ADVANCE PRAIS
REGENERATIVE DESIGN FOR CHANGEMAKERS

"Regeneration is not a set of practices or ways of 'doing good' vs bad. It is a paradigm that can be used to take a more profound look at everything. Dresdale has taken that to heart and is turning social constructs we hold upside down. Read Regenerative Design for Changemakers for the ideas here. There is some very very exciting rethinking. But read also for her process of questioning 'groupthink' about subjects we hold near and dear in our society and social systems. And if you look deeply, you will be disrupted and question your attachment. That is the purpose of a regenerative paradigm. Dresdale takes us to school on what we can no longer accept without reflecting. What subject would you like to apply regenerative design to and use Dresdale's radical questions?"

– **Carol Sanford**, CEO of The Regenerative Paradigm Institute and best selling multi-award winning author of *The Regenerative Life, The Regenerative Business*, and more

"Projects to regenerate degraded farms and landscapes that fail tend to do so because of the people involved rather than the land-based practices or plant species. Personal burnout, organizational challenges, and oppression issues frequently derail project planning efforts. Regenerative Design for Changemakers provides a unique contribution to the field of social permaculture, with an applied toolkit and valuable insights from Dresdale's professional experience to help redesign our lives and projects for fertile success."

– **Eric Toensmeier**, author of *The Carbon Farming Solution* and co-author of *Edible Forest Gardens*, and former lecturer at Yale School of Forestry

"Regenerative Design for Changemakers and its companion course harnesses the social permaculture design process, mindfulness techniques, and creativity to support changemakers in designing holistic, regenerative plans for our social change projects and our lives. Read Abrah's book and find opportunities to train with her!"

– **Naima Penniman**, Program Director of SoulFire Farm, Co-Founder of WILDSEED & Climbing PoeTree

"So often I avoid books about environmental decline, climate change, and ecosystem breakdown. Too scary, too heartbreaking, too overwhelming. But this guidebook combines hopeful inspiration, hands-on solutions, and user-friendly science that is accessible and relevant to everyday life. Thank goodness for changemakers like Abrah Dresdale who are charting a path toward a livable future."

– **Elizabeth Lesser**, Co-Founder of Omega Institute, and author of the New York Times bestseller, *Broken Open: How Difficult Times Can Help Us Grow*

"Regenerative Design for Changemakers provides an accessible toolkit of ideas, information, resources, self-reflection exercises and inspiration for surviving, thriving and building effective community projects in the chaotic and sometimes overwhelming times we live in. You'll want to dive right in and try out some of the many practical suggestions for making personal and community level change."

– **Paul Kivel**, educator, activist and author of *Uprooting Racism: How White People Can Work for Racial Justice*

"*Regenerative Design for Changemakers* was ahead of its time when it was created, but now it's right on time! It's a radical guide for deep systems change for creators, organizations, and changemakers looking to make a regenerative impact. Not only has this book shifted how I approach my personal life, I've also used it with my teams and organizations I consult for. It's a must read for creating a regenerative new future that works for everyone!"

– **Erika Rose Santoro**, Senior Director of Creative Strategy and Programming at Kripalu Center for Yoga & Health

"Life—with 3.8+ billion years of evolutionary trial and error—is the ultimate regenerative designer. In *Regenerative Design for Changemakers: A Social Permaculture Guide*, Abrah draws upon the principles of permaculture (which in essence are lessons from life) and frames these in a compelling way to help evolve your leadership for transforming social systems. Accessible, comprehensive, and critically timely, this provocative handbook is a must have for any change agent wanting to bring ancient wisdom to our modern challenges."

– **Dayna Baumeister, Ph.D**, Co-Founder of Biomimicry Institute and Biomimicry 3.8, and Co-Director and Faculty at Arizona State University's Biomimicry Center

REGENERATIVE DESIGN FOR CHANGEMAKERS:

A Social Permaculture Guide

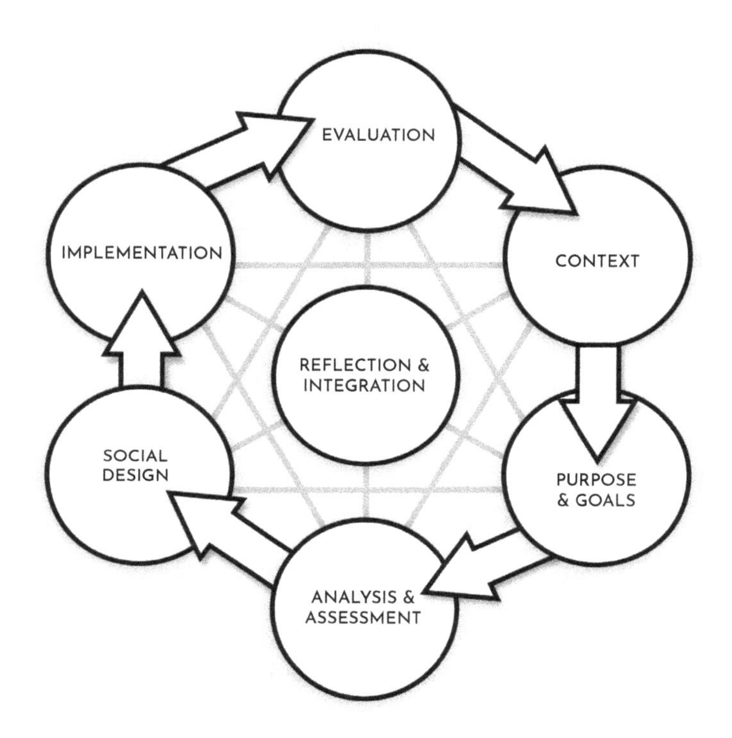

ABRAH DRESDALE

Kingston, NY
Unceded Lenape & Mohawk Territory
CULTURE SHIFT PRESS

REGENERATIVE DESIGN FOR CHANGEMAKERS: A SOCIAL PERMACULTURE GUIDE

1st Edition 2021

Photographs by Abrah Dresdale
Cover design by Phyllis Labanowski
Book layout and charts by Alexis Neubert
Diagrams by Abrah Dresdale
Illustrations by Keith Zaltzberg-Drezdahl
Edited by Revan Schendler, Erin Martineau, and Judith Brand
Written on unceded Nipmuck, Pocumtuck, and Abenaki territories

Published by Culture Shift Press
Kingston, NY USA

ISBN: 978-0-578-85745-9

www.abrahdresdale.com

To my beloved stepfather, Joseph Jordan Berenis, who lived a life full of passion and catalyzed concentric rings of change in every realm he touched. May his memory be for a blessing.

ACKNOWLEDGMENTS

I am so deeply grateful to all of the powerful changemakers who have influenced me and to my accomplices who have supported me during the creation of *Regenerative Design for Changemakers:*

Keith Zaltzberg-Drezdahl, my sweetheart and husband, for his role as devoted midwife to this book, and championing my career always and often; Connor Stedman, for supporting me in all sectors of my life, including thought partnership for many aspects of this book, emotional grounding, and eternal steadiness; Vivian Black, Hilary Costa, and Mark Benjamin, chosen family who have lifted me up and cheered me through every threshold of this book's formation; Eunice Torres, for standing by me and reminding me, "You're A Strong Jewish Woman."

Jasmine Fuego, my co-founder at Regenerate Change, for all your fiery catalyzing energy and love; Adam Brock and the rest of the team at Regenerate Change—Asia Dorsey, Jordan Williams, and Lila Rimalovski—for your ongoing enthusiasm for the work and all you've taught me; My co-coach Leora Fridman, for buddying me so often, and developing Exercises 23 and 40 with me!; My friend and colleague at UMass Amherst, Lisa DePiano, who mentored me and helped me see a path forward in the discipline of social permaculture; My unconditionally supportive colleagues Madeleine Charney at UMass Libraries and Jennifer Abeles at the Franklin County House of Corrections—you've both made such a difference in my life!; Ethan Roland Solaviev and Eric Toensmeier, for your allyship, thought leadership, and contributions to the body of this work from the bad old permaculture days.

Key organizations that I've studied with and who's ideas surface as threads throughout this book: Center for Whole Communities, Undoing Racism Organizing Collective, Movement Generation, and The Conway School; Omega Institute and its Center for Sustainable Living, for piloting the first Regenerative Design for Changemakers course in 2015, and for being a spiritual and professional home to me every summer for 20 years; Carol Sanford, a teacher, elder, and regenerative badass who has influenced my thinking on triads, pentads, paradigms, and more; Naima Penniman and Alixa Garcia of Climbing PoeTree, cultural artist friends whose words and profound projects have grafted themselves into my consciousness since our 20s.

My book layout designer, Alexis Neubert, for her graphic skills, great communication, and dedicated patience; My cover designer, Phyllis Labanowski, for her beautiful art and belief in the project; The incredible Katie Andrews, who technically assisted me with publishing research and skillful website redesign; The many contributing editors of the book at various stages: Revan Schendler, Erin Martineau, and Judith Brand at New Society—thank you!; Erin Kassis, Z Estimé, and Ellie Lobovits, friends who creatively resourced me through the final decision of how to publish after Covid-related disturbances in the publishing world.

The incredible authors and cultural creatives who generously offered advance praise for the book: Carol Sanford, Eric Toensmeier, Elizabeth Lesser, Naima Penniman, Paul Kivel, Erika Rose Santoro, and Dr. Dayna Baumeister; The unstoppable changemakers and thought leaders who've inspired me to keep reaching for the future we are collectively calling forth: Dr. Martin Luther King, Jr., Grace Lee Boggs, Winona LaDuke, Cornell West, Dr. Joanna Macy, Cherie Brown, Leah Penniman, Van Jones, Michelle Obama, Martín Prechtel, Dr. Robin Wall Kimmerer, and adrienne maree brown.

And last by not least, my benevolent ancestors and my parents, who raised me to believe in my capabilities, and my stepfather who so often said, "Av, you always land on your feet."

This book was written on unceded Nipmuck, Pocumtuck, and Abenaki territories in a place today known as Shelburne Falls, Massachusetts.

CONTENTS

INTRODUCTION

Welcome

You've arrived, here on the planet at this time in history. You are one of the billions of people who have joined the forces of life during a crucial tipping point. Together, we are dreaming the world into its unfolding future. What message, sealed within the chambers of your heart, do you have to offer the world on the brink of ecological and social crises, a world spinning off its axes and toward an unforeseen transformation? How will you reveal that message, actively and authentically, to yourself? And how will you communicate your unique message to the other brave ones on the planet today?

A Note from the Author

All of my life I have been a translator and a poet. I use images, patterns, diagrams, and language to tease out parts and pieces of complex systems and communicate them to diverse learners. I've written this book with a *popular education* approach, acknowledging that a wide community of justice workers and systems thinkers are the source of collectively held knowledge and liberation. Even though I teach at a university, I have deliberately chosen to create exercises and write material that are accessible and relevant to a wider array of readers, rather than writing for an academic audience and sourcing information solely from peer-reviewed literature. From teaching war veterans to incarcerated students to readers like yourself, nothing gives me more joy than to share powerful change-making tools with others. Together, we can unearth the blueprint of our purposes, carve out the contours of our goals, and develop our platforms for delivering our messages to the world with clarity and conviction.

Regenerative Design and Permaculture

Once we are clear on our calling, how can we design the long-term health of our collectively held projects in a regenerative manner? When there is a *disturbance* to our personal well-being or to our organizing work, how can we practice resilience in community, adapting to the new conditions that we could not have anticipated? I believe the answer involves living our lives in accordance with regenerative principles. The process begins in section I of this guide with developing *self-awareness* and *personal resilience* for changemakers (a permaculture ethic of People Care). Section II lays out a Regenerative Design Process for organizations, institutions, and communities that seek to become leaders and catalyze lasting change at the intersection of *environmental regeneration* (another permaculture ethic of Earth Care) and *social justice* (and a third ethic of Resource Share).

Just as environmental designers regenerate wild ecosystems and permaculture designers regenerate biological systems in partnership with people, anyone can apply the same design process to heal and regenerate their personal lives and the wider social systems that surround them. I invite you to join me and many others on an eco-social learning journey of personal and collective transformation.

Drawing upon the whole systems frameworks of regenerative design, permaculture, and cycles found in nature, this guide offers a practical step-by-step process for your change-making work.

What is regenerative design, exactly? One working definition I use is: a design approach that supports a system's ability to adapt, transform, and evolve its capacities over time with internal feedback and self-regulation. Systems that are *regenerative* renew their resources, build beneficial *reciprocal relationships* with other systems, and have the flexibility and intelligence to adapt to fluctuating situations with emergent properties. In contrast, when we design a system to be sustainable, the goal is to replicate rather than evolve its functions over time, sustaining the original conditions that it serves. Nor are sustainable systems intended to respond adaptively to disturbances, compromising their resilience and ability to contribute to changing circumstances over the long run. For instance, a sustainable approach to soil management would involve maintaining the same level of organic matter, nutrients, and minerals rather than losing fertility over time. Regenerative soil management, in comparison, would actually increase the soil health and evolve its ability to be productive even through worsening weather conditions brought about by climate change. In addition, regenerative design takes a whole systems approach to challenges; it attends to the unique elements and functions within a system *and* the health of the system as a whole while evolving its capacity to respond to changing conditions.

REGENERATIVE VS. SUSTAINABLE

Regeneration refers to a system's ability to evolve its own capacity and to build beneficial reciprocal relationships with other systems. These connected systems increase and distribute resources over time.

The regeneration paradigm is drastically different from a sustainability paradigm, where the goal is to sustain (rather than degrade further) the current conditions.

Permaculture overlaps with and complements regenerative design. It's a practice of mimicking the patterns and principles found in nature and applying them to the design of systems that serve people while regenerating the land, rather than extracting from it. Permaculture incorporates three things, broadly speaking:

1. **An international movement**
2. **A design system**
3. **A positivist attitude** or response to global challenges: putting our attention on places where we can make change rather than slipping into cynicism or hopelessness.

Both permaculture and regenerative design represent a synthesis of best practices from Earth-based cultures around the world, and they pair these practices with an intentional design process focused on planetary regeneration. It's important to note that the co-founders of permaculture, Bill Mollison and David Holmgren, two white Australian male academics, did not invent the land-based techniques of permaculture in the 1970s. These practices had been developed over millennia, mostly by Indigenous Peoples. By naming "the shoulders we stand on," as my social permaculture colleague Lisa DePiano says at the beginning of permaculture courses, we acknowledge these histories and resist practices of appropriating the knowledge of Indigenous Peoples. Today, there is a nascent but growing movement to "*decolonize*" permaculture [See Further Reading Section].

Permaculture is distinct from many other fields of design such as landscape architecture or industrial design because it bows itself to the inherent elegance and efficiency found in the natural world. A core skill in permaculture and regenerative design is pattern recognition. Permaculture design principles derive from repeated patterns and processes found all over the natural world. For example, capitalist economies contrast the way that trees in a forest share resources to revive sickly neighbors—using an underground mycelial network of symbiotic relationships with fungi—because the health of neighboring trees is necessary to keep the forest ecosystem intact. In this way, each individual tree may thrive. The practice of permaculture is also place-based, involving deep observation of social and ecological contexts. Many fields of design do not take a rigorous approach to understanding contextual conditions. Instead, design outcomes tend to serve a small few or neglect to meet the needs of the inhabitants, human and nonhuman, of a place.

WHAT IS PERMACULTURE?

A practice of observing nature, and then mimicking its beneficial patterns and processes, as we design systems that meet human needs while regenerating the health of ecosystems.

A prevalent *Paradigm* within the permaculture movement views human beings as integral to ecosystem health. As such, the permaculture design process and the various strategies it employs provide pathways for people to play a vital role in the regeneration of landscapes, the built environment, and social systems. This Paradigm is uncommon and can seem ludicrous. In contrast, the result of mainstream design thinking tends to divide people and nature, placing people inside buildings and paved environments, and quarantining nature in protected preserves. Permaculture also differs from other design approaches by the measure of its ethics: Earth Care, People Care, and Resource Share. Ideally, each design decision considers these three *permaculture ethics* and works to address them simultaneously. Rafter Sass Ferguson has authored several peer-reviewed papers on the subject, such as "Permaculture" and "Permaculture for Agroecology: Design, Movement, Practice, and Worldview." They are excellent resources for understanding permaculture more deeply. Adapting permaculture frameworks to social change projects yields resilient, life-affirming social systems cast in the image of our master teacher: the natural world.

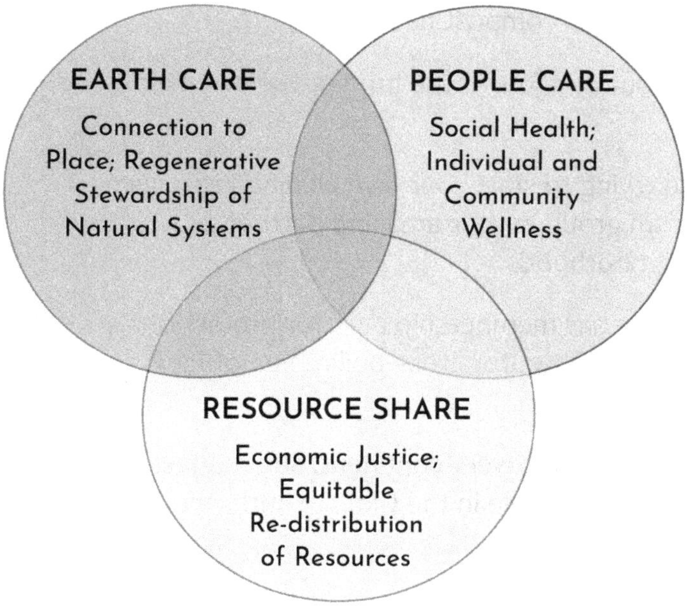

EARTH CARE
Connection to Place; Regenerative Stewardship of Natural Systems

PEOPLE CARE
Social Health; Individual and Community Wellness

RESOURCE SHARE
Economic Justice; Equitable Re-distribution of Resources

PERMACULTURE ETHICS

Permaculture Principles

Derived from the inherent intelligence in nature and rooted in relationships, *permaculture principles* offer us wisdom from the wild places of this planet. These are organizing or guiding tenets that inform the design decisions we make moment to moment. Applying these principles across scales—from the individual to the organization to the larger social system—amplifies the power of conscious design modeled from nature's wisdom.

Various teachers present a range of permaculture principles. The following sampling comes from Mollison, Holmgren, and Dave Jacke. More principles will be introduced throughout the book.

When I teach permaculture principles, I invite students to play a card game. They match up four sets of cards: the principles, their definitions, an ecological example, and a social example. Here are some of those permaculture principles with their social examples:

Stack Multiple Functions: A food hub in the middle of town provides a space for a year-round farmer's market, certified commercial kitchen, aggregation infrastructure, and incubator services for local food businesses.

Use On-Site Resources: Residents' needs in a low-income neighborhood are not being met by city programs. Members of the community start a neighborhood mapping project to make an inventory of the assets, skills, and needs within the community, matching people and resources in order to meet needs locally.

Plan Redundancy: Members of a student club share leadership by taking turns facilitating meetings, planning agendas, and training new members to learn these skills. If one leader gets busy or graduates, the club doesn't fall apart.

Turn the Problem into the Solution: You get a flu from overworking at your social work job. Having to take time off to recuperate becomes an opportunity for much needed rest and reflection.

Design for Functional Interconnection: Formerly incarcerated people train at a community farm to learn organic farming skills and start a new career. They grow six key crops that a local food entrepreneur buys wholesale to make nutritious soup that is sold to the prison to increase residents' nutrition. The prison supplies the farm with food scraps for their compost needs.

Relinquish Control: A good event planner will plan herself out of a job. At the time of the event, she can sit back and enjoy the show.

Work with Nature: Rather than reinventing the wheel and trying to start your own eliminating racism group, you could learn about the existing Uprooting Racism group in your area and partner with them on shared actions and coalition-building among neighborhoods.

Use Edges and Value the Marginal: A collective working space has membership tiers for professionals and graduate students who work side by side. Their proximity allows for cross-pollination of ideas and sharing of resources.

Value Diversity: A climate justice organization involves leaders from every continent, and not just as token board members. The organization is thus accountable to people in the Global South who are currently the hardest hit by climate disruptions.

Seek the Least Change, Greatest Effect: At your local food security council, you help focus on changing the policy for your school district's food procurement practices. Now all the schools in your area allocate 25% of their food budget for local fresh food. This one policy change increases children's nutrition, supports farmers, boosts the local food economy, and decreases the distance that food is transported, increasing freshness and reducing fuel.

In the spirit of participatory evolution, here are four more explicitly social principles I have added to the body of permaculture knowledge:

Lead from Our Lineages: Workshop facilitators name the "shoulders we stand on" at the beginning of any class as protocol, making transparent their orientation to their work and giving credit to the frameworks that shaped them (these can be our ethnic/cultural/religious lineages and/or our intellectual/artistic/political lineages).

Stand Squarely in Our Identities: In a social change group that has built safety over time, the convener names or shows their more hidden identities (e.g., gay, raised poor, differently abled) and welcomes members to do the same. This modeling creates a culture of inclusion where others receive permission to bring their whole selves and speak from their identities. This environment of encouraging vulnerability fosters group cohesion and draws strength from the diversity of a group's members.

Build Connection First: Before diving into logistics at the beginning of a community organizing conference call, each person goes around and shares something about their week that they're grateful for. This practice builds intimacy and humanity into our shared work, creating more surface area for critical connections that serve as the foundation for collective movement building.

Practice Love: You practice engaging your capacity for compassion with those you already love. This repeated action helps you start to feel compassion for those who you would traditionally see as your adversaries. In seeing each other's humanity, we can reconcile mental oppositions and transform perceived binaries.

Social Permaculture

The growing field of *social permaculture* means many things to different people. To me, it is a healing art practiced by *culture workers*—people who are dedicated to transforming broad-scale systems toward greater wholeness and regeneration—in service to coordinated *culture shifts*. With this body of work, we can observe the brokenness of the world, from the infinitesimally small to the macro level, and still perceive the possibility for regeneration within it. We can design pathways for the wholeness and true essence of each system and its respective elements to emerge. I invite you to define this core concept of social permaculture for yourself (see the end of each chapter: Social Design Lexicon).

The DNA for the social permaculture curriculum in this particular book comes from frameworks in psychology, ecology, holistic studies, social justice movements, permaculture design, and systems thinking—all in service to social regeneration across interconnected scales of change. Many people, organizations, and communities have created and refined the exercises and ideas that I bring together, with their explicit permission, in this guide. (Please see the Further Reading section for resources and more information by chapter at the end of the book.) Many of the examples in section II draw from the field of food systems, my area of professional study, and climate justice, a topic relevant to all. However, regenerative design can be applied to any content area.

I want to humbly acknowledge that I am not an expert in all things I write about this book. Instead, I lay out a swath of interconnected ideas that I believe are important for changemakers to think about critically for themselves. I encourage you to try on these ideas or frameworks against your own thinking before you accept them or before you reject them. They are invitations to you.

There is a part of me that is terrified to make this body of work public to the world, for at times I've felt trepidatious to write about and lead on these complex topics. It feels important to vulnerably name this self-doubt. In so doing, I hope to model that, as changemakers, we must assert our visions and leadership, even (and especially) when we do not feel fully ready or expertly competent in the areas we seek to make change. This is part of the risk it takes to grow, to step out of the shade and produce fruit as our unique, sweet offerings for the world. Fortunately, or unfortunately, we might be the best people for the job...

> ***Leave safety behind. Put your body on the line. Stand before the people you fear and speak your mind—even if your voice shakes. When you least expect it, someone may actually listen to what you have to say. Well-aimed slingshots can topple giants.***
>
> – Maggie Kuhn, founder of the Gray Panthers

Making the Power of Paradigms Visible

A holistic mending of the world, from the individual to institution to social system, can only develop roots and thrive if the dominant worldview of separation from all of life around us dissolves. Humbling ourselves, we can look to nature as an interconnected model of regeneration. Regeneration is dynamic by nature, and it reflects a Paradigm of supporting the inherent intelligence of systems to evolve their current limitations using internal resources and self-modulation. This type of dynamic equilibrium can be found in nature, such as in forest dynamics of blowdowns, microbursts, fire, and succession. Ecosystems are resilient because they embrace and adapt to the ever-changing dynamics of an alive world. Regeneration comes after storm disturbances in the form of increased soil fertility, new sunny openings in a dense wood, and growth of more biodiverse species.

We can spend lots of time creating innovative solutions, but if they only address *end of the tailpipe* problems rather than issues at their source, then we're just spinning our wheels and may frustratingly end up where we began. Instead, permaculture urges us to engage with a regeneration Paradigm by learning from these patterns in natural systems and their dynamics, and then looking for points to intervene in a system that can nodally affect different degrees of change. Taking

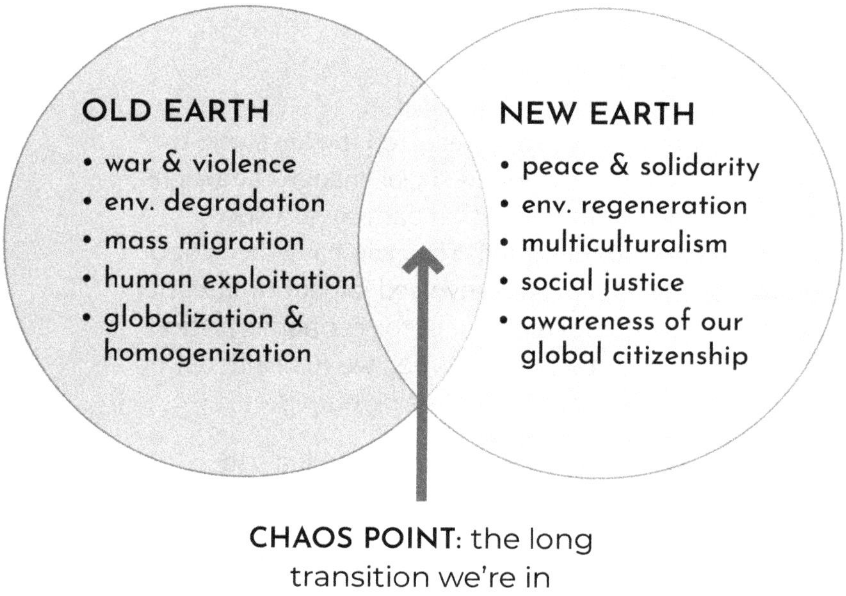

OLD EARTH

- war & violence
- env. degradation
- mass migration
- human exploitation
- globalization & homogenization

NEW EARTH

- peace & solidarity
- env. regeneration
- multiculturalism
- social justice
- awareness of our global citizenship

CHAOS POINT: the long transition we're in

time for analysis is a key strategy of effective changemakers. The *higher up in the watershed*, so to speak, that we can position our interventions, the more influence our designs will have downstream. Having a map of the territory and making key decisions about where to intervene to shift dominant (and often destructive) Paradigms is essential. This guide encourages that level of big-picture design thinking.

Skip Backus, Chief Executive Officer of Omega Institute for Holistic Studies, describes the context we are all living in today as a *chaos point*. A new Paradigm is needed to make the transition from what he calls an Old Earth to a New Earth. As we observe patterns, understand systems, and embrace our global citizenship, we can shift from the role of consumer to producer, and ultimately, to co-designer with all of life.

Evolving the worldviews or Paradigms that predominate is an extremely effective yet highly difficult task that influences all decisions and practices downstream. Many Paradigms and practices of capitalism, such as the *exploitative Paradigm* and *assembly-line mentality*, have led to the development of systems that are out of alignment with nature's cycles. Many "broken" systems illustrate this point. Consider the public health crises in the US, and the chaos of health insurance bureaucracy and corruption. Or the inherent inequities of our educational system and its disparate student outcomes, from incarceration to Ivy League graduation to staggering levels of debt accrued by young people. These systems do not mimic the inherent checks and balances found in ecosystem dynamics that create a distribution of resources. Nor do dominant social institutions follow nature's cyclical rhythms of emergence, growth, reproduction, and decay. Rather, endless growth and consumption in the form of corporate profiteering trump the well-being of the whole. Without a holistic investigation of why these systems (healthcare, education, etc.) benefit only a tiny fraction of society, we can never develop *whole solutions*. Linear mental models, used to rationalize unjust and exploitative systems, produced what Joanna Macy, white Buddhist scholar and founder of The Work That Reconnects, calls *"the mess we're in."*

The *sustainability Paradigm*, touted by numerous visionaries and environmentalists, has good intentions and moves us beyond the exploitative Paradigm. However, do we really want to sustain the "mess we're in"? Or do we need something that goes further, a new Paradigm that can evolve the sources of the current norms and practices—which gave way to the crises we are mired in today?

Instead of Paradigms that value linear thinking and exponential growth, we can observe cycles in the wildness of nature. And, instead of a reductionist Paradigm that compartmentalizes each element in an ecosystem, we begin to see webs of tight-knit and long-standing relationships based on reciprocity. With a whole system lens, we can learn how to regenerate the "broken" systems of our societies and design systems that can evolve their own capacity and self-regulate over time.

Building Blocks of Regenerative Social Design

Consciously and proactively designing the social dimensions of any project is often the keystone to creating systemic change. How come? Even the most beautifully envisioned social change campaigns will not succeed over the years if the human systems, such as communication pathways, work agreements, finances, and community relations, are not carefully designed. They can have the best of intentions, but lose momentum or even disintegrate if the changemakers involved fall out of integrity with themselves or one another. Occupy is an example of a hopeful movement for economic justice that dissolved due to internal group dynamics and external societal factors. When we rush into action without first engaging in a conscious analysis and design process, we risk capsizing our vision.

The seven stages of the Regenerative Design Process apply across scales from individuals to interpersonal relationships to organizations, institutions, and communities.

Social design begins with the individuals that make up groups which collectively constitute social systems. A commitment to evolving our personal patterns, especially as *changemakers*, is essential for broad-scale social regeneration. This includes:

- becoming cognizant of and owning our mental and behavioral patterns
- committing to integrating the parts of ourselves that were severed or wounded
- leaving our comfortable nests and taking risks that increase our competencies
- cultivating our capacity to lead and make changes in the wider world

If we neglect this dimension of internal and behavioral change, there is a high risk of replicating the same mental models and oppressive dynamics of the systems we seek to transform. Additionally, it's important to emphasize "how" we engage with our collective projects (our approach and personal conduct) rather than focusing on the "what" (the content or deliverables).

Through our social design endeavors, we have the opportunity to expand our capacities as agents of change. Exercises in this guide focus on literacy of the self, undoing oppression, structural analyses of social systems, and implementing effective approaches for whole systems change-making that sustains and evolves over time.

"It is not incumbent upon you to finish the task [of mending the world], but neither are you free to absolve yourself from it." This powerful exhortation from the Jewish manual of ethics, *Pirkei Avot*, to me implies the importance of attending to personal healing, accountability, and *cultural regeneration* as we do our collective social design work. In the courses I teach, we create a safe container (different from a Comfort Zone) so that everyone can explore inner barriers to change. These can include the effects of intergenerational trauma, structural oppression, and/or the role of internalized messages of social superiority or inferiority. Through the exercises in this guide, I invite readers to engage in healing practices as a means to collectively incite change in the oppressive practices of the larger systems that should serve and protect us all.

Take a moment to consider: What are your personal practices for engaging with difficulty or tension? What supports you in leaning into discomfort, in a way that's safe but that stretches you to grow? For some, meditation is a way to sit with pain or conflict, observing it rather than suppressing it. For others, it may be a commitment to not shy away from challenging social interactions with people from different backgrounds or identities.

Offerings Emerge from Lineage and Identities

Lead from our lineages and *stand squarely in our identities* are two guiding principles of my consulting and educational work. And so, *Regenerative Design for Changemakers: A Social Permaculture Guide* is informed by the social justice ethos and connection to the Earth I feel most intimately feel through my Jewish lineage and outward facing identities.

At some point, I made the conscious decision that the structure of my change-making projects would emerge from my lineages, ancestral and intellectual. This decision has brought power and clarity to my work, and it has, in turn, increased my ability to connect with other powerful visionaries across differing lineages and orientations.

The DNA for this book is as syncretic as my set of personal identities...

I am a New York Ashkenazi Eastern European Jew, raised Reconstructionist (a "liberal" branch of Judaism) in Woodstock, NY. I spent much of my childhood at my grandparents' home in Rockland County, NY, where they kept Kosher, spoke Yiddish, and attended Orthodox and Conservative synagogues. Within three generations—and even in the course of my lifetime—the assimilation and loss of culture in my family has been enormous, including changing our last name, relinquishing Kosher practices, and only occasionally attending synagogue. My contact with family customs from the old country and the ways my family assimilated to survive as Jews in the New World has taught me about contrast, what it means to be "other" and what it means to become "white."

My mother converted to Judaism before I was born. My cultural and religious identity is Jewish, but I also find it useful to claim "mixed-heritage" as an identity and learn about the patterns and inheritance from my Anglo-Protestant family. They are Southerners from Mississippi whose lineage traces back to Ireland, England, Sweden, and Germany. Holding the contradictory values of my New York Jewish family and my Deep South Protestant family has helped me to become a "bridge person," seeing connections across disparate worlds. Although I do not descend directly from Holocaust survivors, reckoning with the fact that my people (gentile Germans) tried to annihilate my people (Jews) has also been a profound experience of an intimate embodiment of paradox.

I was raised in two exceptionally different home environments after my parents' divorce at the age of three. I have four unique and at times conflict-prone parents and stepparents (three of which are therapists, oy vey!).

I am a queer person who has, since adolescence, loved people who identify as female, male, gender queer, and transgender. I came out at a difficult time, before there were Gay-Straight Alliances to support queer youth. As such, I learned the critical skill of code-shifting, which I believe has helped aid my role as a translator and bridge-builder.

I am an unapologetic feminist and womanist. I identify as a genderqueer female or femme. I use she/her/hers pronouns, and I am fluid with my gender in a way that is authentically me.

As a queer person, femme, and Jew, I weave together scraps—from the ways in which I and my female ancestors, Jewish ancestors, and queer community have survived oppression—into a transformed tapestry. The pain of fragmentation in my life has led me to seek edges ripe for reconciliation. From my story, I have cultivated an ability to relate across groups with different value systems and to find and translate commonalities. I seek wholenesses that can contain multiplicity and paradoxes, without needing them to blur into one unified expression.

My cultural artistry work reimagines worlds where healing, wholeness, and connection wash over and permeate the accretion of intergenerational trauma and worldviews of hatred, having seen too many factions form in my family, communities, and histories. It is from this position that I have approached the writing of this social permaculture guide, from the development of its very personal content to its pedagogical approach.

My intellectual lineages are diverse and colorful. Teachers and organizations who have shared their wisdom with me about the Earth, connections to the Holy, pathways to healing, and Jewish tradition include: Rabbi Shefa Gold, Rabbi Jill Hammer, Rav Kohenet Taya Shere, Rabbi Jonathan Kligler, Rabbi Gershon Winkler, Kohenet Dori Midnight, Ellie Lobovits, Rabbi Arthur Waskow, Rabbi Batya Friedland, Rowena Pattee Kryder and the Stream of Wisdom Institute, Phyllis Berman, Yigal Deutscher, Deliah Rosel, Cara Silverberg, Maggid David Arfa, Rabbi Zelig Goldin, the JOFEE (Jewish Outdoor Food and Environmental Educators) network, Jewish Farm School, Jewish Farmer Network, *Nishmat Shoom*, Wilderness Torah, and my *Rosh Chodesh* priestess circle.

I've also studied with and been invited to participate in ceremonies with Diné elder Shanadii, Dakota Sundance Chief Calvin Pompana, Odawa Peacemaker Paul Raphael, Haudenosaunee Tree of Peace Society founders Jake and Judy Swamp, the Thirteen Indigenous Grandmothers, and Native elders at the Sun Ray Peace Village.

The communities to which I have belonged and learned with—from design thinking to justice work to cultural healing—include: The Work That Reconnects, Omega Institute for Holistic Studies and the Omega Center for Sustainable Living, Carol Sanford Institute, Center for Whole Communities, International Re-evaluation Counseling Communities, Systemic/Family Constellations, Hebraic Futurism Movement, Franklin County Jail educators circle, Northeast Prison Garden Educators Collaborative, Rwandan Restorative Justice community and Africa Conflict Transformation Fellowship, WildSeed Farm and Healing Village, Settler Colonialism Jewish Community of Practice, Living Routes, Sadhana Forest, Encounter Programs, Wild Earth, the Art of Mentoring network, Vermont Wilderness School, Her Feet on the Earth, Conway School of Landscape Design, Wildflower School of Botanical Medicine, Danish Institute for Study Abroad Architecture Program, Synthesis of Ulster County, transformative justice and prison abolition circles, anti-racism and decolonization circles, land-based reparations networks, queer community, carbon farming and climate justice movements, regenerative food systems and food justice movements, permaculture movement, emergent strategists, and the Regenerate Change network.

Jewish Ethics and Cycles That Frame This Book

Quite beautifully the three ethics of permaculture echo those of the Jewish ethic of *Tikkun Olam*, or mending of the world. Earth Care points to its emphasis on environmental stewardship. People Care expresses the healthy communities dimension of *Tikkun Olam*. Resource Share resonates with its equity and justice imperative. These values of healing and justice from my lineage and Jewish education help to shape the book's content and curriculum.

In service to mending my own disconnection from the wild places of this planet, I practice building relationships with the world beyond my doorstep—the seasons, the celestial bodies, the rocks, and the rivers—through Jewish ritual. From this wellspring of embodied experience, I combine a Hebraic view of nature's cycles as a way to organize section I of this book. There are many points of overlap between Earth-based Jewish practices, Indigenous practices globally, and permaculture today.

Throughout the year, Jews honor the seven directions that surrounded us in the wilderness, the East, South, West, North, Above, Below, and Center. During the autumn harvest festival of *Sukkot*, for example, we shake the *lulav* (a wand of palm, myrtle, and willow sprigs) and *etrog* (a Middle Eastern citrus fruit) in each direction. The roots of these practices extend back to a time when my Hebrew ancestors had a much more place-based connection to the land.

Each of the *arba ruchot*, or "four winds" in Hebrew (compare to the four directions honored by many Indigenous Peoples), holds an archetypal energy associated with the location of the sun. The sun rises at dawn in the East. Then it moves to its zenith in the middle of the day. For those of us who live in the Northern hemisphere, the sun moves towards the Southern sky. It then descends at sunset in the West, and it slips into hiding from view at midnight, designated as the direction North. With the *arba ruchot*, we can also map natural cycles, as Rabbi Gershon Winkler does in *Magic of the Ordinary*. Below is my interpretation, informed by Rabbis Jill Hammer, Zelig Goldin, and Winkler, of cycles mapped onto each wind:

- **East Wind** (*Mizrach*): sunrise, springtime, new beginnings, birth, childhood
- **South Wind** (*Darom*): high noon, summer exploration, growing pains, adolescence
- **West Wind** (*Ma'ariv*): sunset, autumn, in-gathering and harvest, adulthood
- **North Wind** (*Tzafon*): midnight, winter, integration, old age, death

Cycles of seven are considered sacred to the Jewish people. If the four directions of solar orientation map onto a horizontal plane to the East, South, West, and North, there are three other directions in Judaism: two that extend vertically, above and below, to create a three-dimensional sphere, and a third "direction" at the center.

From the skies **Above** come the rains, the life force that permits living beings to thrive on this watery planet. Gifts of *shamayim*, or the heavens above, offer us rain and clouds for cleansing renewal. The rains soak us in tears that bring us through grief into sobering clarity.

From the ground **Below** we are gifted with the solidity of the earth, soil, and bedrock. The qualities of *adamah*, Earth, are connection, gravity, and relationship with all life.

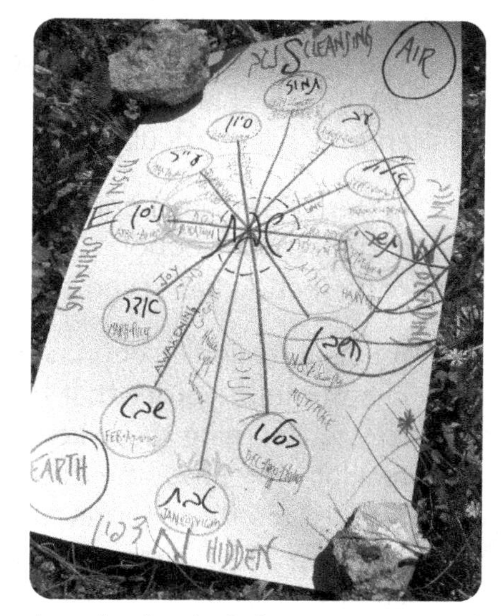

Jewish wheel of the year mapped onto rhythms in nature

As with every cycle, the ending of one gives way to the beginning of another. In the Jewish wheel of life, the place from which we end and begin, from which we stand and extend an invisible line out to each of the six directions, is the **Center**, "the seventh direction." Imagine a person standing in one place and shaking a *lulav* and *etrog* in the six directions.

The Center is the place where we rest and reflect on the activities of the other six directions. Jews (and other religious groups) are commanded to reflect on the six days of creation and to rest on the seventh day, *Shabbat*. It is this center point to which we return, and return again, to shake softly and listen. To say, *"heneni,"* or "Here I am." In a healthy individual or system this center place, or seventh direction, is a place of peacefulness and integrity, the point from which all other directions radiate.

Inspired by these rhythms and other Jewish sacred cycles of sevens (counting of the *Omer* for seven weeks, counting every seven years to mark *Shmita*), I have organized this book into two sections of seven chapters.

Section I, Personal Regeneration for Changemakers: The Self as a Blueprint for Systemic Change, brings the reader on a seven-step journey. The first four chapters embody the archetypal stages of nature's cycles, echoed in the chapters' themes by the stages of human development. The last three chapters reflect the directions of Above, Below, and Center and their archetypal associations. By the end of section II, after completing deep self-reflection work, we arrive again at dawn. The incoming light of the East illuminates a new path forward into the second half of the book.

Section II, Designing for Organizations, Institutions, and Communities: A Recipe for Social Alchemy, moves readers through the seven phases of the Regenerative Design Process with a self-selected project as the focus. The aim is to design organizations, institutions, and communities in accordance with the life-giving regenerative patterns of nature and the ethos of social justice.

The last/seventh chapter of each section offers a break for rest and integration, to silence oneself and listen deeply below the buzzing of the chapters that came before.

From Patterns to Details: Book Overview and Content

The permaculture principle of *design from patterns to details* advises that we identify big-picture patterns first and then dive into understanding and designing details within those patterns. This approach is particularly helpful when we engage with complex systems.

In the spirit of this principle, I will explain the broad pattern of this book. It entails this introduction and then two sections with repeating elements: an overview at the beginning of each section, and each section has seven chapters.

A Social Design Lexicon page at the end of each chapter lists the italicized key terms from the chapter in the order that they appear. Throughout the book, I use terminology that may be new to you. Learning these key concepts will increase your facility in talking about social change-making. The first time these terms appear, I italicize them. I invite you to articulate what you understand these terms to mean in your own words, based on their context in the reading, your own understanding, and/or looking them up. (Note: Book titles and words in languages other than English are also italicized, but these are not Social Design Lexicon words.)

A Further Reading resource list for each chapter appears at the end of the book. Many of the concepts, frameworks, and exercises have numerous articles, books, websites, and podcasts to explore deeper. I attribute the originators of work I reference in the body of writing and have organized those references and additional resources by topic at the end of the book.

Another note about language: the phases of the Regenerative Design Process and other terms related to the process are capitalized throughout the book. This emphasis is meant to call your attention to how these commonly used terms are functioning as design jargon in this context.

Now, for the details...

This introduction serves as a map of the journey you are about to embark on.

Section I focuses on the individual, the changemaker, as a site of systemic change. We explore our patterns in the form of our values, social identities, leadership approaches, and health of our relationships. This groundwork yields more vitality and resilience for us and, in turn, for the social designs we create and sustain.

The focus broadens in section II from personal regeneration for changemakers to designing regenerative projects within organizations, institutions, and communities. You'll learn the Regenerative Design Process by applying it to a tangible social change project of your choosing. You'll progress through the phases of the Regenerative Design Process, with theory, exercises, and production of design outputs, which collectively comprise the Social Design Lab. Section II provides new material, and it also refers to and scales up many of the frameworks from section I.

Regenerative Design Process Overview

Section II guides readers through a Regenerative Social Design Process through which we:

1. Consider the **Context** of the social ecosystems in which our change-making projects occur
2. Clarify and articulate (to oneself and to the world) a project **Purpose** and **Goals**
3. Create **Analyses and Assessments** that reveal unique Opportunities and Constraints
4. Join the Goals with the Analysis and Assessment to yield an elegant **Social Design** that is responsive to the Context and realizes the project Purpose
5. **Implement** a robust, multi-staged plan that moves the Design from ideation into action
6. Determine holistic criteria, tools, and benchmarks to **Evaluate** the project impact and degree to which the Social Design achieves the project Goals
7. Take the time and space for ourselves, to exhale, rest, **Reflect** on, and **Integrate** the work we've created

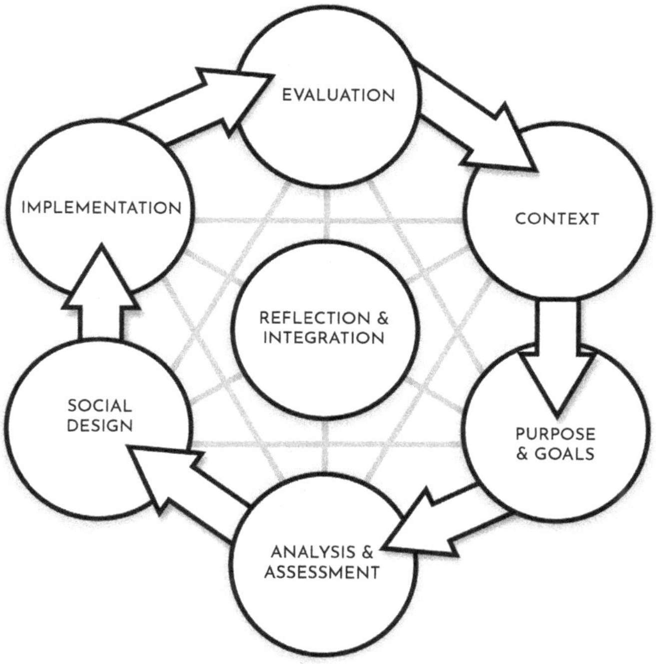

EVALUATION
CONTEXT
PURPOSE & GOALS
ANALYSIS & ASSESSMENT
SOCIAL DESIGN
IMPLEMENTATION
REFLECTION & INTEGRATION

SOCIAL REGENERATIVE DESIGN PROCESS

As they would say at the Conway School of Landscape Design, my alma mater, "Trust the process!"

Consider Your Approach to Using This Book

It's not easy to embark on projects to change our own habitual patterns, let alone transform society's "broken" systems. Here are a few suggestions for engaging with the invitations in this book:

- Define a period of time in which to read and absorb this guide, such as two months or a 14-week college semester. Try not to rush ahead, but rather imbibe different stages of the process, from personal exploration and reflection (section I) to professional/project development (section II).
- View your first round of incorporating tools from this book as a laboratory, an incubation period for your regenerative design skills.
- Imagine at the beginning what it will feel like to have successfully completed this book, and what types of creativity, agency, and leadership qualities you will embody.
- Write out your personal goals for embarking on this journey, using *present tense active voice*—an important, yet subtle tool permaculture teacher and author Dave Jacke employs. Presenting your goals as if they are already happening allows your mind to incorporate the new reality of your goals being met, and it calls forth support from the universe that you need to do so.
- While working your way through this book, use a journal to record your goals and their ongoing refinement, your responses to exercise prompts, and your insights. Your journal will serve as a precious archive of your learning journey. Throughout the book, you will see "***Journal***" with suggested questions for you to reflect on. Sometimes these journal prompts will be preceded by **Reflection and Integration** pauses that offer you moments of still introspection to shift gears from taking in information to slowing down to integrate, to check in with yourself, and witness your own reactions, emotions, and thoughts. This practice mirrors the recurring phase in the design process used in this book, Reflection and Integration.
- In section II, you will find **Social Designer Tips** offered throughout. See if there is a creative way for you to engage with these tips, writing them on Post-its and putting them up in your work space or creating a special section to record them in your journal. They are meant to be supportive signposts while you learn a complex process without a mentor being there to guide you.
- At the end of each chapter, a **Social Design Lexicon** will list key terms. Articulate in your own words what they mean and grow your competence in communicating central ideas of social systemic change.
- Consider (seriously!) setting up a buddy system with other changemakers:
    1. a ***Learning Buddy*** with whom you can process the material and share your responses to self-reflective exercises
    2. a ***Wellness Buddy*** to support your self-care goals, including motivating each other and even sharing wellness experiences
    3. an ***Accountability Buddy*** to ensure you follow through on steps to implement your social design project

You may want the same special person in your life to serve as all three types of buddies. However, I have found that each of my loved ones offers unique strengths, and developing a clear understanding of their strengths lets me reach out to different friends and family members to take on these important roles. Spreading my buddy system across three or more people builds connections and redundancy and fosters resilience in my various personal and professional projects!

Permissions

This guide can be a stand-alone resource for individual readers or used in educational settings. It encapsulates the curriculum (plus so much more!) from the Regenerative Design for Changemakers training, offered through my organization, Regenerate Change (more information at regeneratechange.com). You have permission and are encouraged to adapt the curriculum and share the exercises and frameworks for educational, organizational, and/or professional development purposes. Please always credit the book, authored by Abrah Dresdale, and attribute the originator of the exercise or framework, where an outside originator is noted. [Please see copyright stipulations on copyright page to ensure you're in integrity with this agreement. Thank you.]

Blessing

The Aramaic expression *Abra K'adabra*, "I create that which I speak," takes on new meaning as each of us emerges as creative designers who can collectively articulate and strategically implement the future we wish to inhabit. The personal is political. As each of us learns from the struggles that have held us back, may we wield the power of our tender personal stories to create new cultural stories—imbued with justice and love. *Tikkun Olam*!

Please see Further Reading related to the Introduction on page 227.

Social Design Lexicon for Introduction

Review the following key terms and write down what they mean to you.

Popular Education:

Disturbance:

Self-awareness:

Personal Resilience:

Environmental Regeneration:

Social Justice:

Regenerative:

Reciprocal Relationships:

Permaculture:

Decolonize:

Paradigm:

Permaculture Ethics:

Permaculture Principles:

Social Permaculture:

Culture Workers:

Culture Shifts:

End of the Tailpipe:

Higher Up in the Watershed:

Chaos Point:

Exploitative Paradigm:

Assembly-line Mentality:

Whole Solutions:

"The Mess We're In":

Sustainability Paradigm:

Changemaker:

Cultural Regeneration:

Lead from Our Lineages:

Stand Squarely in Our Identities:

Design from Patterns to Details:

Present Tense Active Voice:

Learning Buddy:

Wellness Buddy:

Accountability Buddy:

Personal Regeneration for Changemakers: The Self as a Blueprint for Systemic Change

SECTION I

Overview

PERSONAL REGENERATION

As a changemaker, you are necessarily part of your designs. As an individual, you are a site for systemic change.

The worldviews and messages we incubate inside ourselves radiate out and affect all that we touch, all that we create. As changemakers, we are necessarily part of our designs. As individuals, each of us is a site for systemic change. If we don't actively and thoughtfully design our inner landscapes (i.e., our emotional, spiritual, and mental health) in a way that brings about vitality and regeneration, we will necessarily radiate old, outworn patterns into our outer lives (i.e., our relationships, family systems, and work). In order to imbue health and wholeness into our social change-making creations, we too, at the center, need to embody these life-giving qualities. This direct link between our inner landscapes and our outer creations is why section I of this book deeply explores the self.

Change-making, by its very nature, cannot come from our well-worn neural pathways of the mind; it needs to come from all of our intelligences combined. A whole systems approach to problem-solving must include our somatic, emotional, and intuitive faculties. When we try on the Paradigms of sustainability versus regeneration, what happens in our bodies, in our hearts? How does it feel intuitively to work toward sustaining what surrounds us versus regenerating a new world? What shifts occur inside us when we put each of these worldviews in the palm of our hands and feel its qualities? These guiding questions point even more so to the importance of deepening our relationship with the self and fine-tuning our own being as an instrument that can detect when, where, and how change is needed.

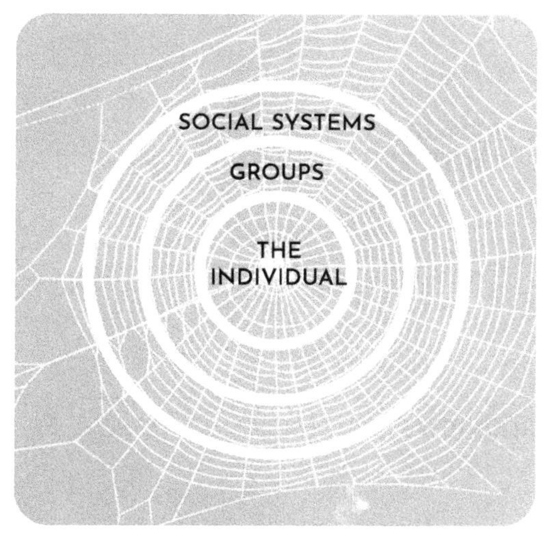

NESTED WHOLES WITH WEB PATTERN

Introduction to Nested Wholes

Every system—whether an ecosystem, organization, business, or society—is an orchestrated web of individuals, each playing their part in contributing to the whole. When we embark on systems change, we must consider both the details and the bigger picture. All living systems, including human systems, are fractals. Our cells make up organs, which in turn make up body systems, which collectively build an organism. The same organizing principles apply across scales of these fractal systems. We call this a Nested Wholes framework. Before we can consciously redesign groups such as organizations, institutions, or communities to align with regenerative principles, we must zoom in on their building blocks:

the individual humans involved and invested in the social system at large. If we neglect the wellness and functioning of each of the individuals, the larger whole becomes vulnerable to disturbances through the cracks in its members.

> *Fractal strategies suggests wholeness in our organizers yields wholeness in our future.*
>
> – adrienne maree brown, *Emergent Strategy*

Tree as Metaphor for the Self

This Nested Wholes framework places the individual at the center of several larger social systems. These nested rings can be likened to a cross-section view of tree rings, with the self located in the tree's core, its *heartwood* (a technical botanical term!). Radiating out, the heartwood serves as the structural strength from which the sapwood expands, protected by the outer bark and cork layers. If this heartwood (the self) is not upright and healthy, neither will the growth rings—one's personal evolution, creations, and the ripples left in our wake.

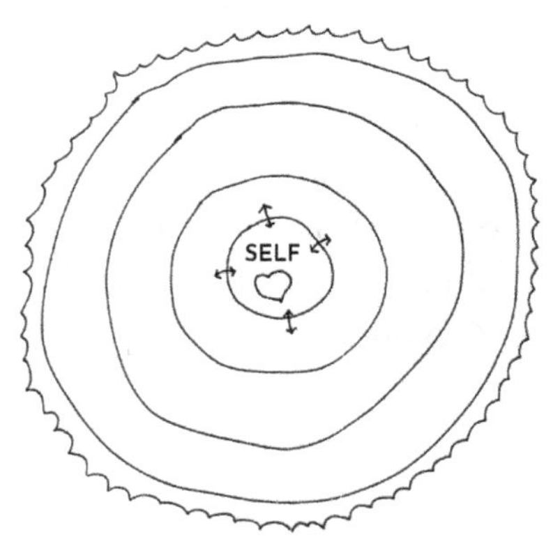

Our Heartwood Radiating Out Into All We Create
Credit: Keith Zaltzberg-Drezdahl

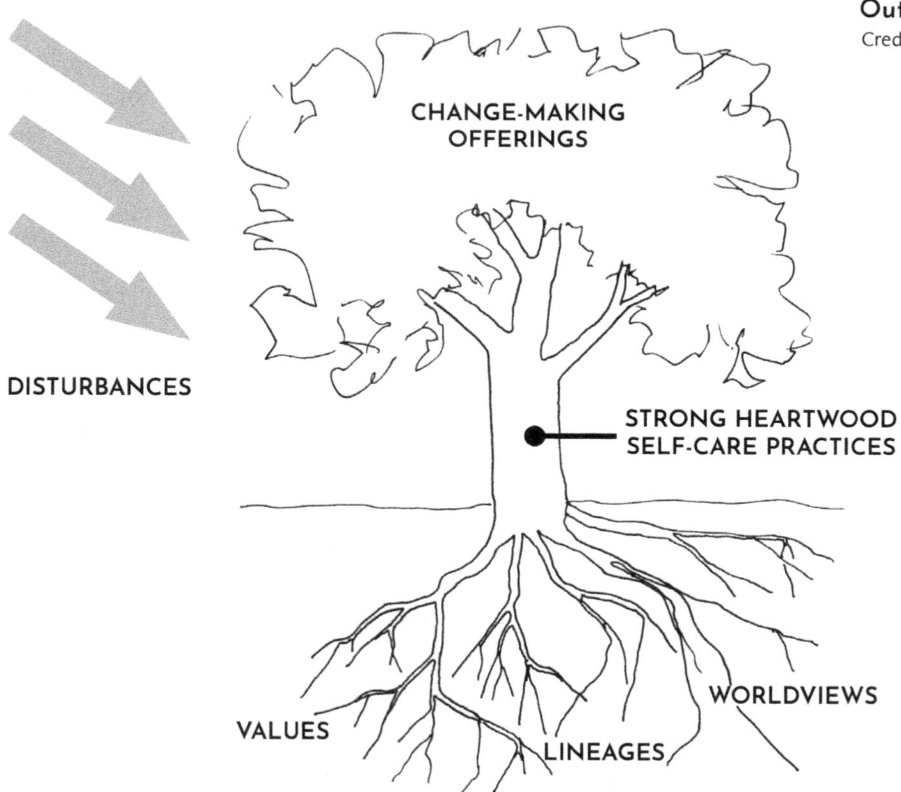

Elevation View of Tree: Resilient with Broad Roots and Healthy Heartwood
Credit: Keith Zaltzberg-Drezdahl

Stepping back, we can consider the elevation view of a tree, facing it head on. The root system is much like our personal rootstock: it represents our *values, lineages,* and *worldviews*. Considering our change-making endeavors, we can then ask ourselves: What are my Holistic Goals for my life and my Purpose? How can my root system support my efforts to catalyze change above the surface, growing my tree's crown and developing fruit as my change-making offerings to the world? How can my offerings be in reciprocal relationship with my roots, helping to bring healing to the collective roots of my peoples' past? The breadth and depth of our roots provide a counterbalancing force for our branches, our change-making reach and impact, to spread further year after year.

Alas, there are other forces and factors to consider beyond our personal ecosystem of tree. When big *disturbances* in the weather arise, our tree has a greater chance of resilience in the face of a storm's blowdown or landslide when we are in active relationships with others. A concrete example of this phenomenon is the flourishing of mutual aid networks in the wake of the coronavirus disturbance as an expression of relational resilience. These relationships—the interlocking of our roots with those of others—might be with personal supports, such as mentors, aunties, and allies, as well as with groups in the form of alliances, coalitions, and networks. Diverse, redundant, and abundant relationships are as essential for survival in the 21st century as they were generations ago.

Practicing self-care regularly at our innermost core ensures our trunk is full of wholeness and vitality. A strong heartwood and strong relationships means that our tree and our change-making offerings will endure in the face of adversities that will surely come.

Identifying the various forms of disturbances that can threaten us may be difficult to face, but it's essential to proactively prepare for them to increase our chances of long-term resilience. Forms of ecological disturbance, many of which are symptoms of climate change, include: wildfires, landslides, tornadoes, hurricanes, floods, and drought. We also have social disturbances to contend with, such as economic collapse, forced displacement, structural oppression, lack of housing, and military rule. We can even name inner cycles of disturbance that threaten the health of our tree, such as low self-esteem, anxiety, depression, internalized oppression, and addiction. What kinds of disturbances can you think of that pose threats to your ecosystem?

In my worldview, healing can travel backwards in time, not just forwards for the future generations. When we engage in ongoing repair and healing processes with our ancestors and lineages, we're also less vulnerable to disturbances in the conditions that surround us. And when our roots lock arms with the roots of neighboring trees, our power multiples. Oak trees lead by example, demonstrating to us the strength that comes with relationships and coalition-building in our change-making work. Not even hurricanes the size of Katrina can bring us down when we weave our roots together in the darkness underground. There, our ancestors of different lineages and worldviews are sitting together sharing stories and food, supporting our courageous actions from the unseen realm in times of turbulence.

> *When Hurricane Katrina slammed into the Gulf Coast, almost everything lost its footing. Houses were detached from their foundations, trees and shrubbery were uprooted, sign posts and vehicles floated down the rivers that became of the streets. But amidst the whipping winds and surging water, the oak tree held its ground. How? Instead of digging its roots deep and solitary into the earth, the oak tree grows its roots wide and interlocks with other oak trees in the surrounding area. And you can't bring down a hundred oak trees bound beneath the soil! How do we survive the unnatural disasters of climate change, environmental injustice, over-policing, mass-imprisonment, militarization, economic inequality, corporate globalization, and displacement? We must connect in the underground, my people! In this way, we shall survive.*
>
> – Naima Penniman, quoted in *In Praise of Trees and Forests* by Claudia Mauro and Nalini Nadkarni

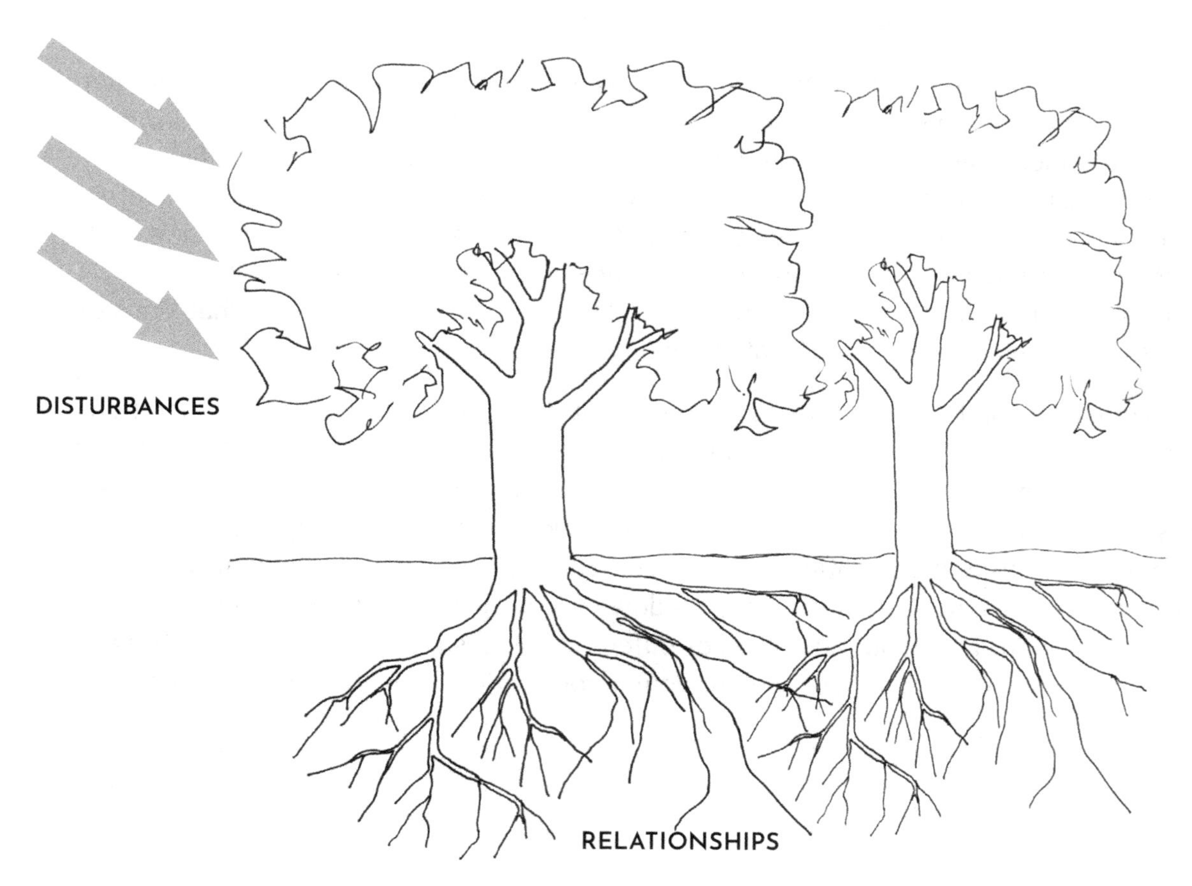

Relationships Increase Our Resilience in the Face of Eco-Social Disturbances
Credit: Keith Zaltzberg-Drezdahl

Embracing Change Ourselves

The more that we cultivate strong trunks and root systems, the wider our branches can grow and the more life they can support, offering oxygen from our leaves and fruits from our prolific flowers. Fruit trees do not actually need to produce fruit in order to survive. The number one limiting factor for fruit production is the amount of sunlight a tree receives. Likewise, for us humans, we can hide in the shade and still sustain, because practices of fecundity are not needed for individual survival. We can sink our roots into the Paradigm of sustainability, just settling for what we have. But to evolve our collective capacity, to regenerate new growth, we can choose to make precious gifts of fruit, our metaphorical offerings of nourishment to the world. This regeneration Paradigm or worldview goes beyond the individual self. It compels us to share our abundance with those around us, and then to drop seeds, generating whole new forests for the future ones to come. In order to do this, we need wide root systems linked in solidarity with others, strong and healthy heartwood, and lots of sunlight, rather than the safety of playing small in the shade.

The more that we can embrace change ourselves by stepping out and into the sun and be seen, the more we can say yes to our own healing and regeneration. For it is in the light that we leave the safety of stagnant predictability behind and become the leaders we were born to be by gifting others with our sun-ripened fruit and seeds of a new tomorrow.

Section I of this book asks you, what do you need to thrive in the sun? What helps you grow your core self, and produce offerings to change the world? And what do you wish to leave behind in the shadows, to turn to compost, to feed new life, regeneratively?

Please see Further Reading related to the Overview of section I on page 229.

Social Design Lexicon for Overview of Section I

Review the following key terms and write down what they mean to you.

Fractals:

Nested Wholes:

Heartwood:

Values:

Lineages:

Worldviews:

CHAPTER 1: THE ROOTS OF OUR VISIBLE SELVES

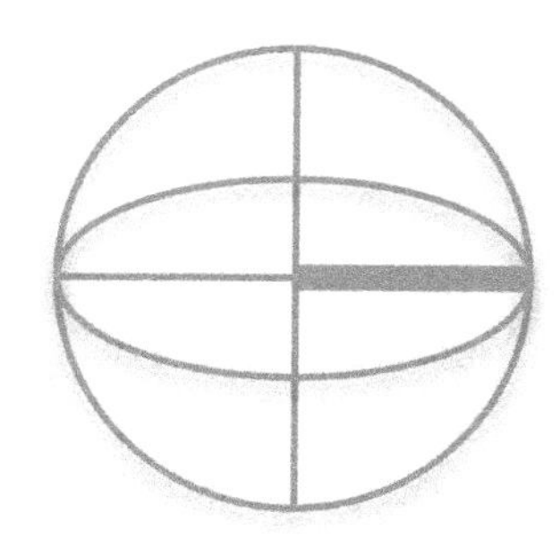

EAST: ROOTS/FORMATIVE DEVELOPMENT

When we hold a mirror up to ourselves with a sense of curiosity, unexpected inner landscapes reveal themselves. Inner and outer observation is a core skill in permaculture that we can apply across new terrains of Social Design. Through regular practices of social observation, we can learn about ourselves as social creatures and the quality of our connections to the other members of our *social ecosystems.*

Location of self is a framework that asks a researcher/writer to locate or orient themselves in relationship to their area of focus. This comes from feminist theory and praxis, and is now broadly used in the field of social justice and identity politics. Location of self can be a helpful starting point in consciously engaging with the design process. In the context of regenerative Social Design, this initial orienting work is essential. We can learn to understand ourselves and our position in relation to various societal dynamics of history, power, and privilege so that we may become mindful designers, aware of the impact we have on the systems in which we thoughtfully intervene.

Locating the self within a landscape of complex social interactions parallels the permaculture concept of Zones of Use, a land-use planning tool for designing efficient systems and relationships among the systems' elements. How can we develop an understanding of the relationship between *Zone 00*, or the Self, and the rest of the zones of a social landscape? In permaculture-informed farm planning, the common element and connector across all five zones, from Zone 0 (the house) to Zone 5 (the wild lands), is the farmer or land steward (Zone 00). The Self is then both the nucleus of the zones and the steward traversing them. As the Zones of Use model suggests, we necessarily are part of the ecosystems' health to which we are attending. Understanding ourselves, our own significance, and the nuances of our relationships to other elements of the social ecosystems around us can reveal important information about the gifts, limitations, and *Unconscious Assumptions* we bring as designers of social landscapes.

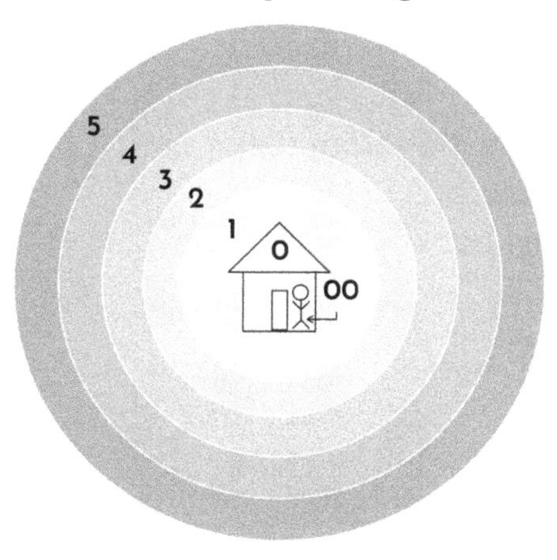

ZONES OF USE CONCEPT DIAGRAM

Not only does practicing *literacy of the self*, a term coined by mindfulness teachers and dear friends Daniel and Taylor Rechtschaffen, greatly strengthen the integrity of the social change projects we design, it also brings new opportunities for personal growth. The joy of being in tune with oneself, understanding how to navigate different situations while honoring the self, and how to connect deeply with others from an authentic place of self-knowledge are part of our birthright as humans. Such skills are not commonly taught in school. The Mindful Life Project and other mindfulness programs, however, teach these tools to school-age children. We can cultivate these abilities as personal acts of liberation and self-love. By practicing these skills, we regain agency around how we choose to use our time, our bodies, our life sparks—rather than defaulting to messages of social conformity.

Underground Roots and Ancestral Wells

To understand the origins from which our self grew, let's begin with our roots: our identities, our ancestry, and our unique socialization. In exploring our roots, we can become literate in our own positionality within larger social systems—from our families, to our neighborhoods, to our workplaces, to the larger systematic structures of our societies. Standing firmly in our roots, we are better equipped to grow stronger relationships across difference and support agile alliances among groups.

A wealth of wisdom remains stored in the *cultural taproots* of our lineages. In this process of digging into our ancestral past, we will likely gain invaluable gems as well as have to face the shadows lurking under a veneer of family secrets. We may feel grief as we turn back the pages, learning more about the historical systems of resource extraction and wealth accumulation in the hands of a few. Our picture of where structural power dynamics have advantaged or disadvantaged our ancestors and us becomes more complete. After research and deep processing, those of us who have benefited from these systems may decide to give up unearned power and resources through the form of *reparations* or other restorative processes.

In regenerative agriculture and permaculture, we teach about the pitfalls of growing crops in a monoculture, where one species predominates for tens to thousands of acres. This agricultural system, justified by efficiency, is not resilient in response to disturbances such as pests or disease. We can see this *monoculture mentality* reflected in the homogenization of human culture. When we design polycultures that have multiple species of perennial and annual crops growing in one area, we mimic the inherent diversity and resilience found in nature. This type of farming system can withstand disturbances and still create a yield. Likewise, if we design our lives to step out of the mold of *assimilation* (if we/our families have assimilated) and reconnect to the powerful pluralism of our lineages in a respectful and authentic manner, no doubt we will be stronger in these turbulent times.

In the US and other colonized countries, society has privileged those citizens who conform and assimilate to a homogeneous "normal." There is safety in fitting in. Unfortunately, this safety comes at a cost. We lose contact with our peoples' traditional ways and the connection to aliveness and wholeness that these ways offered our ancestors for millennia. For example, people with light skin color who migrated to the US from diverse places in the northern hemisphere, each with their own set of origin stories, languages, ceremonial practices, etc., have been clumped together into a fabricated racial category of *whiteness*. This form of assimilation was a terrible bargain, where light-skinned people gained racial privilege, but they had to trade it for disconnection from their peoplehood and deculturation, such as the loss of traditional foodways and land practices. This homogenization process is part of how the category of whiteness was created and continues to be recreated.

When we return to the ancestral wells that our forebears dug and we slake our thirst from them, there is no need to drink or steal water from the wells of others. When we draw wisdom and ritual from our own traditions, our impulse to appropriate customs from our less assimilated neighbors' cultures dissolves. Instead, a new Paradigm emerges of sharing water communally around a metaphorical oasis, rather than draining the aquifers of others.

This chapter is dedicated to engaging with the roots of our visible selves—our above ground parts—because systems change must begin in the roots and spread like an underground fire. If only cosmetic change appears on the surface (like the greenwashing of corporate products or the tokenism of diverse representation on nonprofit boards) instead of real changes to Zone 00 worldviews and practices, we will never reach the magnificent visions each of us is here to seed.

Stories of Family and Culture

What do we know of our family stories and mythologies? Some of us who are more connected to our ethnic origins may know family recipes, songs, traditional crafts, or religious practices. Others may only know the names and occupations of two generations before us and lack a cultural connection to our roots. The impact of assimilating into a host culture, while beneficial for survival, has deeply disrupted the *cultural capital* of many families. We are sold experiences or commodities to fill the cultural and spiritual voids we instinctively feel. Many of us don't even know that we feel this disconnection or where to look for true nourishment under the influence of *cultural amnesia.*

It's never too late to start uncovering our family stories and their priceless treasures, along with the tragedies, we may find. The discovery of family names, for instance, can point to our relatives' homelands or their vocations. Tracking patterns of poverty or wealth and all the fluctuations in between can be illuminating. Learning how our families have responded to crisis, to death, to mourning, to renewal, can be inspiring. Learning how devout or agnostic our relatives have been can help us better understand our own beliefs and what may have influenced them. It's illuminating to learn about our inheritances, but it may be difficult for some of us because of adoption and/or family histories of fleeing from persecution, forced violent displacement, and/or enslavement. But even when they're difficult to uncover, there are clues and traces that we can find and research and intuit to slowly discover our family's long lost truths.

Historical trauma is often swept under the rug along with everything else about the past, but its energetic imprint lingers. Often, the assimilation needed to survive in a new host culture is the very mechanism that causes our cultural amnesia. So let's be gentle with ourselves as we embark on learning our family stories.

EXERCISE 1: Ancestral Symbolic Objects

We exist within in a long chain of relatives, those who have walked before us and those to come, and it is an extraordinary privilege to be alive in the present moment. When we understand our work as changemakers within this broader context of time, we can open ourselves to guidance from what ancestral guide Daniel Foor calls "the well ancestors."

Family ephemera contain stories and can elicit sensations or images. Take a moment to think about what you may still have access to from your family of origin. If you were adopted or part of your lineage is unknown, see if there is some artifact or story that resonates with you on an intuitive level, if you are not able to access any archival information from your biological parents' lineages.

Select an object that somehow feels connected to your roots, your family's heritage. It need not be an heirloom if you don't have one. You can also choose a plant or food that has family significance, a type of instrument, or a replica of something that relates to your peoples' past. Notice it, draw it, journal about it, and then share with your Learning Buddy why this object is meaningful to you and what it represents.

With this object, can you think about one of your family's homelands? How far back can you trace where they are from? What languages did they speak and what foods did they eat? How did they worship, if at all? What struggles were they engaged in? Did they come to the place where you currently live by choice or through violent force or fleeing from danger? What messages did they impart to you?

After you spend some time tuning in to the pieces you know and the snippets you have assembled, imagine yourself as a link in the spiral of generations, linking those that have come before you and the generations on their way. Here you stand, alive, today, connected to all of these people across time. What a blessing and privilege! This is a rare moment.

Journal: *Write about this symbolic object and/or share with your Learning Buddy about yourself, using this symbolic object as a focal point for exploring. What values did you observe underlying your stories? Which of these are your own values? How do your roots influence you today? In friendships? In love relationships? In work settings? In community settings? How you think about politics? How you think about the unseen forces or the sacred? How you think about resources? How you think about the Earth?*

What messages from your inheritance did you internalize? Which of these messages is a source of strength and resilience for you? Is there a small offering of gratitude (i.e., a poem, song, intentionally prepared food) you want to give your ancestors for this gift? And which of these messages hinder your growth and healing? Is there a ritual you can create to release these internalized messages that no longer serve you?

This is wonderful exercise that can be easily turned into a group activity and offered in many settings. It has been used in college classes, anti-racism trainings, permaculture courses, Passover seders, and more. Repeating this exercise across time with a group of people can reveal deeper layers of the self and further understanding of our multigenerational histories.

Values, Values, Values

Reflecting on where we've come from and deciding what we want to carry forward and what to lovingly leave behind, we can allow our emerging set of refined Values to guide our decisions and actions. When we live in *integrity* with our Values, our power multiplies. Understanding not just our ancestry and lineages, but also our numerous other social identities, such as gender and socioeconomic class, can shed light on where our Values originate. In the next exercise, we'll get to explore these further dimensions of our inner landscape.

Just as many of us struggle with dedicating the time to define our goals, we can sometimes resist articulating our Values. The Center for Whole Communities has developed "Working With Values" as a core component of their Whole Thinking practices. Take a moment to reflect on the following questions inspired by their work:

- What do you value?
- From what love or pain or longing do these Values arise?
- How are these Values connected to your ancestry or lineages in any way at all?
- What have been the successes, struggles, and risks of leading with your Values?

Journal: *Take a moment to journal or share your responses with a Learning Buddy or group.*

Especially for those of us making change within institutions and organizations, it is imperative that we connect with other leaders who share our Values and who are also willing to take risks in the name of their Values. When we work with others, the process can be slow. Tensions arise between the urgency of the world's crises and the deliberate work of building connections that can slow us down but also strengthen our cause with the power of shared Values.

> *If you want to go fast, go it alone; If you want to go far, go together.*
>
> – A popular proverb (whose origin is difficult to attribute)

EXERCISE 2: Mapping Personal Identities and Histories

How many times have you considered the implications of the various identities you hold or how they inform your Values and worldviews? The more we can understand the privileges we've been granted based on our identities, as well as the various ways our identities are targeted or have been historically, the more effective we will become at pursuing personal healing and systemic social justice. And these two are, of course, inextricably linked.

This exploration of our families' stories is a good starting point to understanding dynamics of *power* and *privilege*. We can go further and lovingly tease apart the layers of our personal social landscapes much like permaculture explores the layers of soil, water, vegetation, and microclimates of a physical landscape. We can explore our tender social layers of race, ethnicity, gender, sexual orientation, gender identity, religious background, and other forms of difference that have strongly shaped our experiences in the world. We can even do the same for our parents, grandparents, and other caregivers. Their identity-based patterns and perspectives have been passed down to us; each of us as descendants carry intergenerational messages atop our unique social composition.

The nuances of these identities and messages go beyond simple categories; their *intersectionality* can contain complex personal, family, and social histories and interactions that help tell the story of where we come from (one dimension of location of the self), and how we have evolved into who we understand ourselves to be today (literacy of the self).

Identity mapping also helps us see ourselves as global citizens of change. Why? From each of our identities, we inherit gifts and challenges. The more we can understand our gifts and challenges as connected to each of our privileged and/or oppressed identities, and not as idiosyncratic or personal characteristics, the more surface area we gain in untangling and re-evaluating the societal messages we've internalized. From there, we can make conscious choices about which beliefs and behaviors we wish to keep from our family's patterning and our unique identities, and which of those beliefs and behaviors we wish to release. With this more intimate knowledge of ourselves in relation to historical and current systems of power, we can extend greater compassion and awareness to others.

This tool of Identity Mapping (used by Power of Hope in Seattle, the Mississippi Coalition for Racial Justice, and other organizations) assists us in connecting the dots between our individual patterns and societal patterns of oppression.

To create your Identity Map:

1. Draw a picture of yourself in the center of a blank piece of paper. Yes, a stick figure is fine!
2. Around this drawing of yourself, write in your different identities for each of these identity or constituency categories. Include lines to connect each category to the drawing of yourself. Please omit interest- or circumstance-based identities that you choose such as "Patriots fan" or "dog owner," and instead stick to mapping identities connected to *power*. The identities we focus on for this exercise are ones that relate to pre-existing power structures that assign certain privileges or discrimination and that *choose you*, in that they are inescapable, such as:

EXERCISE 2: Cont.

- **Ethnic heritage:** geographic area(s), lineage(s), tribal group(s), and culture(s) you come from
- **Racial identity(ies):** keeping in mind that while "race" is a social construction without genetic basis, the *impact* of this social construction is very real
- **Age group:** adolescent, a young adult, in your twenties, thirties, middle age, golden years, elder, etc.
- **Class background:** raised poor, working class, middle class, owning class (those who own the means of production), or mixed class (specify). Class is tricky and squishy. There are always nuances in family backgrounds and upbringing. Perhaps one parent comes from the working class and the other from the owning class. What happens when there are more than two parents who raise a young person? Or if there are attitudes and patterns from one class, but the family income level differs from that class? Also, other experiences that affect class to consider here are families where one or more parents are immigrants or who served as clergy or in the military. How has upward or downward mobility affected your experience of class in any ways? Incarceration? Mental health hospitalization? Notice how these experiences effect the basic categories of class
- **Current socio-economic class:** your current class status may be different from the class(es) you were raised in
- **Gender:** gender is not binary and there are infinitely more genders than male or female. When listing this identity, you can write the gender you were assigned at birth and the gender you currently identify as, if they are different
- **Sexual orientation:** lesbian, gay, bisexual, queer, pansexual, demisexual, heterosexual, asexual, etc.
- **Religious background:** the religion(s) and philosophy(ies) you were raised with, if any, including atheist and agnostic (not knowing)
- **Current religious identification:** if different than the religious practices you were raised with
- **Ability/disability:** is there a hidden or evident disability you live with? are you normatively abled? differently abled?
- **Body type:** fatphobia is very real and painful. Are you someone who has been targeted by it?
- **Relationship status:** single, in a casual relationship(s), a committed open relationship or marriage, a committed monogamous relationship or marriage, etc.
- **Parental status:** are you a parent? A single parent? A parent of many children? Are you raising your child with your spouse? With the child's grandparents? In a polyamorous family with multiple parents? Do you have grown children? Are you raising grandchildren or foster children?
- **Immigrant:** are you an immigrant to the country in which you currently reside? Please note if you are the child of an immigrant, too
- **Nationality:** what country(ies) are you a citizen of? Do you reside in a different country than the one you were born in?
- **Language(s):** are you a native speaker where you live? Is the language that is spoken where you live your second or third language?

Continued on next page

EXERCISE 2: Cont.

- **Education level:** diplomas and/or degrees and/or level of education completed
- **Professional or work-related identity:** food server, unpaid caregiver, entrepreneur, lawyer, student, etc.

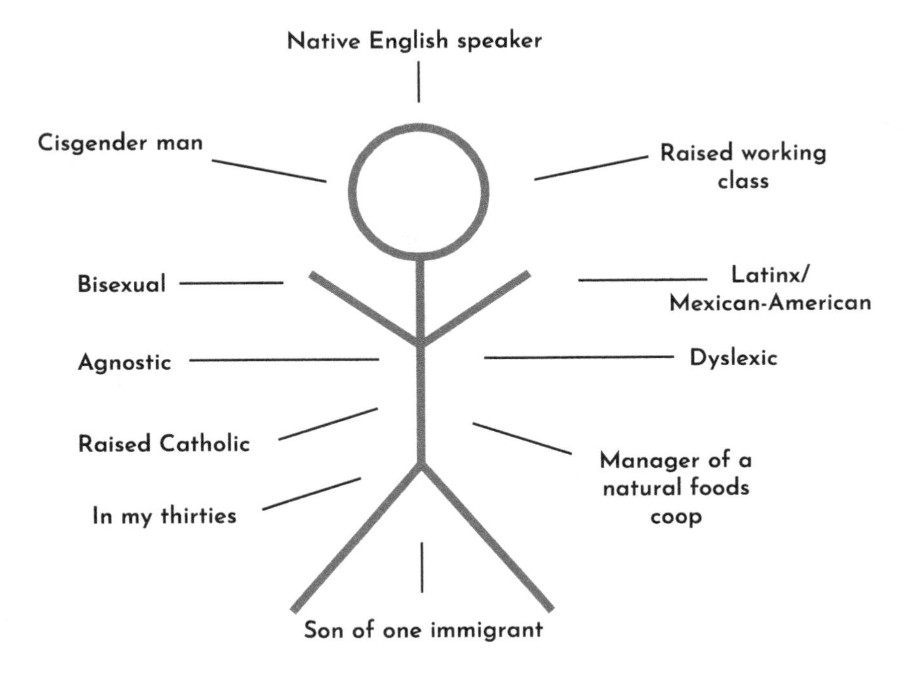

EXAMPLE IDENTITY MAP

Journal: *This exercise is about observing patterns of power, including the dynamics of subordination and domination, privilege and oppression. Through the lens of power, please write a few sentences about each of your identities, addressing:*

- *what you like about each identity (e.g., what are its gifts, benefits, privileges, and/or strengths?)*
- *what is hard or challenging about each identity (e.g., difficulties, societal limitations, and/or experiences of marginalization and oppression?)*
- *what implications do your identities have for you as a changemaker?*
- *which intersections of your identities, such as race and gender or ethnicity and class, complexify or reinforce power dynamics and their effect on you? For example, a son of an immigrant might write, "I like being a son of an immigrant because I know two+ languages and draw strength from the foods, stories, and songs of those cultures. What is hard about being a son of an immigrant is constantly feeling invisible/disregarded in the workplace or in the market because of my accent/not fitting in/being on the margins of both of my cultures, with an added pressure to 'make it' as a man, so that my parent's struggle to immigrate here was not in vain."*

You can facilitate this exercise with a group, and ask another question for willing participants to share with the group: What is one thing you want people who are not in your identity group to know about what it's like to be in this group?

Identity Map Reflection & Integration

This exploration helps to unpack the many facets of ourselves, while also highlighting how our identities have given us greater or lesser amounts of power and privilege. One of the reasons we do this sometimes uncomfortable work of looking at power and oppression is to understand the ways in which we've been systematically divided from each other. In order to create movements of social regeneration, and to restore our full humanity as loving, interconnected beings, we must remove the blocks that have kept us from joining fully with each other. For example, whiteness has allowed light-skinned people to avoid the structural racism that many Black, Indigenous, and People of Color (BIPOC), or *People of the Global Majority*, a powerful reframing that comes from the United to End Racism program, experience on a daily basis. This form of oppression has sliced up the whole world, pitting groups against each other—a strategy that serves the 1% because it keeps everyone else from organizing to create an equitable distribution of resources.

Especially for members of groups who have been assigned societal privilege (white, heterosexual, cisgender male, Protestant, middle or owning class, able-bodied, college educated, US citizens, English speaking, people in their 30s or 40s, etc.), lacking awareness of the sometimes invisible privileges and benefits that come with these identities can make it difficult to share power across differences.

How has this exercise helped you highlight the underbelly of privileged identities and the difficulties that can come along with being members of privileged groups, such as isolation, paranoia, emotional suppression, etc.? Whether we at times land on the side of the oppressed or the side of the privileged, somewhere in our socialization, we all had to be hurt in ways that made us participate in participating in systems of domination and subordination.

Understanding Internalized Oppression

The People's Institute for Survival and Beyond defines *internalized oppression* as "a multi-generational process of disempowerment where you're acting out the definitions of self—as being less than human—given to you by your oppressor." Internalized oppression creates the boxes or personal limitations that we perceive we are in. To make sense of the world, humans internalize illogical and perverse messages, such as racial- or gender-based inferiority, to help create internal worldviews that are consistent with external conditions. We believe the systemic messages of oppression and enforce them on ourselves, and what's worse, we even enforce them on others with whom we share a common oppressed identity. This is how the internalization of oppressive messages keeps systems of power in place: those targeted no longer need an external enforcer to keep delivering oppressive messages. And if one or more of our identities is connected to our lineage, e.g., as a Black Muslim or Mizrachi Jew, the very same oppressions were endured by our parents and ancestors, and those oppressions carried messages that got compounded and passed down to us. These hurtful tape recordings live on inside our heads and within our family's narrative, reinforced by societal patterns of learned behavior, until they are interrupted and brought to light.

Internalizing shame or assigning self-blame is an inevitable outcome of living in an oppressive society that targets everyone, even people with privileged identities. Consider one of the dominant groups: cisgender men. From a young age, boys in the US are typically ridiculed, if not isolated, if they express forms of physical affection, signs of "weakness," or almost any emotion besides anger.

This painful conditioning sets them up to become agents of oppression as adults, toward other men, women, transpeople, and children. Many cisgender men, if honest, share that they feel that they are inherently bad simply because they are a man. This is a form of internalized oppression that we often overlook, and yet it is a linchpin in widely accepted norms of *toxic masculinity*: male domination, sexism, homophobia, state violence, classism, and many other forms of oppression. Re-evaluation Counseling and MERGE for Equality are two examples of anti-oppression organizations that understand and teach about the importance of the role of internalized oppression for identity groups with power. MERGE, for instance, states that it focuses on, "transforming masculinity to advance gender equality...through developing emotionally and socially connected boys."

For those of us who have identities that are not assigned societal power (e.g., gender non-confirming, disabled, poor), it's important that we become agents in our own liberation struggle to undo the effects that historical patterns of oppression have had on us. Hierarchical societies would like oppressed groups to believe and internalize the message that "shortcomings" are personal failures (for example, showing rage, acting neurotic, being controlling, feeling stupid, looking to others for approval). However, these prevalent patterns that persist within identity groups are *symptoms of the oppressive conditions* in which they were socialized. Characterizing these as "shortcomings" serves to excuse the mistreatment of people and to justify assigned inferiority. As changemakers, it's important to understand and be able to identify this twisted tool of oppression.

We can intervene in this insidious cycle by examining the messages that we have internalized and that our people have endured over time (we can also define "our people" beyond blood or cultural lineages and broaden it, e.g., working-class people, queer people, women healers). The first step involves identifying the internalized oppressive messages acting inside each of us, their hosts. Understanding how these messages function goes hand in hand with making an active decision to stop these messages from dictating our lives and using us as their vessels for anchoring the cultural story of division and oppression. This work is difficult, and it is even more difficult to do alone. Breaking up our *isolation*—a strategically generated condition of the oppressive society—by connecting with others with shared identity(ies) in caucuses or support groups allows us to hear one another's stories, listen for resonance, and imagine together our collective liberation.

Social Ecosystems and the Self

Social permaculture is about understanding the multifaceted human connections and our roles in these social ecologies. We can design for regenerative partnerships much like elements of ecosystems produce ecological health together. Through meditating on the associations embodied in ancestral symbolic objects, we have reached back in time to find our connection to our roots and the stories of our families. With Mapping Personal Identities and Histories, we have looked inward at ourselves in relation to external power and the dynamics of privilege. Now we can ask: Who am I right now in relation to others in my personal life story? What do I need to give and receive in order to feel fulfilled? What exchange can I foster in order to interlock my roots underground with neighboring trees for our mutual resilience?

As Zone 00 creatures, moving amidst many overlapping social ecosystems, we can zoom out to better understand ourselves and the *social niche(s)* or positions we occupy. How do we effect other Zones of Relationships (see chapter 6) and situations around us? How do these Zones of Relationships affect us?

To become excellent social designers, we must first know what makes us feel safe, happy, nourished, and loved in group contexts and what makes us feel triggered, threatened, insecure, and scared in the presence of others. Rather than letting feelings catch us by surprise and dictate our experience or thwart our progress, we can become literate in our inner landscapes, which allows us to anticipate these feelings and cultivate ways to work with them. We can create conditions that bring about nourishment and happiness so that we can enjoy our role as social designers and keep up our motivation. Or when a turbulent sea of difficult feelings arises, we can navigate our responses so that we can persist on the course we've set out on. To become intimate with our inner landscapes we also want to ask: What are our needs? What are our offerings or yields? What conditions, people, or feelings seem as if they prey on us? Who are our allies on whom we can rely? As we come to observe and understand our own selves better, we can make requests of others on our behalf, take responsibility for our Unconscious Assumptions, and grow in compassion and understanding for those with whom we collaborate.

EXERCISE 3: Social Niche Analysis

For this exercise, we apply the concept of an ecological niche (a multifunctional role or job within an ecosystem) to ourselves within larger social ecologies. When we understand our niche in the world, we can avoid competition, or what Dave Jacke refers to as resource partitioning. An example of *resource partitioning* from the natural world is the evolutionary strategy of warblers, a type of songbird. Various types of warblers feed on different insect species that they hunt within their own respective height levels within the same forest. They partition their resources so that they avoid competing for food with each other.

Following the warblers' strategy, how can we design ways to thrive alongside others, even in societies that foster individualism and reward competition? How can you use your gifts for the benefit of all and seek mutualistic support in places where you lack certain abilities or feel insecure engaging your abilities? Creating a Social Niche Analysis for yourself and asking others in your social ecosystems to complete one for themselves is a good place to start. Then, see how your yields may link up with what others need and vice versa, designing for *functional interconnection.*

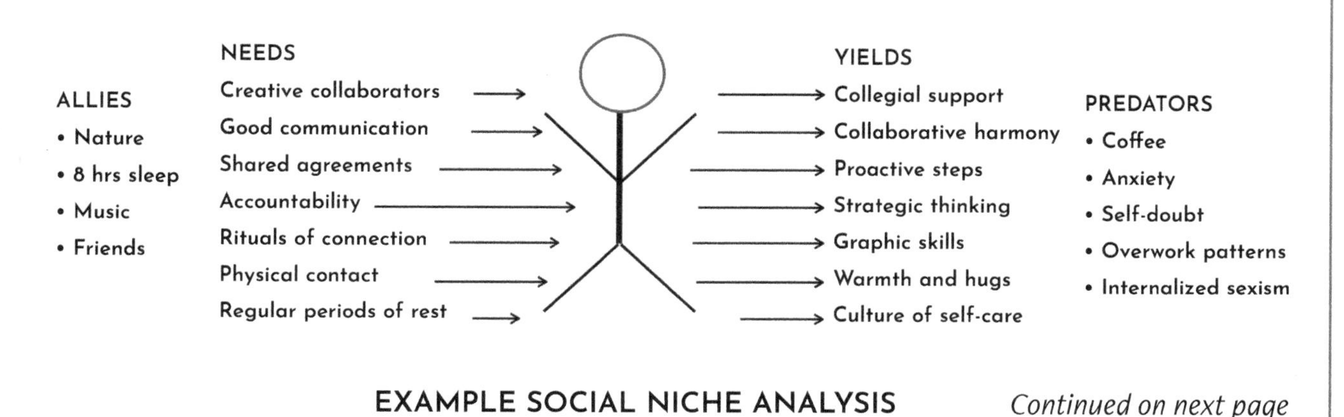

EXAMPLE SOCIAL NICHE ANALYSIS

Continued on next page

EXERCISE 3: Cont.

1. Choose one of the social ecosystems you belong to as the Context of your analysis, for example, the ecosystem of your place of employment, your home, or your mosque or synagogue.
2. Draw a Social Niche Analysis for yourself. Include in your diagram: a drawing of yourself and your needs, yields, allies, and predators. Make sure to use arrows coming in toward yourself for needs and arrows going out from yourself for yields.

Journal: *Begin to play with the analytical approach of regenerative design. What did you notice about your niche? What do these Observations reveal about your role in your defined Context? What Interpretations of the Observations can you make as they relate to the Values you named above? What are some of your Interpretations of your Niche, both as an individual and as a designer of change? Write five Observations and three Interpretations for each Observation.*

(Note: Observations address the "What?" or the patterns you observed. Interpretations address the "So what?" or how these patterns matter in relationship to Values. See chapter 10 for more details on the Analysis and Assessment process.)

Based on the overall pattern of your Social Niche Analysis, which of the following roles from nature would you say you play? Here are some I've thought up:

- ***Soil builder:*** *breaking down waste and turning it into fertility for all*
- ***Cross Pollinator:*** *connecting ideas, people, and places to build stronger social webs and fertile possibilities*
- ***Water catcher:*** *pooling resources when they are available and sharing them later on when they are most needed*
- ***Nitrogen fixer:*** *transforming substances or frameworks and making them accessible and abundant to beings who could not access them independently*
- ***Slope stabilizer:*** *helping to protect the precious resources we still have and maintaining their integrity*
- ***Wetland filter:*** *reducing the toxins bit by bit and slowing down the pulses that seek to overwhelm the system*
- ***Nurse tree:*** *creating habitats and conditions for fledgling life to have a chance to thrive*
- *Or, generate your own nature niche analog that best suits your approach in the world!*

Please see Further Reading related to chapter 1 on page 229.

Social Design Lexicon for Chapter 1

Review the following key terms and write down what they mean to you.

Social Ecosystems:

Location of Self:

Zone 00:

Unconscious Assumptions:

Literacy of the Self:

Cultural Taproots:

Reparations:

Monoculture Mentality:

Assimilation:

Whiteness:

Cultural Capital:

Cultural Amnesia:

Integrity:

Power:

Privilege:

Intersectionality:

People of the Global Majority:

Internalized Oppression:

Toxic Masculinity:

Symptoms of Oppressive Conditions:

Isolation:

Social Niche:

Resource Partitioning:

Functional Interconnection:

CHAPTER 2: EMERGING FROM THE LAYERS WE'VE BEEN ENVELOPED IN

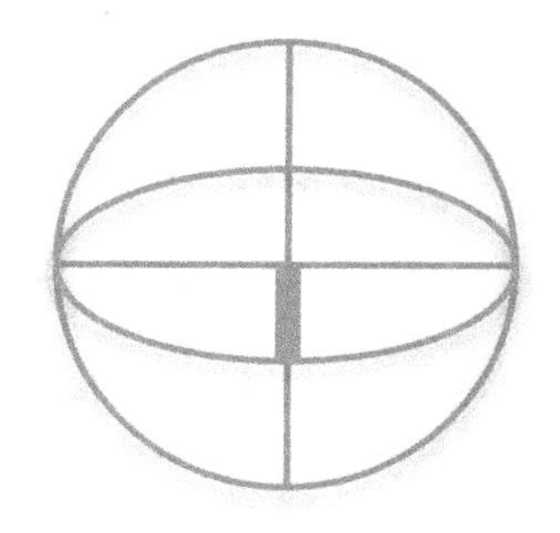

SOUTH: SHOOTS AND FLOWERS/ADOLESCENCE

As we learn to read our internal landscapes, to understand more deeply our metaphorical roots and the outward-facing identities we carry, we sharpen our literacy tools that can detect the protective layers that envelop us, yet also separate us. Oftentimes they can be difficult for us to perceive. Such protection may have been necessary for a period of time, but our tender centers have outgrown their dormancy. In order to emerge like a determined sapling, cracking through the concrete, our old limiting constraints require some careful disintegration. In this chapter we will learn processes for lovingly peeling back the chaff of our outer casing and allowing new light to reach our dormant potential. Much like the twists and turns of adolescence, this work of undoing the barriers that have separated us from each other—such as messages of racial superiority and/or inferiority—is no joyride, but brings with it maturity and an expanded sense of connection and agency.

Building Meta-Capacities: An Antidote to Discouragement

Discouragement: it's epidemic. Multi-billion dollar industries invest in making people feel discouraged, which in turn drives consumption (of material goods, food, drugs, sex, exciting new experiences, etc.) to try to alleviate the discouragement. And round and round the capitalist wheel goes, extracting material resources, exploiting workers, trashing the planet—all generated by our feelings that have been manipulated to compel us to consume.

Developing *meta-capacities* is a process of becoming self-aware of the ways in which we conduct ourselves. We can start by noticing any degenerative *patterns of disempowerment* that limit us. And we can replace them with regenerative *patterns of agency* that embolden us. More specifically, we can cultivate our ability to:

1. observe the places where we feel discouragement or defeat
2. dis-identify with feelings that thwart our creative actions
3. redirect these chronic feelings toward gaining sovereignty from our self-limiting thoughts
4. take actions that create breakthroughs in places where we encountered seeming obstacles

How can we dismantle the *mental boxes* we find ourselves in, and use them to fuel creative change in our lives and communities? Below are some suggestions that Connor Stedman uses in the Ecological Literacy Immersion Program that we co-teach at Omega Institute. We can "metabolize" those mental boxes! On the following page are some suggested ways to transform common mental boxes we may find ourselves in

MENTAL BOXES		METABOLIZING DISCOURAGEMENT
"I can't"	⟶	"Who can?"
"I don't know"	⟶	"Who does?"/ "How can I learn?"
"I don't have enough money"	⟶	"Who has money that I can influence?"
"That didn't work"	⟶	"Let's try something else."
"I'm afraid"	⟶	"Who can do this with me?"
"I'm overwhelmed"	⟶	"What's most important?"
"I'm stuck"	⟶	"I'm about to discover..."

Notice specific limiting thoughts inside your head and record the most common phrases. Then create your own reframing of them. Try putting these new messages up on Post-its around your home or find other ways to be disciplined about metabolizing old limiting thoughts. It's a muscle that can be exercised and strengthened.

There are many other ways to emerge from the right angles and tall walls we perceive/believe surround us:

- **Listen to another perspective.** Doing so actively contradicts the belief that there is only one reality, the one you are living in. Listening to another perspective expands your understanding that your view is only one of many.
- **Become aware of your own boxes.** These are the "recorded conversations" in your head. In permaculture we observe and track patterns. You can be the observer of your inner landscape and identify recurring inner dialogue. Mindfulness and meditation practices are particularly helpful here.
- **See into your box.** See its walls and objectify them, rather than identify with them. How can they become an object that you write about, sing about, make art about? The more we can see these walls clearly, the more we can peek over them to consider what else is possible.

EXERCISE 4: The Boxes We Find Ourselves In

Before you read further in this chapter, take a moment to list the types of boxes, the constraints (real or perceived), that you feel stuck in. For instance, it might feel like you are in a tight financial box and can't seem to get ahead. Or you might be having a creative block and feel unable to produce your next song or painting. Perhaps an addiction has its grip on you. List the categories of boxes (financial, creative block, addiction, etc.) you are struggling with at the moment:

______________________ ______________________

______________________ ______________________

______________________ ______________________

Now, go back to the Mapping Personal Identities and Histories exercise in chapter 1, page 12.

Journal: *Take a moment to write responses to these questions and/or share them with your Learning Buddy.*

- *Which of the boxes that you have listed might be related to larger societal messages or narratives running in your head? Which are unique to you?*
- *How many of the boxes that you listed here relate to larger patterns of power, privilege, or oppression connected to your various identities?*
- *How have messages that you have internalized and now hold as beliefs combine with the constraints of very real circumstances to land you in these boxes today?*

EXERCISE 5: Nine Dots

An engaged experience of boxes helps us to learn more about their rules and their secret passages. To experience this, please draw nine dots on a piece of paper. Without picking up your pen, draw four straight and connected lines to connect all nine dots. Once you've made a few attempts, you can locate the solution at the end of the chapter on page 34. Then read on.

The purpose of this exercise here is to represent symbolically the boxed-in limitations we project, often unconsciously, onto situations. Creativity offers infinite solutions for any one problem. The trick is finding the access point to our creative genius below the thick protective layers we've built.

When we came into this world, we had a willpower that never gave up, at first. Think of the strength of a baby's cry. Through various messages and feedback we received in childhood, such as "stop dreaming, that will never happen" or "you live in la-la land" or "it's not worth it," we started to lose some of our personal agency and constructed mental barriers boxing in our dreams. As adults, we have built up our stockpile of discouragement, making it easier to get deterred, even in a simple exercise. If you figured out the solution—congratulations! Here's the good news and the bad news: the box is in our heads.

Difference, Power, and Privilege

We can start to unravel these multigenerational global stories of feeling boxed in to one corner or another by applying an analysis of difference, power, and privilege. Patriarchy and male domination, or caste systems and slavery, for instance, have been boxing people in place on this planet for millennia. These oppressive systems still operate, and their effects are compounded in the psyches of each new generation. Epigenetic research now shows that these experiences of oppression become recorded in our very genes and are transmitted to the next generation.

Intergenerational traumas may persist as unconscious material running in the background. It is important to face what we are up against in the social contexts we're designing for. Structural violence is one cause of the protective layers we've developed to cope with the trauma that's accumulated over generations. This buildup of trauma and related scar tissue needs gentle, dedicated attention from each of us, toward ourselves and others, to gracefully heal these compounded hurts. The fields of *restorative justice* and *transformative justice*, from interpersonal to international reconciliation efforts, offer brilliant ways forward on this path. There is much to learn from communities leading on this front, from South Africa's Truth and Reconciliation Commission to Rwanda's traditional community-based court system, Gacaca, to Canada's restorative justice programs for court diversion.

A commitment to ongoing and rigorous sociopolitical systems analysis reduces the likelihood of replicating old unconscious and harmful patterns. This type of commitment is especially important for those whose privilege allows them to choose when they do and don't want to look at the impacts of power and oppression.

Understanding the concepts of difference and privilege is one lens that I've found helpful for analyzing social power.

A significant pattern we can observe in all of nature, including humanity, is diversity. People are different from one another in thousands of ways. Our social systems and interpersonal relationships are as diverse and complex as the natural world. This diversity is normal, natural, and healthy.

What is contrived and unhealthy is how differences have become stratified into boxes over time. Those with certain identities have gained economic, social, and political privilege over others. Those identity groups (such as the ruling class, monarchs, imperialists) have gone on to build systems of power to reinforce their privilege. They have used these systems to coerce others to actively oppress and disempower those with non-privileged identities.

It's illuminating to visually map the most basic building blocks of oppression that keep us divided from each other. Kaylynn Sullivan TwoTrees and Mathew Kolan, who teach at the University of Vermont and on our teaching team at the Ecological Literacy Immersion Program at Omega Institute, have created a useful frame for examining racism, sexism, classism, homophobia, anti-Jewish oppression, and other forms of structural discrimination. They identify four steps in a process they call Privilege as Practice:

1. **Differences** (natural genetic diversity of any species)
2. **Differences ⟶ Preference** (over time, certain differences become preferred)
3. **Differences ⟶ Preference ⟶ Privilege** (these preferred identities are assigned privileges)
4. **Differences ⟶ Preference ⟶ Privilege ⟶ Power** (those with power build systems to uphold their privileges over time within the structures of a society)

Social systems analysis must go hand in hand with action—stepping out of our small comfortable boxes, taking risks and moving toward each other, together designing the bold new world we yearn to inhabit.

Mapping What's Conscious and Claiming What's Not

Imagine an iceberg towering above the surface of the ocean. It appears enormous, mountain-like, and yet most of its mass is under water. The visible portion is only a small percentage of the whole. In a similar way, our surface-level opinions and actions may only represent a small fraction of our whole selves. Deeper components such as *worldviews*, belief systems, unexpressed gifts, residual trauma, and neurological patterning all lie below the surface. These less conscious aspects of ourselves can create unintended consequences in our work and our personal well-being when they remain submerged.

The well-known map of Competence Cycles, or Four Stages of Competence, serves as a useful visual tool to understand how our own icebergs function.

Know what you Know (KK) Quadrant/conscious competencies: our Comfort Zone, where we are skilled and we know it.

Know what you Don't Know (KD) Quadrant/conscious incompetencies: our edge, where we are aware that we lack skill, and accept or feel insecure about our lack of competence.

Don't know what you Know (DK) Quadrant/unconscious competencies: where our hidden gifts reside. Bringing them up into our awareness, usually with the help of a friend who can reflect these gifts back to us, allows us to engage with them more powerfully. When we can't see our own gifts or don't take ownership of them, it can be a liability to us and others.

Don't know what you Don't Know (DD) Quadrant/unconscious incompetencies: where we find out we were wrong, where we are off base and couldn't tell. Bringing our unconscious incompetencies up into our awareness offers us a chance to work deliberately on improving our skills.

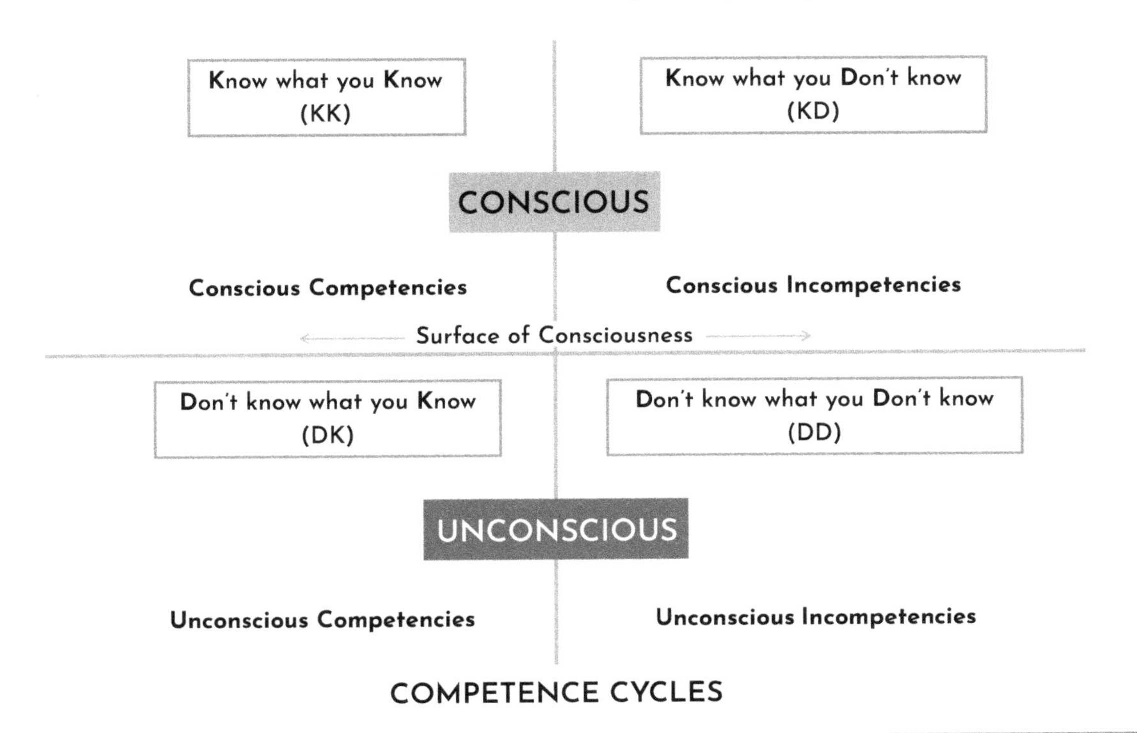

COMPETENCE CYCLES

EXERCISE 6: Strengths & Gifts, Unconscious Assumptions & Hurts

Moving forward in designing change can be counterproductive if we lack awareness of our own selves. If we are not conscious of the patterns we embody and radiate outward, we run the risk of recapitulating the same, often unconscious, dynamics that we are seeking to transform in our change-making projects. A popular saying, frequently attributed to Albert Einstein, aptly sums this up: "Insanity is doing the same thing over and over again and expecting different results."

When we work to claim our full range of conscious and unconscious corners, and from that place make new choices, then we grow as individuals. This process, repeated over time, is one way we can regenerate ourselves anew and engage in personal change-making.

After reading through the above frameworks and synthesizing your insights from chapter 1, please reflect on:

What **Strengths** and **Gifts** do you have personally (from who you are intrinsically, from events you have experienced in your lifetime, from gifts assigned to you by your family or society)? Please list at least five of them here. If this is difficult to do, then ask your closest loved ones what strengths and gifts they see in you:

1. ______________________________
2. ______________________________
3. ______________________________
4. ______________________________
5. ______________________________

What **Unconscious Assumptions** and **Hurts** do you hold (from your personal life, your family story, or societal conditioning)? Again, if this is difficult to do, then ask your closest loved ones what they observe in you:

1. ______________________________
2. ______________________________
3. ______________________________
4. ______________________________
5. ______________________________

Journal: *Before you fully acquaint yourself with the Regenerative Design Process (the focus of section II), please journal about how you would design a shift in one specific aspect of your personal life. Examples might be healing a relationship with a family member, transforming your work habits, expanding your artistic expressions, or improving your health and nutrition.*

Articulate three Goals for this aspect of your life. Then, make some Design recommendations. Questions to address: How you would harness your strengths and gifts in service to this shift? In what ways would you thoughtfully work with your Unconscious Assumptions and hurts to design a shift in this aspect of your life?

Unconscious Assumptions

Becoming more aware of the DD/"Don't know what you Don't Know" quadrant in the Competence Cycle can often bring discomfort. Instead of using ableist language of "blind spots," we call this material our Unconscious Assumptions. This corner is where an "oops" moment may take place in a social interaction, when someone or a group of people kindly or angrily point out something beyond your awareness.

In cultures that appear to be addicted to comfort, we can ask, what are people attempting to cover up? Is there a deep discomfort with conflict? For others, we might ask, are there intolerable feelings of terror that people urgently wish to avoid? Does an entire ethnic group or class of people feel shame or remorse, or anger and grief, about their status in society and the historical events that led to up to these circumstances?

We may attempt to avoid conversations, situations, or whole groups of people different from ourselves who might illuminate these painful parts of our personal and/or societal iceberg. But periods of discomfort, accompanied by moments for pause and integration, are worthy of celebration. They can lead to growth and the development of new capacities, as we move material out of our lower unconscious quadrants and up to our conscious awareness.

Without taking risks and venturing to an uncomfortable edge from time to time, we can never know what's possible beyond our perceived limitations, nor realize our unlimited potential. Much like adolescent growing pains, if we want to progress, we will have to feel some burn.

Understanding these aspects of the DD quadrant is another powerful way to explore the contours of privilege. This unconscious corner is where our lack of awareness about our own privilege can fester. It is hard to see something that is stuck on our back. We cannot see it unless someone else or some series of situations lets us know that something is stuck there. Privilege is similar: We cannot see the unearned privileges we have until we hear another voice or version, until we contrast our experience with that of someone who does not have the same privileges. It takes a lot of looking and dredging up that which is below the surface of our consciousness, of seeing the walls and then deconstructing the boxes we've been assigned.

As we commit to taking steps toward change and relinquishing some of our privilege, a flow much like an ocean's current begins to course through us. We move the unconscious material of our iceberg up from the ocean's depth and toward the surface waters of our consciousness.

Our unconscious material become conscious incompetencies, shadowy places that we know are there. From this awareness, we can take steps to move our awareness of our own privilege into the quadrant of KK, or conscious competency.

Likewise, in the places where we try to hide our gifts from ourselves—for fear of being too bright, too outrageous, too powerful—we can begin to name and claim our gifts as we move them into the light of our consciousness. Liberation is contagious and spreads to others like fire. The more we can access our collective liberation, the more we can direct our shared power to join movements for healing, justice, and cultural regeneration.

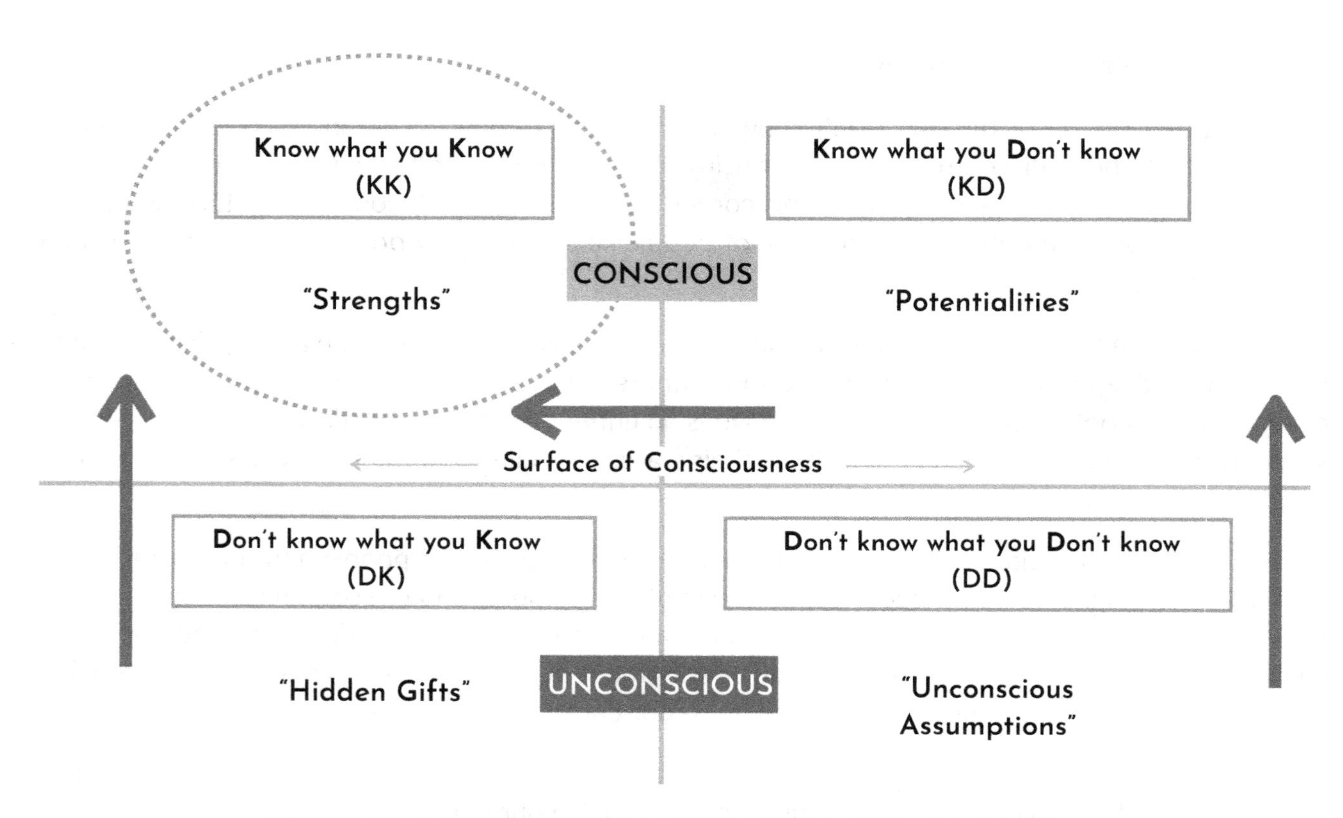

MOVING UNCONSCIOUS MATERIAL TO THE SURFACE

Tracking and Transforming Our Patterns: Zone 00 Justice Work

As we experiment with creating new regenerative cultures, each identity group in our social ecosystems (e.g., age group, religious sect, Indigenous Nation) must be valued and included. Nature does not leave out anyone or anything in its marvelous workings. So too can we create new systems that produce no waste, no throwaway people or places. With this blueprint of nature as our model for rebuilding our broken relationships and inclusivity, it then becomes impossible to ignore systems of power that have purposely divided and disadvantaged certain groups of people, systems with which we often collude consciously or unconsciously.

Our hearts would never choose to participate in systems that have historically divided people and dehumanized everyone in the process. And yet, the ways in which the world is set up and interlocks with the hurts we carry makes it nearly impossible to do otherwise. But even in the midst of these coercive oppressive systems, our species has done its best throughout history—despite the dominant Paradigms of each period and the limited tools we have had available—to resist and reform these systems. An excerpt from the article "A Critical Mass for Real Food" in *Yes!* magazine, authored by Anim Steel, co-founder of The Real Food Challenge, beautifully illustrates this point:

> A wooden door on a busy London street below a hand-painted sign reads "print shop." You'd probably miss it if you were just passing by. If you were standing outside of it in one morning in 1787, you might have seen 12 men, mostly Quakers, go inside for a meeting.
>
> To imagine a world without slavery then would be like imagining a world without oil today—and who would be crazy enough to propose that?
>
> That meeting sparked the beginning of the British Anti-Slavery Society, and the very first citizens' campaign of its kind. Its members ran petitions, lobbied parliament, and staged book tours, pioneering many of the social movement tactics we still use today. When those men walked through that door, the whole world economy was built on slave labor.
>
> In 10 years, this group of 12 swelled to hundreds of thousands. And in just a few decades, it did the unthinkable: It ended the slave trade throughout the British Empire.

I am hopeful that humanity will continue on with resistance work, pairing it with the power of our imaginations to envision and transform systems based on wholeness and reciprocity. As Chinese American thought leader Grace Lee Bogs put it, "We need to connect visionary work with resistance work; one is not possible without the other. Both are essential parts of a more holistic movement for change." And social permaculture teaches us how to identify the patterns and principles of a system, which is essential for making changes that can disrupt and transform it.

As we boldly step forward on a path toward justice, we must face the shadows of our culture(s) or nation(s) that linger in areas beyond our awareness. Many of us around the planet have conditioned patterns that are enforced by oppression and *worldviews of scarcity*—the notion that we need to exploit others and hoard resources if we are to survive. These conditioned patterns make it difficult to observe, or even want to observe, structural patterns of social inequity. These issues are not only outside of us. We absorbed these messages from what Jungian psychoanalyst Clarissa Pinkola Estés calls "the over-culture"; part of them reside in our own worldviews and unconscious lower quadrants. Justifications for upholding social inequity based on differences between people have been internalized and normalized by both oppressor and oppressed.

Understanding our personal patterns, as an element of any system, is equally important to becoming literate in the system at large. We can apply the metaphor of tracking animals out in nature to tracking our journey through our internal landscapes. *Inner tracking* (or self-observation) aids us in uprooting patterns of oppression that we were indoctrinated with, and in understanding our own role in acting as diligent agents working on behalf of oppressive systems. We can interrupt this cycle starting with self-observation. We should not do this out of feelings of shame or charity toward our oppressed kin. Reclaiming the parts of our minds that were colonized by misguided and divisive ideologies such as racism, classism, and xenophobia is extremely healing. In so doing, we can live bigger lives, expanding the relationships and experiences we can have as part of a multicultural and super-lovable human family. This mental liberation is a gift we get to give ourselves. It also serves *multiple functions*: It uproots the mental constructs of oppression held inside individuals, one person at a time. In turn, these individuals can stand in *solidarity* with those who are still oppressed and build coalitions for lasting change.

> *Many of our white brothers, as evidenced by their presence here today, have come to realize that their destiny is tied up with our destiny. And they have come to realize that their freedom is inextricably bound to our freedom.*
>
> – Dr. Martin Luther King, Jr., from "I Have a Dream" speech

To be an ally in solidarity with those who have less privilege than ourselves means we are growing in *power-with* and relinquishing *power-over*. Patterns of white supremacy in a multiracial place of work, for instance, can include white people being the dominant speakers in a meeting, setting the agenda without soliciting input from Black, Indigenous, and People of Color (BIPOC) colleagues, or making unilateral decisions on behalf of those who are BIPOC without consulting them. These are examples of power-over dynamics. To embody and practice a power-with approach necessitates building authentic relationships, trust, and redistributing power. In the workplace, for example, white people would listen first before speaking in meetings, collaborate with BIPOC colleagues in setting the agenda well in advance, and participate in democratic decision-making facilitated by those who are BIPOC. And white people will need to relinquish any compulsions to micromanage how these shifts in power occur, understanding that BIPOC colleagues may not do things in the same way.

Perhaps the next step on our developmental journey in uprooting oppression is learning how to grow from being an *ally* who backs others into an *accomplice* who stands with others on the front lines, shoulder to shoulder. Although the word "accomplice" is typically used to talk about wrongdoings, I want to repurpose it. Going beyond ally-ship sometimes means putting your body on the line or breaking the law. "Ally" as a verb, however, has more gravitas than "ally" as a noun; it's something you do, an action. To ally a group of people or an individual from that group is a practice in that we can take on. In forging these relationships, we peel away our learned fear of "the other" and intentionally release our desire for insular safety. We can actively dismantle the guarded layers that we were indoctrinated with as young people and that circumscribed our lives within smaller and smaller social circles. With a commitment to this righteous Zone oo justice work, we can track and transform the struggles for power-over that live inside all of us.

> *Justice is love in public and tenderness is love in private.*
>
> – Cornel West, Seeds of Change Conference at Omega Institute

Unpacking Racism

Racism hurts everyone, and it functions as one of the primary wedges that keeps humanity divided. In a world without racism, coordinated efforts across cultures and countries toward collective planetary regeneration would become much more possible.

When we hear the word "racist," some of us often think about a person rather than an institution or organization. Racism is an ideology, a socially constructed belief system and societal enforcement of privileging and empowering select groups over others for exploitation and resource gain. Racism, then, points to power structures that perpetuate injustices that go beyond individual acts of bigotry. Even if a person with racial privilege is not engaging in interpersonal acts of racism, it is still critical that they work to dismantle structural racism and their internalized sense of racial superiority. When we remain inactive in the movements to end racism, we collude with structural racism and the continuation of trauma and inequality.

Racism is a relatively recent social construction, only dating back to the 17th century when scientific racism, based on pseudo-scientific phrenology studies of human skull sizes, evolved as a way to justify inferiority and superiority within the human species. Identification of Jews as a "subhuman" group during the 13th and 14th centuries in Europe was perhaps a template for what later morphed into racism based on skin color and physical characteristics. Four hundred years later, we still live with the devastating effects of this worldview, including health disparities, mass incarceration, resource inequity, state-sanctioned violence, and countless deaths.

Racism divides the people of this planet from joining in a coordinated effort toward economic justice and planetary regeneration in a time of human atrocities and climate crisis. An understanding of the specific role of racism in this "chaos point" in history can serve as our North Star for designing change.

A clear analysis of who has power and who does not across lines of difference helps clarify the role of power in racism.

> *Racism = Prejudice + Power*
>
> – Patricia Bidol-Pavda, Developing New Perspectives on Race

How can you tell what someone's race is: by their hair? Their name? Country they live in? Skin color? Facial features? Their language? The answer to all of these questions is a resounding no. What then is race? Geneticists have shown that there is no biological basis for racial distinctions. These distinctions occur solely in the social realm. When we try to pinpoint race, we begin to see it is a powerful social construction used to manipulate people and justify the appropriation of resources.

What is prejudice? How does it function? Prejudice can operate in many circumstances and across scales, from structural to interpersonal. Federal policies produce *structural racism* and inequity based on racial prejudice. The Federal Housing Administration (FHA) in the US, for example, denied Veterans of Color returning from World War II access to low-interest mortgages and affordable homes.[1] Another example of structural racism in the US is that people working as farm laborers and domestic workers were not covered under Social Security until recently. These jobs were disproportionately held by African Americans and Latinxs (a gender-neutral term for people with Latin American heritage), who could not accumulate savings from these benefits and pass down wealth to their children.

Racism can also occur on an individual basis between people. Fearful socialization of "the other" creates a cultural milieu that normalizes oppression and sanctions individual acts of discrimination. For example, landlords or hotel staff may refuse to rent an apartment or a room to a Person of Color, a common practice with few legal consequences. These *interpersonal acts* of racism are painful and dehumanizing, can have personal and professional consequences, and can trigger exasperation, anger, and despair about the effects of larger structural oppressions that people keenly feel on a daily basis.

Prejudice can be directed across any line of difference; even those with less racial privilege can discriminate against those with more racial privilege. However, racism necessarily includes a power-over dynamic. When someone with less racial privilege discriminates against someone with more racial privilege, this act does not fall under the definition of racism that I use and that experts in the field are using. Some call this form of discrimination "reverse racism." But following the definition of Racism = Prejudice + Power, reverse racism cannot exist, because there are no structural systems of power or historical patterns backing those with less privilege. When a person with racial privilege discriminates against someone with less racial privilege, that does fall under our definition of racism. A power-over dynamic is involved. It is especially essential for people with *white privilege* to grapple with this seemingly nuanced understanding of power. For those who have been targeted by racism, this nuance is not subtle at all. It is an example of how Unconscious Assumptions work for those with privilege.

The Illusion of Racial Superiority

Deconstructing the ways our minds have been colonized—with unhealthy and unnatural messages about our inferiority and superiority to others—helps to liberate us from our mental boxes. In particular, we can decide to look at our own feelings of superiority. Again, it's important to understand that white people should not do this work to alleviate feeling badly about oneself as a white person. Nor should this work be undertaken in order to look good or "woke" in the eyes of others. Instead, white people can make a positive, proactive choice to do this work for our own growth, to dissolve a pattern of withholding, inside ourselves. And we can do this work in connection with other white people rather than in isolation.

For those of us who struggle with feelings of superiority at times, the dismantling of these feelings and perspectives allows us to access a much wider slice of life and experience a greater extent of belonging. When we clench our muscles in learned disdain for others, we lose access to connection with most of the world. This posture is extremely painful and isolating, held in place under a mirage of believing we "got the better end of the stick." No amount of financial wealth or racial privilege can compensate for loneliness and, ultimately, feelings of insecurity—the other side of the coin of superiority.

For white readers, below are some clues that are helpful in unpacking the internalized superiority that most, if not all, white people have felt at some point. Knowing that defensiveness and what white scholar and author Robin DiAngelo refers to as *white fragility* are socialized into most white people from an early age, please be aware that some of the points on this list may not feel accurate for you at first. Take time to digest them. If you are white, consider how you might possibly carry these patterns, consciously or unconsciously. At the same time, we can hold the knowledge that all people, including white people, are good people, and that no single person is responsible for present-day or historical racism. No one came into this world looking to be an oppressor, and all individuals in oppressor identity groups were systematically hurt when they learned to play the role of the oppressor through painful socialization, as the saying "hurt people hurt people" from Rabbi Yehuda Berg suggests. (Think of boys/those raised male who are ridiculed for seeking affection from others, crying, or showing signs of vulnerability. This painful treatment leads to boys' isolation, repression of their humanity, and anger, setting them up for their role in the larger systems of male domination and patriarchy as they become adults.)

The process of looking at the illusory walls of the box of racial superiority can feel like growing pains we experience during adolescence. Disturbances to the status quo lead to discomfort. When Donald Trump was elected president, many white liberals were shocked and for the first time felt the kind of national duress that many US citizens of Color, immigrants, and Indigenous communities had been experiencing for centuries. However, discomfort is necessary for systemic transformation, and will lead to all peoples' liberation, including white peoples'. In the wake of Trump's presidency, we've seen more women and candidates of Color successfully winning state and national seats in Congress, being appointed by the Biden administration, and not to mention, electing a Black Indian-heritage woman vice president. This is not quite systemic transformation, but this trend is certainly beckoning it forth.

We all must do this essential uprooting racism work together. Racism divides the working class from organizing to demand better pay and working conditions. Along with classism, racism separates the 99% (those who are not in the elite owning class) from mobilizing a movement for resource redistribution. Racism even separates people into different entities working to address environmental disasters. How much stronger would a movement to protect the environment be if the white environmentalists working on land and water preservation could bridge the gap to work with Native communities resisting fossil fuel extraction on their sovereign territory, and with Black, Indigenous, and People of Color around the globe working as activists for climate justice?

White folks were not born asking for positions of social domination, and it is not our fault, but it *is* our responsibility—since we are the ones alive now—to take leadership in cleaning up the multigenerational mess of *white supremacy*.

Indicators of Internalized Racial Superiority

To identify when racial superiority is at work inside us, we need signposts. Here are a few mental and behavioral indicators from the People's Institute for Survival and Beyond's training Undoing Racism, for people who benefit from having light-colored skin, by which they have greater ease in accessing housing, education, employment, healthcare, etc.

- **Denial of Racism:** claiming "color-blindness" or that everyone gets to choose their lot in life/a worldview of "meritocracy"
- **Individualism:** wanting to be treated as an individual and resisting being collectivized/grouped with other whites

- **Distancing:** separating from other white people rather than thoughtfully intervening and "calling in" white friends, co-workers, and family members when they show their racism
- **Escapism:** highlighting ways that one has been victimized or targeted as a diversionary tactic, in order to avoid looking at one's own behaviors or racism at large
- **Presumption of Authority and Competence:** believing "white is right," the historical legacy of European colonialism/white people being in charge and setting the standards by which all people are judged

EXERCISE 7: Responding to and Transforming Feelings of Internalized Racial Superiority

Here's where all of us, BIPOC and white people, can engage in some honest self-reckoning. This can be a long process, so it's important to be gentle with ourselves as we take on the undoing of hundreds of years of racism, on the heels of thousands of years of oppression and slavery!

Journal: *Questions to write about or explore with a Learning Buddy:*

- *What active role do I have in keeping my individual beliefs and defending my worldviews?*
- *What aspects of privilege and interpersonal power-over dynamics do I unconsciously collude with? How might these power dynamics be impacting others? How do they impact me?*
- *What active role do I have in keeping oppressive and exploitative institutional structures going?*
- *Which of the indicators of racial superiority can I honestly say I exhibit?*
- *How has racism separated and damaged me/my family/my people?*
- *Who are my Accountability Buddies and Accomplices in transforming these patterns—so I don't have to try to do it alone?*

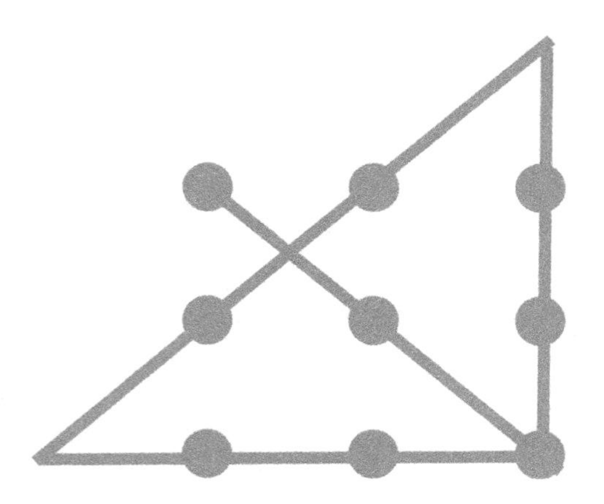

9 Dots Solution

Here's the solution: you need to draw outside the box that you perceive is there!

Please see Further Reading related to chapter 2 on page 231.

Social Design Lexicon for Chapter 2

Review the following key terms and write down what they mean to you.

Meta-capacities:

Patterns of Disempowerment vs. Patterns of Agency:

Mental Boxes:

Restorative Justice:

Transformative Justice:

Worldviews of Scarcity:

Inner Tracking:

Multiple Functions:

Solidarity:

Power-over vs. Power-with:

Ally vs. Accomplice:

Interpersonal Acts of Racism vs. Structural Racism:

White Privilege:

White Fragility:

White Supremacy:

CHAPTER 3: CHOOSING TO BEAR FRUIT RATHER THAN HIDING IN THE SHADE

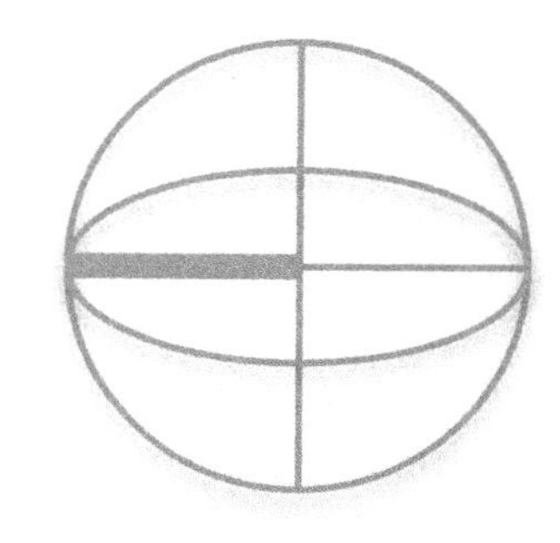

WEST: FRUIT/ADULTHOOD

There is a wealth inside you. You know it. You can feel it in your roots, in the strength of your structure, in the expression of your soft leaves opening. And yet every tree can choose to refrain from bearing fruit. To produce glorious fruit is a decisive action, not one by default.

Bearing fruit is also courageous: By putting your effort into its flesh, storing your secrets in its seeds, new orchards can take your place when you've fallen. To show the fruits of your labor can be vulnerable, exposing such gorgeousness to the outside. To bear fruit often involves a sacrifice somewhere else in the energy bank of one's life. This labor of love is available to all trees, but only some who sprout up in the shade of the canopy will take the journey of growing tall and up into the light, transforming sunlight into fruitful offerings for the generations to come.

How does nature create a symbiotic balance so that the mother tree can sustain her own nourishment while also sharing her offerings with the world so it too can be nourished? This is the challenge of the initiated adult: striking a balance between stopping before extending oneself to the brink of exhaustion and playing small with all the protections of fearfulness or self-preoccupation. Without marked rites of passage, we wander blindly into adulthood (or the maturation of our projects), without the awareness that we have crossed a *threshold*. The importance of taking time to notice this change, and even marking it with a ritual, cannot be understated. Being witnessed by others and externalizing our transitions so that they happen not just internally, but also anchored in community rituals, fortifies us as we enter a new stage. How can we bring forth our *hidden gifts* through consciously crossing a threshold that opens us to the trials, the joy, and the tenderness of being fully alive?

This chapter weaves together what we have explored in chapters 1 and 2. After becoming rooted to the Earth and sending new shoots of awareness from the darkness up into the light of day, we come to a place of terrestrial unfolding. In this phase, supportive branches bearing fruit emerge. When we are in service to something greater than ourselves, we can both produce a bountiful harvest and feel deeply nourished in a *loop of reciprocity*, exchanging our breath with the world's.

Personal Regeneration and Radical Self-Care

Our creations are reflections of ourselves. If we are not mindful of the quality of our personal inputs (food, social environments, media, etc.), our masterpieces will be flawed. As cultural artists at the core, it is important for us changemakers to cultivate inner balance and awareness so that our projects develop new concentric rings in the image of our own health. Consider what happens when our central heartwood, to recall the metaphor from the structure of trees, develops injury or rot?

The integrity of our new growth rings erodes, and ultimately our strength is undermined over time. The Jewish practices of *Shabbat* and *Shmita* are cultural blueprints in the Islamic-Judeo-Christian tradition that prioritize observing downtime, every week on *Shabbat* and for a whole year every seven-year cycle during *Shmita*.

The Zones of Use permaculture planning concept introduced in chapter 1 is helpful for understanding the importance of self-care. From Zone 0 (the house), to Zone 5 (the wild lands) on a farm, there must be a healthy steward traversing the zones. This steward, Zone 00, is the nucleus of all they are tending. If they do not care for their body and soul—Zone 00—then the Zone 0 house becomes chaotic. And if the house is not maintained, the Zone 1 garden goes neglected. When these first few zones are overlooked, that neglect ripples out, and the chickens in Zone 2 and sheep in Zone 3 are not well cared for, and the orchard in Zone 4 develops disease, and the babbling brook in Zone 5 gets sullied, and so on.

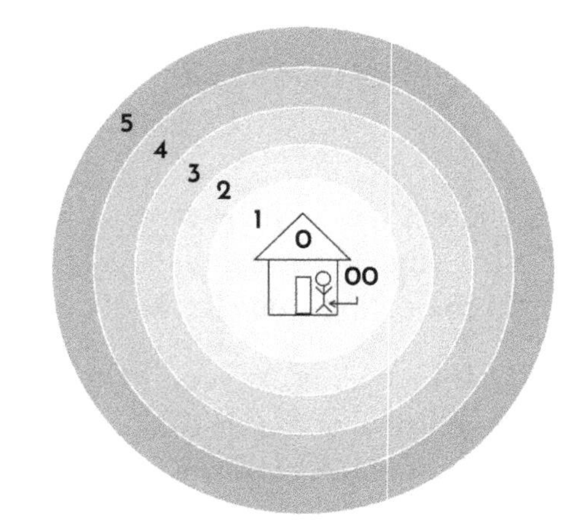

ZONES OF USE CONCEPT DIAGRAM

Tree Rot at the Center Radiates Out

The permaculture model of Zones of Use reveals the importance of ongoing personal regeneration. Not only is it essential that our projects are carefully planned and attended to, we also have to attend to ourselves: we are precious and our lives are gifts that deserve devoted care. By treating ourselves with kindness, rest, and nourishment, we set the standard for the projects we are stewarding and model the same for others. We create a culture shift in the concentric rings around us when we practice these values at the center. Huge liabilities for any project occur when a team member shows up drained on a regular basis—which can look like a loss of integrity with agreements, resentfulness, or even resignation. "Disease" at the core radiates out and affects all the projects that surround it.

This chapter offers you a cornucopia of exercises to help you cultivate practices of personal regeneration, abundance creation, and generosity.

EXERCISE 8: Personal Wellness Goals

Inspired by what you uncovered in your exploration of Values, Values, Values (see page 11), can you articulate three to five Personal Wellness Goals? Goals focused on self-care help changemakers navigate professional decisions efficiently and with confidence. We can develop the ability to discern in the moment which response aligns with our Goals: a clear "No," a considered "Not now, I'll have to get back to you later," or an enthusiastic "Yes! That aligns with my Values and Wellness Goals."

Using present tense active voice, a powerful approach from Dave Jacke, articulate your Personal Wellness Goals for a defined period of time (two weeks, six months, etc.). Writing your goals in complete sentences with a clear subject and active verb puts your statement in active rather than passive voice. It declares who or what is the instrument you need for realizing your Wellness Goals. Articulating your goals as if they are already happening (in present tense) allows your mind to incorporate the new reality of your goals being met, and it calls forth support from the universe to do so. Avoid future tense such as, "Daily exercise *will revitalize*..." or conditional tense, "Daily exercise *could revitalize*...if I..." Instead, write something like, "Daily exercise revitalizes my body with health and energy." Consider writing concrete Objectives for each goal, using bold to highlight key ideas, and vary the subject rather than starting each goal with "I do XYZ."

Journal: *Take a moment to articulate these goals in writing and then share them with a Wellness Buddy (different from a Learning Buddy)—someone who you know and love and who could benefit from these exercises and having you as their Wellness Buddy! We will return to your wellness goals later in the chapter.*

Discussion 1: Personal Regeneration and Gratitude

With your Wellness Buddy, take turns to each discuss the following:

- What do you think the importance of preventative self-care is for visionary leaders, community organizers, and other changemakers? How often do you see this modeled or how often do you model it yourself?
- What do you think the role of gratitude might be in the healing or mending of the world? What role might gratitude play in the lives of those of us who are changemakers, who are often motivated because we perceive the brokenness of the world?
- What is one small commitment you can make right now for practicing gratitude today or this week?

EXERCISE 9: Comfort Zone / Edge Zone / Panic Zone

One way to increase literacy of the self is by learning to identify and consciously working with our Comfort / Edge / Panic Zones.

We are in our *Comfort Zone* when we feel relaxed, safe, and confident. This zone is our home base, where we go to recharge and restore ourselves to a calm baseline.

Our *Edge Zone* is where we grow the most. When we take on challenges, try new things, and take risks, we find ourselves in our Edge Zone. This zone is often where we often feel the most alive—with our senses alert and adrenaline pulsing through us. The permaculture principle *edge effect* is at work here, pointing to the rich potential for growth that lies at the edge where two areas meet, such as the fertile soil where a river and a field come together.

If we choose to always stay in our Comfort Zone and avoid the edges, then we miss opportunities to peek over the walls of our boxes and expand our *cultural competencies*. However, if we stay in our Edge Zone for too long without retreating to our Comfort Zone to recharge and reflect on and integrate new teachings, then we can easily become overextended.

Degenerative patterns of overextension ultimately lead us into our *Panic Zone*. We feel strung out, which means it's time to return to where we feel comfortable and can recuperate. There are physical dangers to our health and negative impacts on our relationships when we stay in our Panic Zone for periods of time.

We can identify the circumstances that move us across these zones and do our best to design our physical and social environments to support our mindful navigation of them. However, life circumstances, such as living in a war-torn region, refugee camp, prison, or psychiatric hospital can limit our agency to change our conditions and can constrain our choices. In these situations, environmental stresses can turn someone's Edge or Panic Zone into their baseline. In such conditions, it is especially important to spend moments in the Comfort Zone with practices that are feasible and nourishing, such as singing, meditating, reading, writing, and loving. Even a quick visit to the Comfort Zone can serve as a restorative, though temporary, touchstone.

The purpose of this exercise is to increase our awareness about our choices and to design our life circumstances so that we can maintain healthy disciplined movement between our Comfort Zone (where we recharge and gain stability) and our Edge Zone (where we expand into new territory and develop increased agency), while not moving so far out that we hit our Panic Zone (where we can't function or end up engaging in some form of self-harm or harm to others).

When we traverse in a healthy way between our Comfort and Edge Zones, we become more effective at taking on new challenges that lie just beyond our repertoire, such as public speaking, starting a business, or advocating for social change.

EXERCISE 9: Cont.

Journal Part 1: *Write which* behavioral *and* physiological indicators *you exhibit when you are in each zone. Practicing mindfulness techniques can help identify indicators.*

Example Comfort Zone indicators: being affectionate and generous with people around you, smiling frequently, having good digestion, waking up feeling recharged

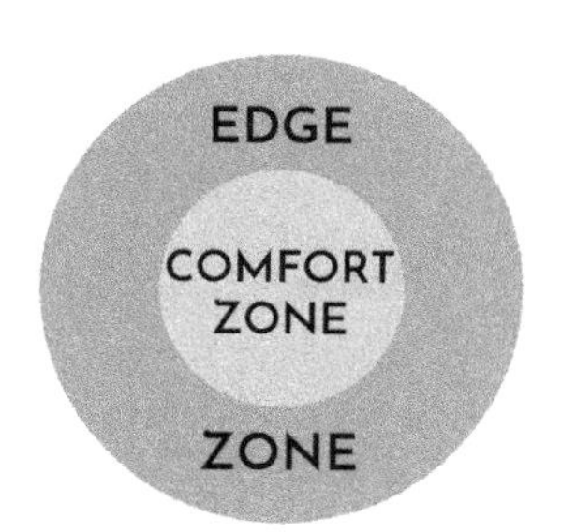

Example Edge Zone indicators: resuming an old habit or addiction such as drinking coffee in the afternoon or spending multiple hours on Facebook, sense of exhilaration and aliveness, being unable to sleep, experiencing shortness of breath

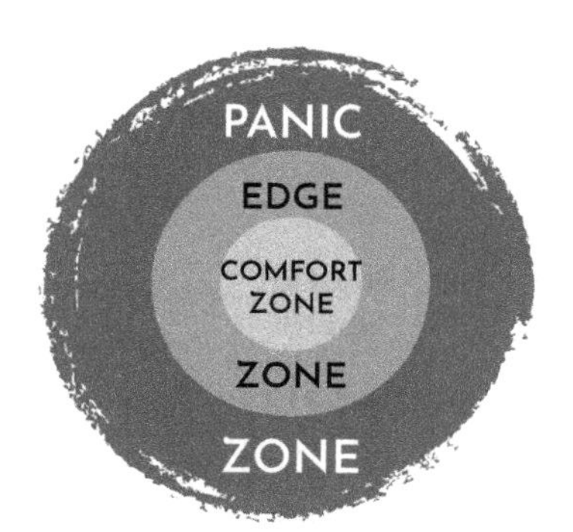

Example Panic Zone indicators: making reckless decisions, returning to out-of-control and dangerous addictions, experiencing dissociation, feeling a flood of adrenaline and fight-or-flight urges

Journal Part 2: *Write your responses to the following questions:*

1. *When working in groups (at your job, in community organizing, with family), where have you seen co-workers, collaborators, or family members move across these zones? Are you able to identify when they are in their Edge or Panic Zones? What behaviors do they exhibit and what is your response? You can invite your co-workers, housemates, etc. to complete this exercise, and have everyone share their indicators and how to best to support each other when Edge or Panic Zones prevail.*
2. *Zooming out, what is the baseline of the culture in your organization, family system, workplace, etc.? Is it normal for people to operate in the Panic Zone, running around and putting out fires all the time? Or, are people gently pushed to grow by frequenting their Edge Zones? How much does the group collectively practice returning to the Comfort Zone to pause, integrate, and recharge before starting a phase of new growth, as nature does with rhythms of hibernation, etc.?*
3. *Have you seen cultural practices where groups are supportive in helping members move beyond their familiar Comfort Zones, but stop each other from stretching too far and overextending themselves into Panic Zones? Can you imagine how your group can support one another in seeking this balance?*

EXERCISE 10: Life Sector Analysis

Holistic lifestyle design requires a whole systems perspective. How can we increase resilience among the seemingly disparate sectors of our life? First, we need a map to see all the sectors in one place and assess the health and wholeness of each one. Then we can design for a vibrant personal ecology that meets our Wellness Goals.

First, identify eight sectors that make up your life currently, for example: home, love life, extended family, physical health, career, spiritual life, artistic life, and finances. Choose sectors that make sense for you!

Then, draw a circle divided into eight equal-sized wedges, and label each wedge with each one of your life sectors (as in Life Sector diagram below).

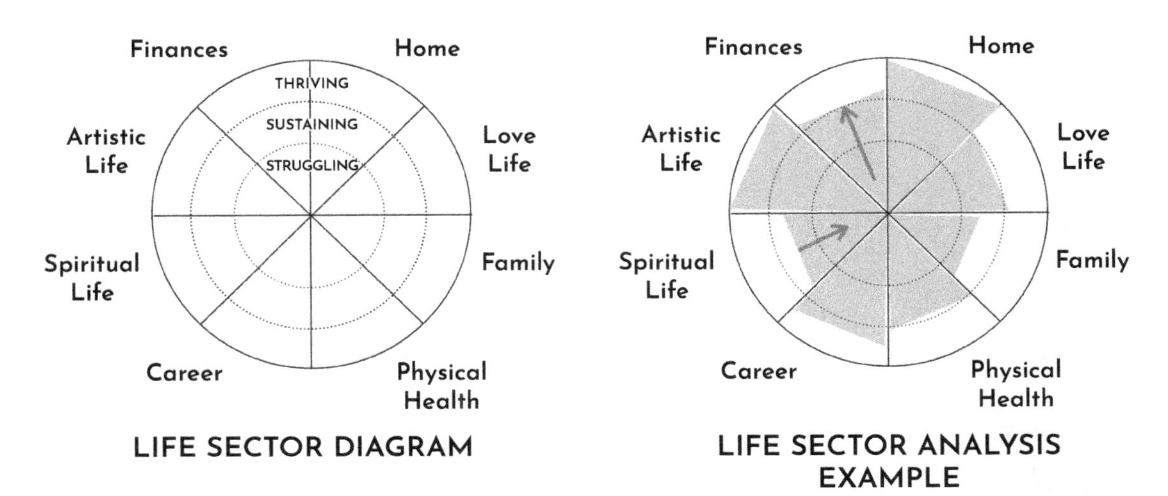

LIFE SECTOR DIAGRAM

LIFE SECTOR ANALYSIS EXAMPLE

Once you have completed this step, shade in each of your sectors with your analysis of how healthy each sector is at the moment (see sample Life Sector Analysis above). As it is here, include rings that represent thresholds of: struggling, sustaining the status quo, or thriving. For example, if your artistic life is flourishing, you might fill in that corresponding wedge into the thriving ring and shade it 90%. If your extended family sector is not exactly thriving, but you are making small progressions with one or two members, you might shade just beyond the sustaining ring for the family sector wedge. This visual representation can help synthesize a lot of information in a simplified form, giving you a snapshot of the health of each of your life sectors.

You can get more creative and exact with your diagram if you choose and include arrows to show directionality of healthiness. For instance, if your financial health is increasing this year, you can draw an arrow pointing outward in that sector. If you've been neglecting your spiritual practices, you can draw an arrow pointing inward to represent a decrease in your spiritual life.

Journal: *What patterns do you observe? Is this diagram reflective of your ideal Wellness Goals? Which areas could use some tending? Which areas surprised you? How is your Life Sector Analysis connected to your Symbolic Objects and/or ancestral lineages? What are some implications you observe in your Life Sector that are related to other identities you hold?*

EXERCISE 11: Cyclical Requirements for Thriving

Giving ourselves permission to say Yes! to thriving is a powerful move. We can design our personal lives in a way that moves our Life Sectors from the struggling and sustaining thresholds and up into thriving. This approach ensures that we are healthy and whole, and so too will be our change-making projects.

Stepping into a fully embodied adulthood involves rites of passages and productive ordeals. These experiences of initiation transition us from our youthful consciousness into being of service to the communities to which we are accountable. This stage of life, *initiated adulthood*, necessarily requires a radical commitment to self-care if we are to sustain the giving of our gifts selflessly to the world around us. On the other side of the self-care coin is self-sabotage: it is important to remember this when we judge ourselves for being indulgent by honoring our own requirements for thriving.

In an exercise from her book *Torah Journeys*, Rabbi Shefa Gold suggests framing self-care in terms of minimum daily, weekly, monthly, and yearly requirements for wholeness and sanity. Take a moment to think about the following: When do you thrive? What brings you delight? What brings you peace? What recharges your battery?

You radiate the energy of the activities you spend most of your time engaging in. How will your personal life and your change-making projects be different if you decide to spend your evenings watching television or looking at Facebook instead of visiting a river or making dinner with a friend?

If we align our personal minimum requirements for thriving with cycles of the natural world, we actively move ourselves away from linear human-created concepts of time. (Note that the dominant grid pattern Westerners use to organize time and landscapes is an inherited legacy from military tactics, used by the Romans and others, designed to divide, control, and conquer.) We can consciously choose to mimic patterns in nature and realign ourselves with her cycles. Sunlight and nightfall govern our daily cycle, the moon's waxing and waning punctuates our months, and the winter solstice lets us know when a new year of returning toward the light has begun. In this exercise, the weekly cycle (or the moon's quarterly cycle) is also included as an expression of several of the world's major religions observing a sabbath every seven days. This periodicity is now reflected in the concept of the weekend, brought to us by labor unions.

The first diagram here is an example of cyclical requirements for thriving. Once you've considered what brings you sanity and clarity, joy and rejuvenation, fill out the second thriving circles diagram. Be specific. Consider how frequently, what amount of time, what portion of day, etc. your being requires each of these activities in order to thrive. Approach this exercise with a sky's-the-limit mentality instead of constraint.

When you have filled out the thriving circles diagram, take out your calendar or appointment book and begin scheduling these dates with yourself. You could start by setting aside time for the first month, and committing to a date by which you will schedule time for the following month.

Continued on next page

EXERCISE 11: Cont.

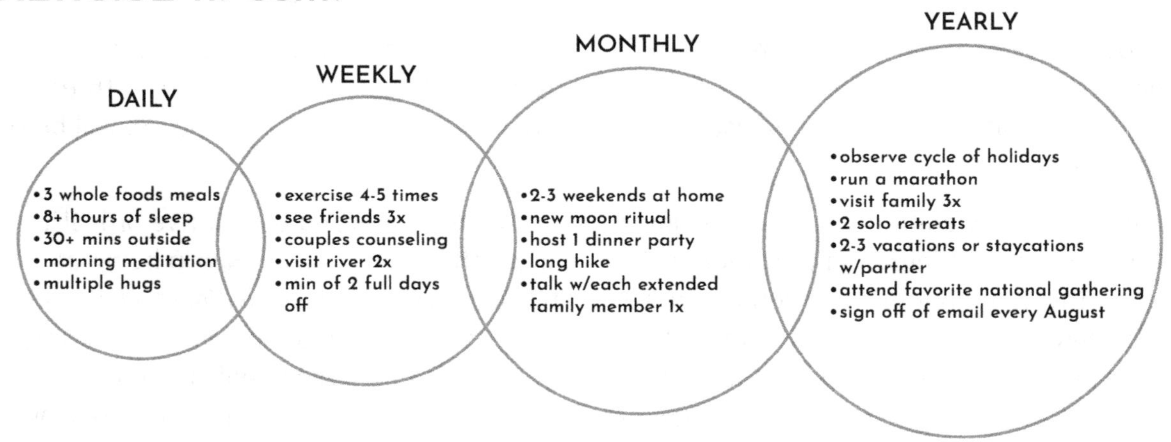

EXAMPLE CYCLICAL REQUIREMENTS FOR THRIVING

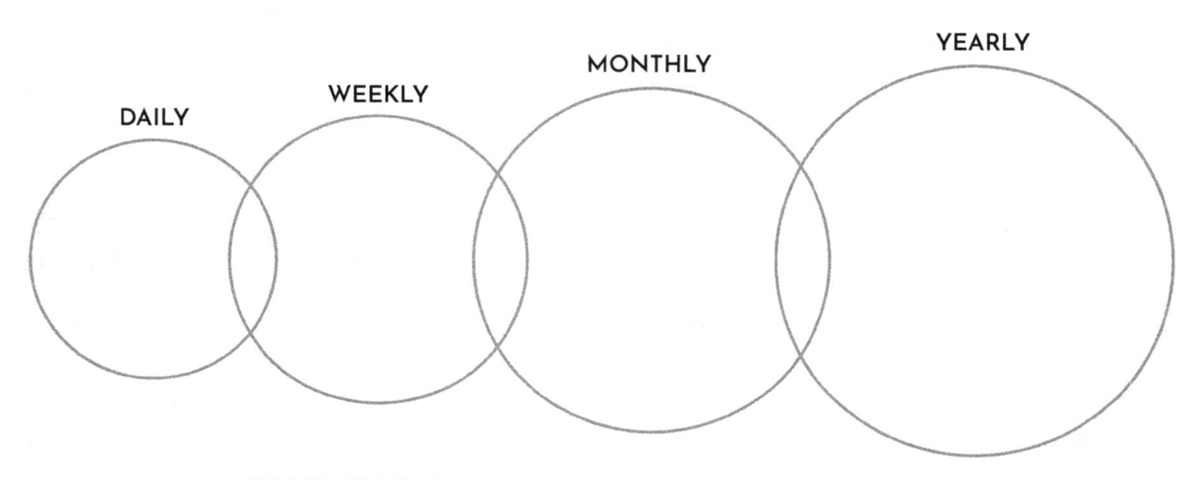

YOUR CYCLICAL REQUIREMENTS FOR THRIVING

Or you could schedule these self-care requirements once every three months. There can be different categories in your calendar as well. You can hold some times on reserve that allow for spontaneous arisings on that day. Another could be a date with a Learning Buddy or Wellness Buddy. Play with it and see what works best for you.

Shifting our habitual patterns, both inside ourselves and in our behaviors, can be challenging, especially if the environments around us reward unhealthy behavior. And likely the habits we generally engage in have been coping strategies that have helped us to survive thus far. We can lovingly thank them for their service, and then begin the worthy but hard work of shifting our default habits into practices that allow us and our projects to thrive.

Embarking on this journey into radical self-care is more fun and much easier with a Wellness Buddy! Who can you share your minimum daily, weekly, monthly, and yearly requirements for thriving with and perhaps even share self-care activities with? Find ways to check in with each other to help the other truly make a shift in old patterns. It will change everything.

Personal Financial Regeneration

The theme of avoiding self-sacrifice through thoughtful, proactive lifestyle design continues in the realm of finances. Money is a painful subject for many of us, and we may have negative feelings about it. We all live in a capitalist system that operates with currencies and markets. Short of living self-sufficiently off the grid, we all participate to greater or lesser degrees in the monetary world. Honoring ourselves and our futures—while living within this monetized system of exchange—with practices of *financial health and regeneration* actually frees up attention that normally goes toward worrying or complaining about money.

Our personal financial ecosystem can be designed in as much accordance with the permaculture ethics of Earth Care, People Care, Resource Share as we put effort into it. On a big-picture level, creating economic systems that incentivize sharing resources with others rather than hoarding them, or caring for the Earth rather than extracting from it, would have monumental implications for the state of peace among peoples and right relationship with the natural world. Where can you move your money to support institutions and projects that align with these ethics, as a decisive act of solidarity? And to which communities do you wish to repair harm done in the past, and to which do you have the ability to make financial reparations toward today?

Before we can thoughtfully bank, invest our money, or make sustained reparations, we have to get out of bad debt—including credit cards or debts we are defaulting on. Some forms of debt, such as mortgages or student loans, are less onerous than others. It might make sense to refrain from paying off low-interest debt all at once, and instead put income into ethical investments.

Then we can start playing around with different forms of economy, such as *solidarity economics*, which includes "alternative" systems that build connection rather than competition. Here are some of the tools in solidarity economics toolbox:

- **LETS** (Local Exchange Trading System), which includes various community-based systems that keep account of the trading of skills and time, and values people's time equally
- **Local currencies**, which incentivize shopping locally and keeping money circulating within the community rather than leaching to large corporations that invest their profits outside of the community and often treat their workers poorly
- **Worker-owned cooperative businesses**, widely known as co-ops; these are a form of democratic enterprise that keeps business ownership and decision-making in the hands of the employees (the worker-owners)
- **Investments in or loans to family and friends**, which are an expression of kinship and mutual support structures. These can also eliminate high interest rates, and prevent interest being pocketed by credit card companies or banks

REGENERATIVE FINANCES

- **Personal reparations payments**, which are different from donations. Financial reparations are one very important way of making amends for individual or structural appropriations in the past and from which an individual, family, business, racial group, or nation has unjustly benefited, such as Indigenous land theft or slavery of Africans and Native Americans.
- **Kiva Zip** and other crowd-lending platforms that offer 0% to very low interest on loans
- **GoFundMe, YouCaring, and other crowd-funding platforms** for creative projects or for personal times of need
- What others can you think of?

Worker-owned co-ops are a particularly powerful business structure for people who are formerly incarcerated. The stigma of a criminal record often means that they are the last to get hired in an application pool and the first to get fired when there are cutbacks in a business. Therefore, the job security and agency that are tied to worker-owned co-ops makes these types of businesses critical for people leaving the carceral system. Evergreen Co-operative in Cleveland, Ohio, and The Composting Co-operative in Greenfield, Massachusetts, are two excellent examples of co-ops that purposefully hire formerly incarcerated workers and embody all three permaculture ethics.

The simplest place to start making conscious financial decisions is by changing the institutions you bank with from large, national, or multi-national banks driven by ruthless profit to regional banks and credit unions that lend to local businesses and community development projects. Resources that list banks to divest from (whose practices are out of integrity with permaculture ethics) can be found in the Further Reading section for this chapter.

When it is time to invest surplus money, there are actually several good options that promote the regeneration of ecologies and human communities! Take a look at Ethan Roland and Gregory Landua's book, *Regenerative Enterprise*, which defines the difference between degenerative, sustainable, and regenerative systems. Carol Sanford's books, *The Responsible Entrepreneur* and The *Regenerative Business*, also explore several business models and specific enterprises to consider investing in.

Financially investing in businesses that regenerate rather than degrade people and the planet can be a powerful strategy for mending our world. In addition to investing consciously in the marketplace, there are numerous opportunities to invest in non-financial forms of capital or wealth, such as land, fruit trees, and livestock (Biological Wealth), or advanced studies (Intellectual Wealth), for instance. Growing all forms of wealth in any project is a benchmark of resilience (see Polyculture of Wealth Analysis Tool, chapter 10, page 161).

EXERCISE 12: Personal Financial Flows and Pools

Money flows in and out of our financial sector, just as water flows in and out of the landscape. Understanding its nature, planning how to capture and harvest it, and determining when to release it and irrigate with it take tools and time. The Personal Financial Flows and Pools exercise is a simple tool to help us understand our personal financial landscape. Please look over this example:

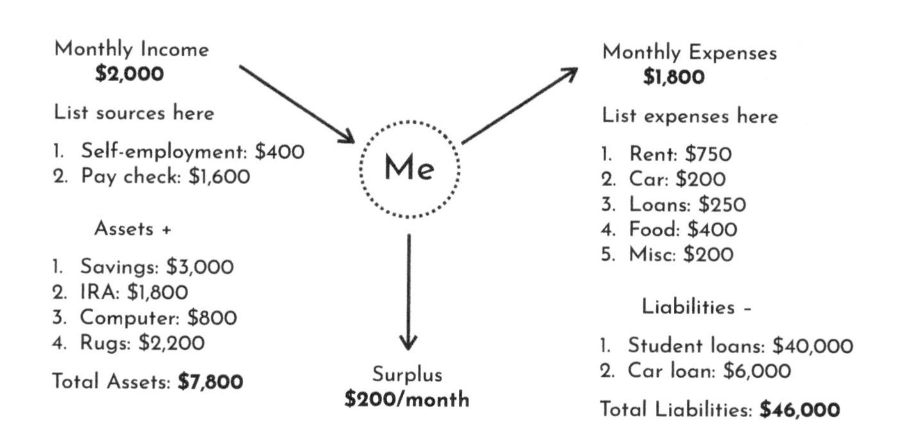

EXAMPLE FINANCIAL FLOWS AND POOLS

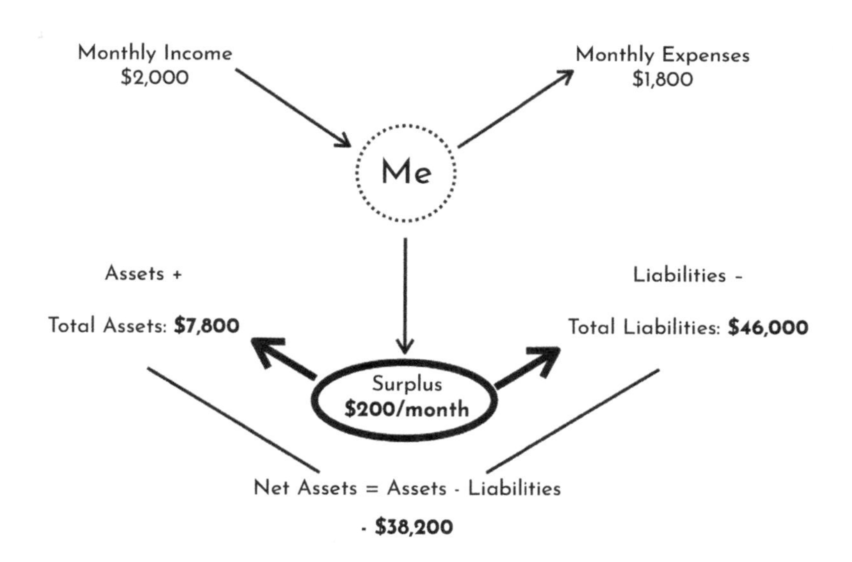

EXAMPLE NET ASSETS AND SURPLUS REDISTRIBUTION

Continued on next page

EXERCISE 12: Cont.

In the diagram below, please list estimates for the following:

- **Monthly income** *after* taxes: If you have seasonal work, estimate your yearly income and divide by 12. If you have more than one job or income source, list them below the Monthly Income line. Put a star next to any passive income (income that no longer requires any or much of your time to generate).
- **Monthly expenses:** If your expenses vary from month to month, estimate your yearly expenses and divide by 12. List your monthly bills under Monthly Expenses.
- **Surplus:** Subtract your monthly expenses from you monthly income and list your monthly surplus here. Then decide how you want to use your monthly surplus: to pay off debt, increase your savings, or some strategic combination of both.
- **Assets:** List your assets and their worth.
- **Liabilities:** List your liabilities/debt and amounts.
- **Net assets and surplus redistribution:** Subtract your liabilities from assets and decide where the surplus goes, into savings/investments and/or debt repayment, and perhaps eventually into reparations if you've unfairly benefited from race and/or class privilege.

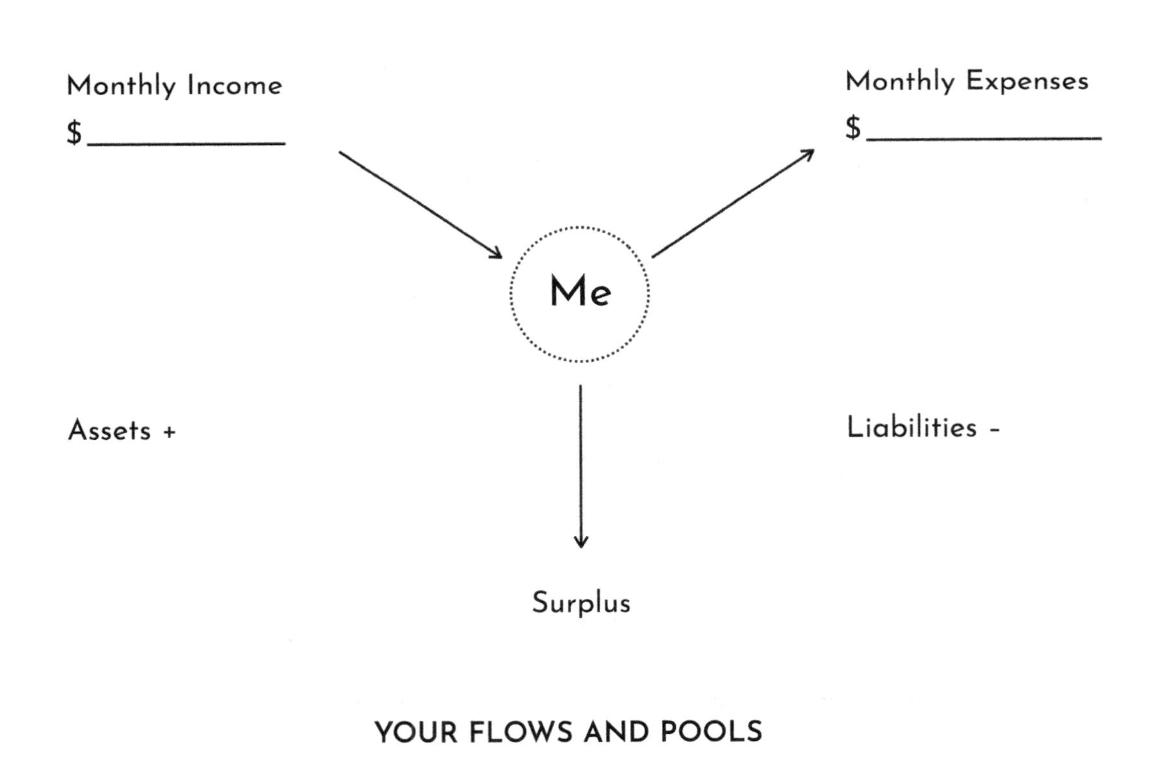

YOUR FLOWS AND POOLS

EXERCISE 13: Barriers, Launchpads, and Threshold Guardians

Keith Zaltzberg-Drezdahl, principal of Regenerative Design Group, my husband, and collaborator on Regenerative Design for Changemakers trainings, developed this exercise to help students understand their inner ecosystem and which parts they can consciously work with to unleash their potential. In this exercise, we use ideas from the Internal Family Systems (IFS) model, founded by psychotherapist Richard Schwartz. IFS combines systems thinking with an understanding of *parts work*, where we give attention to the different parts or voices inside us. Each part gets the opportunity to express its own viewpoint and qualities. Facilitators work with each part on its own and in dialogue other parts to bring about more internal harmony and alignment with Self, which contains all parts.

This exercise is not meant to be a cerebral activity; rather let it elicit spontaneous insights. The first thoughts that arise are usually the truest, so don't overthink it!

Journal: *Write your gut-level responses to the prompts. These gems are signposts for the path, urging you on toward your destiny as a thriving human being.*

- ***Barriers:*** *What feelings or circumstances are holding you back from moving out of the shadows and into the light so that your gifts can unfold? Is it fear of economic scarcity if you take new risks? A relationship that's preoccupying all of your creative energy? A difficult living situation?*
- ***Launchpads:*** *What environment, resources, or support do you need to step into your image of an initiated adult, engaged with change-making that serves the communities you love and to which you're accountable?*
- ***Threshold Guardians:*** *These guardians try to protect you from stepping out in your Edge Zone. They are afraid of you failing, or worse, afraid of you being too bright, too bold, too big. Examples of Threshold Guardian parts could be a defiant eight-year-old, a loyal soldier, or a worried parent. Who are the Threshold Guardians inside you, and what do they need to feel confident in surrendering control to Self (you!)? How can you communicate with them, and incorporate their needs, without letting them sit in the driver's seat?*

Take a moment to honor all your parts and thank them for working together as you step into this initiated life stage, consciously offering your gifts in service to the world!

Please see Further Reading related to chapter 3 on page 234.

Social Design Lexicon for Chapter 3

Review the following key terms and write down what they mean to you.

Thresholds:

Hidden Gifts:

Loop of Reciprocity:

Comfort Zone:

Edge Zone:

Panic Zone:

Edge Effect:

Cultural Competencies:

Behavioral and Physiological Indicators:

Initiated Adulthood:

Financial Health and Regeneration:

Solidarity Economics:

Parts Work:

Barriers:

Launchpads:

Threshold Guardians:

CHAPTER 4: SEEDING A NEW GENERATION OF LEADERS

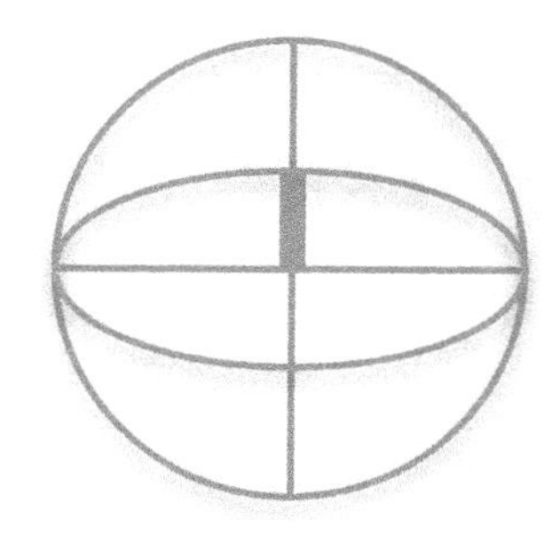

NORTH: SEED/ELDER

Seeds are the blueprint of life, carrying all potential within them. They pack the knowledge of everything that has come before into a tiny vehicle that moves across vast swaths of space and time, preparing to start anew. Their arrival also signals that a senescence in the parent plant is drawing near, a time when energy transfers. In the process of human regeneration, we have the opportunity to transmit our knowledge and wisdom to others. Stepping forth as wise leaders, ripe with experience, we are able to synthesize the fruits of our labor and guide the next generation—of leaders, projects, and Paradigms.

On the week of my 27th birthday, I crossed a threshold on my leadership journey, stepping further into initiated adulthood. Supported by loving human and tree witnesses alike, I chose to go alone into the wilderness, where I fasted, prayed, and slept for three days and nights in the 40 acres of forest behind the Woodstock Jewish Congregation. This land, stewarded by my childhood synagogue, abuts the southeastern slopes of the beloved Catskill Mountains in the mid-Hudson Valley of New York State (occupied Mohawk and Lenape territories), from where I hail. Connection to place and to my Jewish lineage were powerful containers for this transformative rite of passage.

A mentor of mine handed me this poem to take on my solo journey into the forest. I now offer you these profound words of Johann Wolfgang van Goethe as you step more fully into your leadership journey:

> I have come to the frightening conclusion that I am the *decisive element*. It is my personal approach that creates the climate. It is my daily mood that makes the weather. I possess tremendous power to make life miserable or joyous. I can be a tool of torture or an instrument of inspiration. I can humiliate or humor, hurt or heal. In all situations, it is my response that decides whether a crisis is escalated or de-escalated, and a person is humanized or dehumanized. If we treat people as they are, we make them worse. If we treat people as they ought to be, we help them become what they are capable of becoming.

We'll begin this chapter with two exercises that explore the big picture: What is the legacy you want to leave in the wake of your life's full offerings?

EXERCISE 14: Letter to the Seventh Generation

This exercise, adapted from Joanna Macy and Chris Johnstone's book, *Active Hope*, will help guide your imagination as it dreams into this question of legacy.

"I am my ancestors' wildest dreams," is a meme I've been seeing recently (its genius author has been difficult to identify). In that spirit, write a letter to the generations alive on the Earth two hundred years from now.

The context for this letter assumes that humanity has made it through a narrow place, a chaos point, and has emerged into a new consciousness, made largely possible by the courageous leadership of your current generation. This future Earth is imbued with values of social equity and environmental stewardship. People have come to understand the intricate interconnections of all life forms. A beautiful, peaceful coexistence prevails.

In your letter, write to those living seven generations from now, and tell them about what you, their ancestor, and your people had to face. Tell them, from your perspective, the state of the world around you today. Tell them how you persisted, even through chaos and despair, to make things whole.

Consider responding to these questions:

- What obstacles did you face, internally and externally?
- What practices helped you to maintain your sanity?
- What beings were allies to you?
- Which movements were you an instrumental part of, helping to bring humanity to a tipping point and towards a new consciousness?
- What seed of a vision did you hold, and what of your vision became manifest before you gracefully bowed to your death?

When you finish your letter, give it to your Learning Buddy and ask them to return it to you in six months. After you receive it, consider writing a letter back to the ancestors from the perspective of the seventh generation. Express your questions and concerns, and convey your gratitude, respect, and sense of intergenerational connection to these brave ancestors.

Repeat the process again: Have your Learning Buddy hold this second letter, and give it to you another six months down the road. Continue this cycle of writing exercises as long as it feels fruitful for you.

EXERCISE 15: Personal Release Commitment for Leaders

Journal: *Record your responses to the following prompts. You will also want to bring in an Accountability Buddy for this exercise. This type of buddy is someone who will follow up with you over time, helping you stay accountable to your own goals. You can offer to be a buddy to them, too!*

Step 1. Think of someone you really admire who will leave a legacy behind them in alignment with their values and vision. List ten adjectives that describe that person. Please make this list before reading on.

Step 2. Now, imagine that you are all those things you admire, even if those characteristics only exist as tiny seeds inside you. What can you do to move on the path from where you are now toward this glorious vision of yourself? Brainstorm a list of principles or practices you want to engage with to this end.

Step 3. Identify and summarize one old story you have about yourself, or one pattern you know is holding you back from shining as the leader you were born to be. At one time, this story or pattern was helpful and protected you in some way, but now it no longer serves you and can be composted. Through a release visualization or simple ritual that you devise for yourself, gently let go of this old story or pattern. Tell your Accountability Buddy about this process.

Step 4. Next, write down and commit to taking three small steps (that can be accomplished within two to four weeks) toward releasing this old story or pattern and moving towards your brilliant leader self (combining steps 2 and 3). Tell your Accountability Buddy these steps of transformation that you are committing to; together, record the dates by which time you will complete each step. When you do, tell your Buddy you have accomplished them. Make sure your Buddy agrees to follow up with you, and by which method of communication, if they have not heard from you by those dates.

Step 5. Who is the powerful leader living inside you with a legacy to gift to the planet? Write the new story and/or intentional habits that will emerge, what you will feel like, and what leadership actions you're taking.

Regenerative Leadership Development

Nature offers us many models for regenerative human leadership. Even those of us who are *cultural orphans*, a term coined by Huron/Cree/European-heritage author Martín Prechtel, cut off from our ancestors' traditional ways, can learn ecological frameworks for guiding groups and piece together some of what we have lost.

Leadership means making things go well for everyone in the group, including you! As a leader, you are also a member of every ecosystem in which you lead or co-lead. If things are not going well for the leaders, the whole group suffers. We can challenge the *martyr-leader Paradigm*, in which a solo leader sacrifices her health and happiness for the sake of the whole.

In *regenerative leadership*, we don't leave anyone behind or allow anyone to be disproportionately impacted, especially our leaders. What's more, leaders get to express their needs, show where they are vulnerable, and ask for a hand from the group when they find themselves stuck. Transparent leadership humanizes the leader, creates connections, and permits other members of the social ecosystem to express their needs and vulnerabilities, too. It's easier to identify with a person "in charge" when they show their whole selves, rather than appearing as a flawless hero or an impenetrable authority figure.

What would it look like to model leadership and decision-making on the redundancy and diversity found in nature? Ecosystems contain some forms of hierarchy (such as the concentration of energy and biomass through different trophic levels), but they also operate as webs of interconnected, reciprocal relationships rather than unilateral systems of power. The permaculture principle of functional interconnection urges us to mimic the mutually supportive web structure of relationships found in ecosystems.

Degenerative leadership can look like one person out in front, ordering others to "follow me." This recalls the monoculture mentality of an industrialized worldview, where a silver bullet solution, single savior, or one crop (e.g., corn or soy) is the answer to the world's impoverishment. This sole solution becomes the weakest link. It is vulnerable as a singularity, with all nodes of a system dependent on its centrality. If a sole leader ("mono-leader"—the one person with whom all relationships are dependent on) leaves, then the group's functioning rapidly degenerates.

When we engage in shared leadership within our organizations and institutions, we also express the design principles of *redundancy*, or resilience in the face of disturbances, and *value diversity*, or differentiated niches within a collective capacity. With these principles in mind, conventional Western models of decision-making and leadership—many only a facade of true consensus or democracy—may need to be reconsidered for long-term resilience.

> ***Adaptation and evolution depend more upon critical, deep, and authentic connections, a thread that can be tugged for support and resilience. The quality of connection between the nodes in the patterns... [is] separate, aligned, cohesive. Critically connected.***
>
> – adrienne maree brown, *Emergent Strategy*

SOCIAL PERMACULTURE = CONNECTIONS

Social permaculture creates connections in a web of mutual accountability and relationships = increased resilience in the face of ever-changing system dynamics.

We can grow our relationships, just as we grow top soil, for abundance and long-term nourishment.

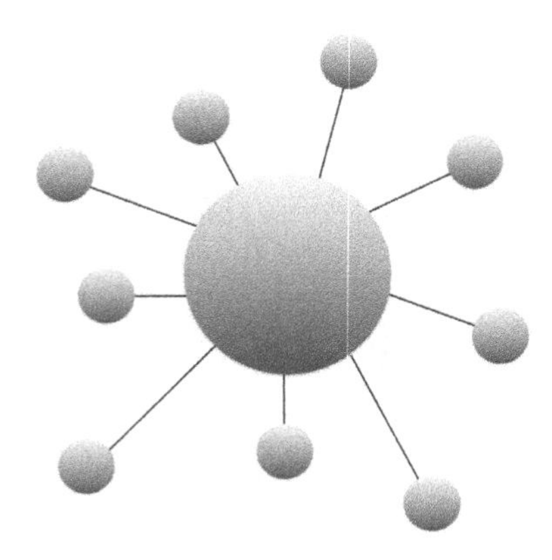

MONO-LEADERSHIP CONSTELLATION: VULNERABLE

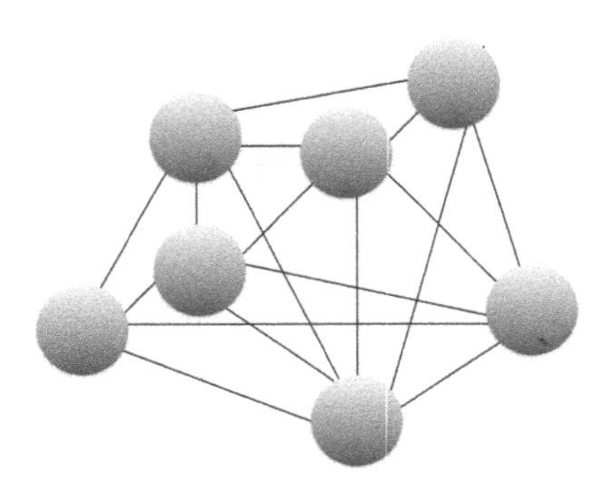

SHARED LEADERSHIP CONSTELLATION: RESILIENT

Shared Leadership Models

There are many *shared leadership* models, which can be matched to the goals and needs of any group or project. Drawing upon a number of decision-making processes brings greater agility and a shared sense of responsibility to a group. Here I'll explore a few that I've found useful in collaborative endeavors.

Consensus-based decision-making processes, such as the general assemblies used by the Occupy movement, are one form of shared leadership. Co-operative living houses, also known as co-ops, often engage in household decisions making through consensus. This process can be very laborious, but the outcome is group unity, even though some compromises may need to occur. Carefully select if this model would work for your team or not, based on its Goals and constraints.

Sociocracy, which is based upon circular leadership rather than top-down hierarchies, is a similar but distinctive approach. This form of governance privileges interdependence, transparency, and decision-making by *consent*, rather than *consensus*. Social permaculture and sociocracy are both whole systems approaches to organizing human systems in a way that supports their highest functions. Sociocracy may be a useful tool for decision-making in social change projects that are based on permaculture principles and design.

Another shared leadership model employs the Eight Shields Framework from the Eight Shields Institute. This model grew out of Jon Young's body of research on the various archetypes that Indigenous Peoples have long associated with the four cardinal (East, West, North, South) and semi-cardinal directions (Southeast, Southwest, Northeast, Northwest). Carl Jung's and Joseph Campbell's work on archetypes also influenced the formation of the Eight Shields. Well detailed in the book *Coyote's Guide* by Jon Young, Ellen Haas, and Evan McGown, this framework has informed leadership practices in the nature connection movement, the Art of Mentoring training program, and the Jewish Outdoor Food/Farming Environmental Education (JOFEE) network.

It is important to note that the content and practices that the Eight Shields Framework organizes are not original ideas of Jon Young, a Western white man, or of Wilderness Awareness School, which he founded. Rather, these practices originated from the perennial wisdom of Indigenous cultures around the world. The Eight Shields Framework organizes these practices, and teaches them to others, mostly to descendants of settlers and immigrants, who are seeking reconnection to the land and cultural practices in the wake of assimilation in the US. The nature connection community has had strong, loving relationships with Native teachers such as Jake and Judy Swamp from the Haudenosaunee Tree of Peace Society, as well as complicated relationships with other Native teachers throughout the Eight Shields' evolution.

Observing the patterns of natural cycles (time of day or seasonality, for example) and mapping them onto the eight directions can inform how a leadership team operates. This approach is a form of *organizational biomimicry*, in which the roles and responsibilities held by each co-leader mimic the patterns in nature. This idea stems from the field of biomimicry, a practice of emulating nature's patterns in the design of innovations and technologies, founded by Janine Benyus and Dayna Baumeister. Much like a web, this system of shared leadership incorporates checks and balances in a way that fosters group integrity.

EXERCISE 16: Four Directions Applied to Shared Leadership

A simpler version of the Eight Shields Framework focuses on the four cardinal directions, a common framework of numerous Earth-based cultures from around the world. While each culture holds different associations with each direction, such as animals or colors, there are also some universally shared associations (see the diagram below).

In this exercise, we map shared leadership roles onto the cardinal directions. In chapter 12, we will do the same with the stages of project development. What cycles and roles from the chart below resonate with your work? How might you reorganize Shared Leadership Roles when working with groups to embody archetypal energies found in nature? (Note: if you live in the southern hemisphere, please reverse South and North.)

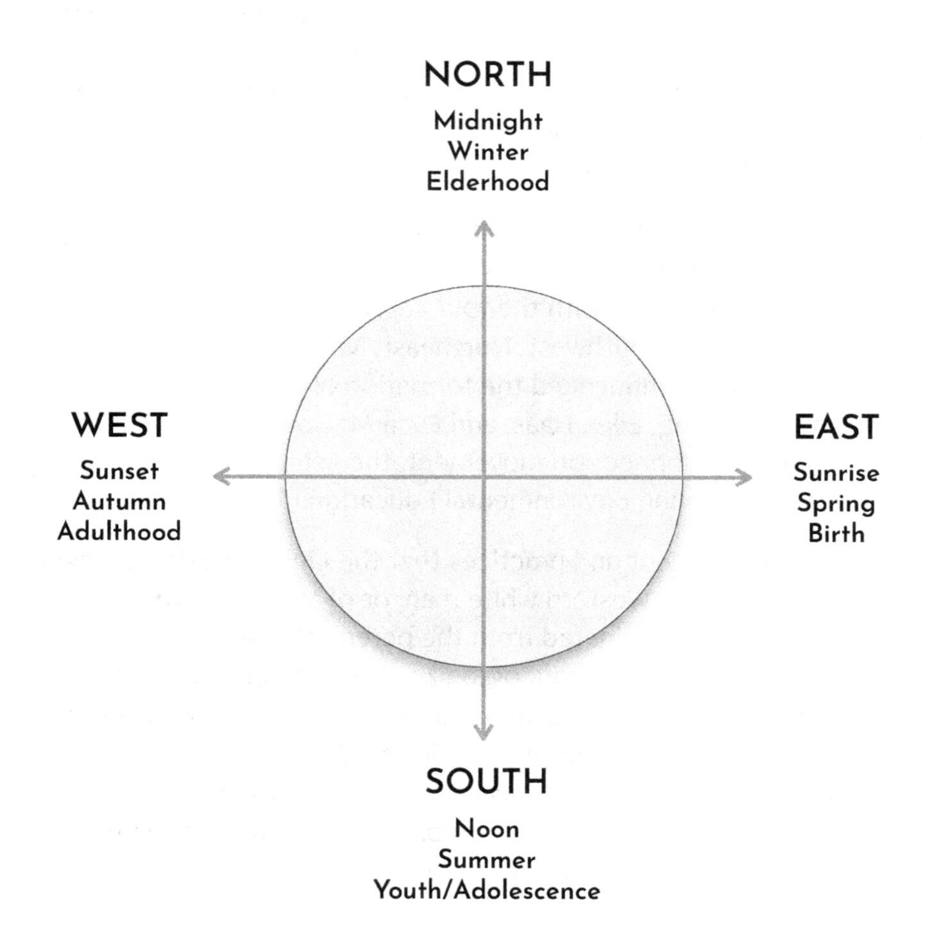

FOUR DIRECTIONS AND THEIR COMMON ASSOCIATIONS

EXERCISE 16: Cont.

CARDINAL DIRECTION	TIME OF DAY	SEASON	STAGE OF LIFE	STAGES OF A PROJECT	SHARED LEADERSHIP ROLES
EAST	Sunrise	Spring	Birth	Inspiration/ New Ideas	**Welcoming presence; builds group connection/unity; focuses on inclusivity; provides inspiration**
SOUTH	High Noon	Summer	Youth/ Adolescence	Action/ Training	**Attends to details, e.g. treasurer, notetaker, timekeeper, fundraiser, marketing, registration**
WEST	Sunset	Autumn	Adulthood	Service/ Creation/ Fruition	**Facilitator, e.g. master of ceremonies, convener, spokesperson, master teacher**
NORTH	Midnight	Winter	Elderhood	Reflection/ Integration/ Senescence	**Knows the big picture; helps the group stay true to the Purpose; sees all the pieces; mentors/ advises; leads from behind**

LAYERS OF MEANING MAPPED ONTO CARDINAL DIRECTIONS

Take a moment to think about a group in which you are a leader or a participant. Who in that social ecosystem is already fulfilling the roles of East, South, West, and North? Fill in their names below and the responsibilities and/or energetics they currently hold. There may be more than one person who comes to mind for each direction: list their names here, too. And remember to include yourself.

East ______________________________

South______________________________

West ______________________________

North______________________________

As an experiment, consider asking your group to try taking on these roles consciously for a meeting. This does not mean people need to relinquish their current roles forever; just try adding this layer and see how things go. Eventually, and this may be a challenge, try giving full rein to each person in their respective direction for a clearly defined period of time, such as planning an event.

If you find your group choosing to adopt this model, then you can take this experiment one step further: see if, over time, your group wants to choose new roles. Rather than selecting roles that play upon people's strengths, everyone has the opportunity to try out leading from a new direction. This will likely move people out of their Comfort Zones, and give them an opportunity to step into their growing Edge and to develop new expressions of their leadership.

Communication Tools

Skilled leaders are also, by necessity, skilled communicators. Without clear communication, interpersonal relationships suffer. Similarly, groups also need to practice good communication between individual members, among the group as a whole, and with the group's leader(s).

There are many helpful communication tools for working together. Active listening, listening projects, and non-violent communication (NVC) are a few of the powerful tools some communities employ. NVC, for instance, focuses on expressing the underlying needs and feelings of each person, rather than communicating them indirectly and hoping others can decipher them. Reciprocity is built into this practice, which generally fosters good feelings among people who use it.

The Peacemaking Principles, articulated in the Peacemaker's story of the Haudenosaunee Confederacy, is another tool, but one that is difficult to translate to non-Native settings. Learning them directly from Native teachers, and learning about Haudenosaunee culture and their origin story, helps to contextualize the principles. Some Native teachers who share these principles with non-Native audiences include author Tom Porter of the Kanatsiohareke Mohawk Community, which holds public events such as their annual Strawberry Festival. Kawisente McGregor, a Mohawk of the Kahnawake Reserve, occasionally teaches at places like Nature Connection Leadership Conferences. Oren Lyons is a Seneca/Onandaga Faithkeeper of the Haudenosaunee Confederacy who shares teachings with wider audiences. You might also consider reading *White Roots of Peace*, Paul A. W. Wallace's powerful book exploring these principles and the influence of Haudenosaunee thought on the three branches of the US government.

Journal: *What peacemaking tools exist in your people's background or faith tradition? What tools for conflict resolution have you observed or learned in the communities you were raised in or are involved in currently? If you were not taught practices for positive communication, then who are the people or the communities that can teach you communication tools as part of your changemakers toolbox?*

Shared Agreements that Build Connection Across Difference

Even if groups have excellent tools for communicating, they do not collaborate well unless they agree to a culture of shared practices and expectations. Articulating group agreements, especially in a multicultural group, is one way to establish clear expectations of how the group will conduct itself and communicate. Generated by the group in the course of a facilitated process, these agreements ensure that participants have what they need in order to share their different views on an issue and their personal stories where relevant.

One purpose of articulating agreements is for people to feel safe enough to leave the cushiness of their Comfort Zones, take risks, and grow in the presence of others. This type of "edge work," where participants engage with tension around topics such as race or male domination, generally cannot be done effectively if people stay in their Comfort Zones. Safe Zones made with clear agreements and accountability protocols support people in stepping into their Edge Zone and engaging with difficult and highly charged topics. Author John Palfrey refers to this space as "brave space." If well facilitated, risk-taking in a community of practice committed to personal growth can be an uncomfortable yet worthwhile process.

For a group that is gathering for the first time and with several members who may be new to group dialogue processes and/or to the topic you're discussing, it's useful for a facilitator to start with a set of agreements, such as "use 'I' statements and speak from personal experience." Then, if there are any additional agreements that participants of the group would like to propose, the facilitator can review or modify them as needed.

This curation of suggested agreements is important because participants may propose agreements that can increase the risk of harm to other participants and/or divide people in a group rather than connect them across their differences.

With a group of people who are facilitators themselves, who have existing relationships with each other, and/or who have a depth of experience with power dynamics and the topic at hand, it makes more sense to take a *self-organizing* approach. The group members can articulate their agreements together and discuss and modify ones for which there is not full group consent. Members can "Vote With the Thumb" to ratify them. A thumbs-up is a consensual "Yes! I vote to include this agreement." A thumbs-down means "No, I do not consent to add this agreement." In this case, the person can offer an amendment and then the group votes again. A horizontal thumb means "I don't know whether I support this, but I won't block it." Here is an opportunity to ask clarifying questions about what the agreement means or how it functions. The process of gaining group buy-in or consent is important for functional group agreements.

Once consensus is met, group members can "call in" one another if they violate an agreement. Rather than calling out someone for making a racist or sexist comment, for example, *calling in* someone creates connection rather than bad feelings. Calling in could mean waiting until later for a one-on-one opportunity to explain why their behavior broke one of the agreements. Generally, calling in someone goes better in private than in the public setting of a group where that individual may likely feel shame, anger, or humiliation, behave defensively, or leave. Calling in supports the growth of the group, rather than its fragmentation. (This protocol is an antidote to the distancing behavior discussed in chapter 2 on page 34, an indicator of Internalized Racial Superiority.)

However, there are times when a group member who is personally affected by a breach of the agreements becomes upset and calls out the person who broke the agreement in an angry or public manner. Especially for people with targeted identities, this outcome is understandable and it brings tension to the surface. Group members can choose to lean into the discomfort and have an opportunity to question the assumptions they hold.

One of my most beloved Jewish elders, Cherie Brown, shares powerful facilitation tools and frameworks in her book, co-authored with George J. Mazza, *Leading Diverse Communities: A How-To Guide for Moving from Healing into Action*. Likewise, the pocket-sized *Guide to Working in Diverse Groups* by Spirit in Action, co-authored by Phyllis Labanowski, another powerful changemaker elder, is a great resource for creating group agreements. They focus on the importance of "inner work" or self-awareness and regulation and "outer work" or our conduct with others. When creating agreements, Spirit in Action begins with these two guiding questions:

- For a relationship between two people in a group, each person can answer: "What do you need from me so that you can step into your power-with me?"

- For an individual relating to the group as a whole, each person can answer: "What do you need from us so that you can step into your power-with the group?"

Here are some of the group agreements that I present to a new group that has never worked together and for whom this may be the first time speaking and listening in a diverse group. Some of these agreements come from the Center for Whole Communities, and others come from social justice-focused permaculture courses I have taught with Lisa DePiano, Javiera Benavente, Connor Stedman, and Jasmine Fuego.

- **Be Present and Curious:** Stay attentive and fully show up to listen to others (including turning off your devices). This helps them speak their truth more completely and allows you to learn from each and every person in a deeper way.
- **Be Relational Before Transactional:** Practice relationship building first, by checking in, sharing a highlight of the day, and asking each other how things are going before diving into a transactional conversation where one person or both people are seeking an outcome: an answer, a favor, a task completed, or other action.
- **Avoid Dehumanizing Language:** Together, the group can generate examples of dehumanizing language, such as referring to a woman as a "chick" or to poor white people as "trailer trash." It's also helpful to develop a shared protocol for calling in someone when they use such language. A community of practice, one that is dedicated to uprooting oppressive speech, can help each other see terms that are problematic or appropriative, such as the common parlance "let's have a pow wow" or "higher up on the totem pole."
- **Presume Good Intent/Attend to the Impact:** When a person or people in the group feel hurt by an expression or action of one member, it is a helpful practice to presume the good intentions of that person, rather than jumping to blame. At the same time, the person who made the comment, regardless of intent, can reach out to address the impact of their comment on the person/people who felt the "ouch" or sting.
- **Take Space/Make Space:** This agreement is about self-awareness and self-modulation. If you tend to withhold your thoughts or be a quiet member of a group, it is important for the group to hear you and for you to speak your thoughts, to "Take Space." If you tend to talk a lot and take up auditory and energetic space, it's good to "Make Space" regularly and just listen, making space for less assertive voices. Inner tracking of one's social identities and patterns of privilege help in this regard.
- **Take the Risk to be Different:** Group conformity is a good strategy for staying safe. When we take risks and show ourselves, we can sometimes stand out as different. In a safe context this is a wonderful thing, giving everyone permission to show their unique selves. We all grow into new terrain, coming out as who we really are, which can be a healing contrast to the harshness of other spaces that incentivize conformity.
- **Use "I" Statements and Speak from Personal Experience:** When we make assumptions and generalize our personal experiences to a group or to all people (making universal "we" statements or saying "everyone knows that...xyz"), a dangerous form of erasing or negating others' experiences can occur. This is true especially when the speaker holds a privileged identity. Sticking to "I" statements also promotes more vulnerability in sharing and avoids Unconscious Assumptions about others' experience.

- **Lean into Tension/Engage With Hard Stories:** As an antidote to the *right to comfort* norm of white supremacy culture (see page 61), and the numbing out of consumer culture, we all can build relationships and learn vast amounts by embracing tension and difficult content rather than turning our backs to it and habitually seeking comfort.
- **Accept and Expect Non-Closure:** *Non-closure* or non-conclusiveness is inevitable when we collectively explore material in our personal and collective Edge Zones, particularly if the content relates to dynamics of power or oppression. Release any need to have a tidy outcome in group dialogue, and you will likely feel a more generative flow than all tangled up.
- **Commit to Self-Care:** In groups of adults, taking care of oneself in the context of the group, whether during an afternoon meeting, a weekend retreat, or a multiyear project, protects the health and cohesion of the group and each individual. Martyrdom is out of style!
- **Stories Stay/Learning Leaves:** Agree to keep what someone shares in the group confidential; however, what listeners realize or what it provokes inside them can be shared elsewhere without referring to the specific details of the personal story.
- **Ask Permission to Refer to Someone's Sharing After the Fact:** Always ask for someone's permission to refer to what they shared if you want to bring it up with them after the fact. The sharer can then say yes, no, or not now. This protocol promotes respect and also extends the safety of the original confidentiality agreement across time. Becoming aware of one's own motivation to ask further questions is important. Refrain from doing so out of personal curiosity.

Tools That Create Connection

Shared leadership frameworks and good communication tools are essential for cultural regeneration. But what else will we need? What other elements have held diverse Earth-based cultures intact for millennia? Prioritizing *connection* over urgency and productivity is a radical act that runs counter to capitalist Paradigms of profit, production, and progress. Furthermore, it contradicts many tenets of white supremacy culture, such as: "quantity over quality; individualism; objectivity; power hoarding; and sense of urgency," as enumerated by Kenneth Jones and Tema Okun in *Dismantling Racism: A Workbook for Social Change Groups*. Magical, unforeseen things occur when we slow down to prioritize relationship over productivity. So what's stopping us?

Connection is our nature, as humans, as elements of the well-connected natural world. The conditions of isolation (from family, from loved ones far away, from community, from Earth) are by-products of modern society. Circumscribed by a new digital era of virtual connection, we have our connection work cut out for us. As we walk toward a new vision of togetherness, we can respectfully implement tools and technologies of connection that traditional peoples have kept alive. We owe gratitude to these teachers who have maintained their customs amidst a globalized and rapidly homogenizing world.

Practices such as customary greeting, singing, storytelling, engaging in rituals, and intergenerational mentoring have persisted around the world for a reason: They create connection, draw out people's gifts, and reflect our shared humanity. These common practices are a means of survival, or else they would not have evolved independently on every continent, with unique expressions reflecting each culture and place.

Today, we can call on these time-tested cultural practices to work against the harmful messages of modern consumer society that alienate us from one another, our own people's customs, and the natural world. We can invite social regeneration from the cultural, psychological, and spiritual cohesion that regular connection practices provide. The Center for Whole Communities leads by example here with their set of Whole Thinking Practices. Throughout their trainings and meetings, they weave these seven practices: awareness, relationship building, creativity, dialogue, hospitality, story, and working with difference.

Similarly, the Eight Shields Institute embodies and teaches students Eight Attributes of Connection, which include empathy, respect for nature, and being truly helpful. Furthermore, they have mapped 64 cultural elements that have been observed to create cultural cohesion within traditional societies worldwide. Giving gratitude, tending to elders, and regularly visiting and spending time in a certain spot in nature are examples of these elements that create connection. Jon Young calls those of us whose families assimilated into Western host cultures in order to survive, but who are on the path of reclaiming connection, the "duck tape" generations. We are the ones who have lifted our heads above the surface of cultural homogenization and isolation, and are working to piece together customs that reconnect us with our lineages, Earth, and one another in a meaningful way.

Connection in Practice

In organizational meetings, educational classes, and community gatherings, try building connection first among people, and between people and place, before addressing agenda items or making decisions. Remember that you are a decisive element and can gently shift the culture of any group you are a member of.

It is important to remember and pay respect to histories that are often occluded and forgotten. One way to do this is by acknowledging *whose land we're on* and—for those of us who are not Indigenous—ways in which our group is benefiting from legacies of land theft and genocide. You may begin an event by talking about the Native people that lived on and stewarded the land on which the meeting or gathering is happening and sharing stories of Native organizing projects there today and how to support them.

You can experiment with these additional practices that foreground connection:

- Begin with a song or telling a story about the place you're in
- Develop a regular opening ritual, such as a brief check-in circle
- Report something "new and good" from each person's life
- Have each person say something they're grateful for
- Invite everyone to say what they want to leave at the door and what they want to invite into the session
- Start with a five-sense meditation or other mindfulness practice
- Invite people to share something that was meaningful to them about the last meeting/class/gathering.

If it's the first time a group is convening and people are introducing themselves, ask people to give their preferred pronouns when they say their names. This same protocol goes for creating name tags. This practice resists the unconscious tendency to make assumptions about people's gender identities and works to remove the gender binary construct of dividing whole humans into men and women. Incorporating this practice helps create an inclusive space for nonbinary, gender nonconforming, intersex, genderqueer, and transgender people.

With regular practices of group connection and inclusivity, we can sustain our work joyfully and persevere together when difficult times arise. Even in our individual interactions, say at a cafe or a conference, the more we can cultivate a practice of connection rather than transaction, the more impactful the ripples from that interaction become. Grace Lee Boggs emphasizes the importance of critical connections over critical mass (quality over quantity) for the long-term success of social change movements. It is a radical act of resistance in the capitalist world to see the beauty in slowing down to make connections rather than disconnecting in our urgency to make "progress." This is how we slowly transform isolation patterns that are a prerequisite for competition and capitalism.

Discussion 2: Unforeseen Costs

In the wake of globalization, industrialization, assimilation, and cultural homogenization (all products of capitalism), what do you think are the unforeseen costs or hidden impacts of losing such cultural practices as communal singing, making art or handcrafts side by side, eating meals together, or offering daily gratitudes? This question can be posed as a class discussion, explored in a dialogue with a Learning Buddy, or written about in your journal.

Please see Further Reading related to chapter 4 on page 236.

Social Design Lexicon for Chapter 4

Review the following key terms and write down what they mean to you.

Decisive Element:

Cultural Orphans:

Martyr-leader Paradigm:

Regenerative Leadership vs. Degenerative Leadership:

Redundancy:

Value Diversity:

Shared Leadership:

Consent vs. Consensus:

Organizational Biomimicry:

Self-Organizing:

Calling Out vs. Calling In:

Transactional:

Right to Comfort:

Non-closure:

Connection:

Whose Land We're On:

Critical Connections vs. Critical Mass:

Unforeseen Costs:

CHAPTER 5: LET THE HEALING RAINS WASH OUR TEARS AWAY

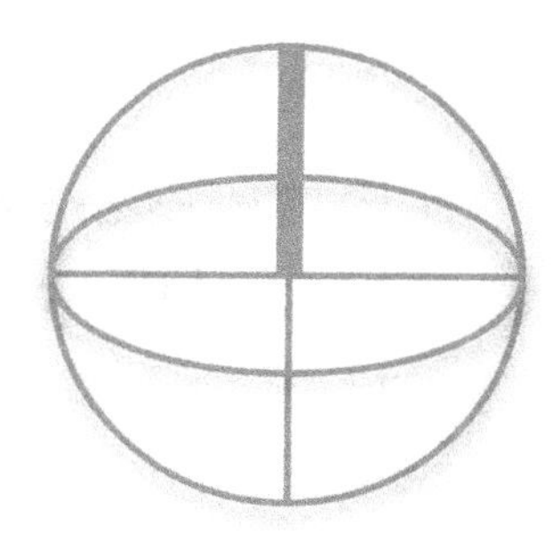

SKIES ABOVE: RAIN AND LIGHTNING/GRIEF REMOVAL

Through each stage of our creative cycles, the sky above covers all that we do. We are held by the clouds, the sun, the blue, the gray. When the heavens become heavy and full, so too do our hearts. When we are ready to release the weightiness of what we've been carrying, so are the clouds ready to let go with the cracking of thunder and lightning. As they release their collection of water droplets from above, we are beckoned to release our stockpile of teardrops below, cleansing our internal landscapes again and again. In nature's hydrological cycle, the rain, thunder, and lightning fulfill a sacred role, assisting humans in our own cycles of *release and renewal.*

Without continual removal of what Rabbi Shefa Gold in *Torah Journeys* calls "the dead ashes," we cannot make space for new, emergent impulses inside us. When we neglect to remove the ashes from the fires kindled by our own life sparks, we become covered in soot and the fire dwindles down. There is no right way to feel our heaviness for a world in crisis or a past ridden with trauma. But it is almost impossible to become a vessel in which new miracles can emerge if we do not devote time to personal release and renewal.

> *"AND ONE MORE THING," says the fire, flashing righteously, "you must remove the dead ashes every day. I cannot burn clean and pure if the refuse of the past is allowed to accumulate within you. Each morning you must remove that which is old and done."*
>
> – Rabbi Shefa Gold, parsha Tzav from *Torah Journeys*

The Regenerative Power of Grief

Metaphors of water and fire help me understand my own nature, because these elements move within each of us through tears and passionate fury. Cycles of rain and cycles of fire both leave behind new landscapes of fertility. Floodwaters, swollen from heavy rains, deposit rich sediment and nutrients that fertilize the fields and forests along our rivers. Forest fires, generated by lightning strikes, leave the gift of ash and potassium in the soil, expose serotinous seeds that require fire to germinate, and create new openings in forest canopies for the understory and low-lying plants to thrive. Humans are also forces of nature that ebb and flow. And our flows should not be dammed like water or suppressed like fire. They are regenerative flows that move us to feel our deepest longings and gratitudes that nourish our love for this world.

> ***There are beautiful wild forces within us. Let them turn the mills inside and fill sacks that feed even heaven.***
>
> – St. Francis of Assisi

Let us honor these wild forces inside us with intentional practices, even if the culture around us seems uncomfortable with emotional release. Many cultures around the world have developed and preserved traditions for tending to grief. Some teachers from these cultures have chosen to share their customs with audiences from outside of their communities. A wonderful resource on the beauty and sacred role of grief is *The Smell of Rain on Dust: Grief and Praise*, by Martín Prechtel. Through storytelling about the reciprocal and essential roles of grief and praise, Prechtel explores the context of *grief-suppressing behaviors* in modern society and *grief-transforming practices* of Indigenous cultures in places such as Guatemala and the Pueblo communities in the American southwest. He also offers suggestions on how to modify practices to make them accessible to those who are new to this work.

Other Indigenous teachers who hold knowledge of traditional grief rituals include Sobonfu Somé and Malidoma Somé, Dagara elders from Burkina Faso. They translate West African grief rituals and teach them to Westerners who have lost connection to the powers of pain and loss, which can be transformational when approached through ritual. Such cultural translation is tricky, but when teachings are given directly by Indigenous mentors, and received with integrity, they are worthy of engagement for those who have lost their own forms of processing grief communally.

In the Jewish tradition, we have a clear designee whose role is to mourn for the community. She is the *Mekonenet*, the mourning woman. According to Rabbi Jill Hammer's work on the *Netivot* or Priestess paths, "The word *Mekonenet* means 'one who laments' but can also mean 'one who makes a nest.' The Mekonenet embodies the pain and truth of change. ... She brings the gifts of comforting the bereaved, burying the dead, healing the mourners, and facing cataclysmic change."

Consciously Working with Grief and Trauma

People have used countless tools to undo old patterns of emotional suppression and move toward greater healing. As changemakers, we must lead the way in pursuing our own healing. We model for others the power and importance of doing this inner work. Our commitment to healing permeates our designs for social change, radiating outwards in the form of acceptance and wholeness rather than in suppression or fragmentation.

Black Organizing for Leadership and Dignity (BOLD) intentionally creates safe spaces for Black leaders to share feelings openly about what's difficult for them in their lives and in their leadership journeys. Creating this space to share tears and stories reinvigorates Black leaders' effectiveness in movement building.

Joanna Macy has developed a profound body of work, The Work that Reconnects, to help environmental activists create spaces for their painful feelings for a world in peril, described in her book, *Coming Back to Life*. There are numerous trainings in North America, New Zealand, Czech Republic, Germany, and the UK. Macy's work has begun to incorporate more analysis of structural oppression, colonization, and the understanding of intersectionality. But, like any predominantly white environmental movement, it still has a ways to go.

Re-evaluation Counseling is another excellent international community for reclaiming our full humanity through facing and "discharging"—by crying, shaking, raging, etc.—the hurts inflicted by an oppressive society. This practice of release involves the participation of one or more supportive co-counselors. After one person has a turn showing their feelings, the other person or people take turns, sharing time equally. This practice also creates beautiful human relationships built on mutually supportive connection.

Family Constellations help individuals process intergenerational family trauma, while Systemic Constellations work with historical organizational entanglements and wider cultural issues, such as healing from genocide, as a form of group work where people play representatives in the issue in need of healing. Both use a phenomenological approach.

How can we acknowledge the role of grief and trauma in practical change-making work? When designing social change projects, a good question to ask oneself is: Are my goals motivated by grief [trauma, wounds, unconscious patterns] or by creativity [gifts, positive vision, my best thinking]? This question comes from James Stark's Ecology of Leadership program at the Regenerative Design Institute. Questions such as this one demand brave self-awareness and turning the mind toward new and different worldviews of what is possible, rather than recapitulating familiar yet often unconscious and wounded perspectives.

My colleague in anti-oppression Jewish leadership education, Cara Silverberg, has been developing *trauma-informed* pedagogy at the intersection of conflict transformation and social justice education. Many of her thoughts on working with grief and trauma somatically can be found in her blog about identity and indigeneity: *On the Fringes of Place.*

We have the beautiful privilege to be alive right now. We are the link between our ancestors and the generations to come. We have the opportunity to actively heal the wounds passed down to us from our ancestors, who did not have adequate resources to stop the cycles of hurts in their lifetimes. With this precious opportunity of being alive, we can create new, regenerative patterns to leave for the children of the future, if we so courageously choose...

Rituals for Release and Renewal

Removing "the dead ashes" of our grief can take many forms, in community or alone. In the spirit of the social permaculture principle of leading from our lineages, I recommend researching traditional customs related to release and renewal practiced by your people (if you are not familiar with them or practicing them yourself already). Are there ways you can redesign or adapt those customs for your context? Below are release rituals, some of which I cherish from my Jewish lineage:

- immersing oneself in a moving body of water at the end of the work week, after big life transitions, or marking the change from one season to the next. Its power is amplified with the witness of others and by speaking aloud what you intend to release (this *mikveh*, or immersion into water as a purification practice, is a personal favorite)
- lighting a braided *havdallah* candle every week on Saturday night, and singing prayers to release the sweetness of the *Shabbat* ending and the sadness that accompanies that release
- convening a monthly *Rosh Chodesh* or new moon group to honor and release what has come to pass in the previous month—a way of becoming ready to receive that which is coming next
- sitting *shiva* (a way of honoring a family after a death) for seven days in one's home and receiving visitors...and lots of food
- on death anniversaries, or *yahrzeits*: placing a rock on a gravestone, lighting a candle for 24 hours, and offering the mourner's *kaddish* prayer
- holding a friend and crying together about a difficult political or personal situation
- communicating with ancestors and asking for their support in healing
- attending a grief ritual to release the collective accumulated pain of a community
- crying aloud to the stars or the mountains during a relationship separation or an identity crisis
- creating a personal mourning cairn, by placing symbolic objects of what is being mourned in a sacred pile, which grows over time (this example comes from the book *The Secret Life of Bees* by Sue Monk Kidd)

A Few Words About Addictive Behaviors and Pain

Addictions can be Band-Aids that we use to cover up painful feelings that yearn to be expressed. The more we tamp down our feelings, the more determined they are to find a way out, even if sideways, and especially when we don't want them to. Addictions only defer feeling our feelings, and, unfortunately, compound them in the process. It is important that changemakers commit to the difficult but worthwhile path of releasing addictions, one by one. In this process, setting up support systems for ourselves to feel the feelings we have attempted to suppress is a necessity. Otherwise, this serious commitment is nearly impossible to sustain. Being clear that this direction forward is for you and in service to living the biggest life possible can help with motivation during the difficult moments of healing.

> ***Sometimes the healing process hurts more than the pain, but the journey through sorrow is worth the ultimate release of all suffering.***
>
> – Alixa Garcia, shared with me at the Center for Whole Communities retreat on Whole Thinking in Booneville, CA

Others may take a more disguised addictive route, what John Welwood of the California Institute of Integral Studies calls a *spiritual bypass*. This coping strategy is another way to avoid feelings—by compulsively attending metaphysical workshops, zealously practicing meditation, or pursuing one certificate after another to blanket our feelings of desperation. Like addictive behaviors, spiritual bypasses do not serve anyone in the long term. Turning to face what we have avoided looking at is difficult and takes time, courage, and support.

We come by such patterns honestly: living in an oppressive society that enforces binary oppressor and oppressed roles has left all of us confused and hurt. When we act out of conditioning, which is reinforced by the over-culture, we remain imprisoned within the constraints of these hurts. Consequently, the Purposes of our social change projects will also be tainted by our patterns unless we transform them. Both modern psychology and philosophical traditions from around the world affirm that our internal states are expressed in our external actions. As within, so without.

When we make the decision to move toward healing, we are gifted with profound layers of personal liberation. What is revealed to us in the process lays the foundation for shared liberation struggles and inexplicable connection with others across difference. It opens our heart to compassion. We can embody the Jungian archetype of the *wounded healer*—originating with the Greek myth of Chiron who was physically wounded, and through the transformation of his own wounds, he became a compassionate teacher of healing and guide for others.

EXERCISE 17: Seven Common Forms of Internal Resistance

Before we move on to face some of the dire conditions on planet Earth, it is useful to identify which patterns of *internal resistance* we use to guard ourselves from our grief. Please read the list below, adapted from Macy and Johnstone's *Active Hope*. Then share with a group or your Learning Buddy—it's best not to do this activity alone—which of these forms of resistance you most often feel when you think about big crises, such as corporate control of the food system, nuclear war, or the militarization of domestic police.

- **I don't believe it's that dangerous**—willful ignorance or denial
- **It isn't my role to sort this out**—individualism, *fragmentation of responsibility*
- **I don't want to stand out from the crowd**—risk aversion, discomfort with standing out, pressure to conform, *culture of collusion*
- **This information threatens my commercial or political interests**—resistance to or invalidation of information/research that may disrupt one's security
- **It is so upsetting that I prefer not to think about it**—suppression and compartmentalization
- **I feel overwhelmed, aware of the danger, but don't know what to do**—paralysis, illusion we have to figure this out on our own
- **There's no point doing anything, since it won't make a difference**—discouragement, despair, it's too late and other *stories of decline*, making the best of life before the final collapse

Journal: *Which of these forms of resistance do you struggle with? When was the first time in your life that you remember feeling these same feelings, e.g., I don't want to stand out or I feel overwhelmed? Describe what was happening in the circumstances around you when you first felt this feeling. Then share what you discovered in a safe group space or with your Learning Buddy—this is the most important part, letting someone else know what you struggle with!*

> *We can exist in both these realities at the same time—going about our normal lives in the mode of Business as Usual while also remaining painfully aware of the multifaceted crisis unfolding around us. Living in this double reality creates a split in our mind.*
>
> – Joanna Macy and Chris Johnstone, *Active Hope*

Turning to Face the Reality of Climate Change

In this section of the book, we will spend time focusing on the psychological and emotional dimensions of facing climate change.

Let's give some attention to the fundamentals of climate change, and explore how they intersect with social injustices. As we do so, we can make space for the feelings that arise, and the healing rains that will follow.

The term "climate change" refers to a complex set of processes that result in catastrophic and often unpredictable weather patterns. When the large industries of the world (agriculture, military, transportation, etc.) burn fossil fuels and release carbon that has been stored underground in stable forms for millennia, the amount of atmospheric carbon increases at an exponential rate. Carbon emissions create a blanketing effect on the planet. Solar rays that enter our atmosphere turn into heat, which is a natural planetary process. The clouds, the oceans, and the landmasses absorb these solar rays and re-emit them as infrared radiation that "warms" the planet. But with the excessive carbon blanketing our atmosphere, this radiated heat remains trapped at levels we have not seen for millions of years, and compounds the rise in global temperature.

The positive feedback loop of "global warming" creates an increase in the movement of molecules, which results in irregular and extreme weather events. Due to the planet's circulation patterns, these storms disproportionately affect the tropics, arid regions, low-lying regions, and the Arctic—four portions of the world that are predominantly inhabited by Black, Indigenous, and People of Color.

Since we are intimately connected with all of life, when life suffers, we suffer. People in the *Global North*, who have thus far been largely buffered from the effects of climate change due to geography and financial wealth, may not realize that part of our individual suffering lies in the planet's exhaustion. We must also understand that this crisis of exhaustion stems from much of the Global North's privilege and overconsumption, which is disheartening and hopeful at the same time; these nations have the power to undo the massive harm they've engendered, if they act swiftly and with clarity.

Soil Desiccation from Colonial Deforestation, Followed by Drought, in Southeast India

One way to gain that clarity is through facing our feelings about the impact of climate change and related environmental crises. The more we can grieve what we have already lost—human cultures and languages, animal and plant species, the special wild places of our youth, beautiful vibrant ecosystems—the more we can allow our hearts their full tenderness. The more tender our hearts, the more we can feel what desperately needs changing and act with decisive clarity, rather than numbing out and sticking our heads in the sand.

One of the best ways to face the crises we're in is to do it with others. Trying to face these challenges alone, late at night just before bed, scanning social media on your device, is not a regenerative way to face the bad news. I recommend reading this segment of the book with a buddy or in a group, where together you can take turns listening to one another process the feelings that come up as you read. Consider using a timer and have everyone share equally. All feelings, from denial to anger to heartbreak, are welcome. What's important is that we are actually looking at these difficult realities, creating the dedicated space to un-dam our feelings, and letting them flow.

As we design our lives and our change-making projects, it's important to do so with the context of climate change in the front of our minds. Denying or ignoring it will not make it go away. Many have begun efforts toward climate change adaptation and mitigation, mostly in communities that are already clearly experiencing the effects on the front lines in the Global South and along the coastlines in the northern hemisphere.

Adaptation to and mitigation of climate change are important, but we must also think beyond these approaches, which come out of the resilience Paradigm, and begin moving toward a regeneration Paradigm. This crisis requires us to consider social and ecological strategies that will contribute to *climate change reversal*, an essential third leg of the climate adaptation–mitigation–reversal stool. It is well documented in Paul Hawken's most recent book, *Drawdown*, that social solutions such as education for girls in developing countries and land-use solutions such as regenerative agriculture involving tree crops can play substantial roles in climate change reversal efforts.

The opportunity to take action toward climate change reversal has a very narrow window. Earth and her creatures are beckoning us, who created this deadly chaos, to step up and act swiftly. My colleague Eric Toensmeier, a white climate change researcher and author of *The Carbon Farming Solution* and Project Drawdown Senior Fellow, shared with me that, "Global emissions have plateaued in the last few years, and need to start going down rapidly (as of 2020). There's a few decades for rapid overhaul of most aspects of civilization, with much of the action needing to take place in the next ten years, and further ongoing actions for the rest of the century." (The first chapter of *The Carbon Farming Solution* provides an excellent climate change overview.)

It's time to rise to our calling as "the ones we've been waiting for," a June Jordan quote echoed in the popular song by Sweet Honey and the Rock, and invoked by former US president Barack Obama. It is not enough to watch a film or two, or have a module on the topic in the classroom. The crisis has already arrived; it is not an issue we can defer to the future. We can do this in connection and strength with others, in a fight for what we love, rather than a fight against the wrongdoers.

> ***Not everything that is faced can be changed, but nothing can be changed until it is faced.***
>
> – James Baldwin

Un-numbing About Climate Injustice

Frontline communities of poor people in the *Global South* do not have the same privilege as people in the Global North to turn their backs on climate change. There are already millions of climate refugees whose homes, farms, and ancestral lands have been claimed by catastrophic weather events, such as the 2010 floods in Pakistan that displaced 11 million people, or Typhoon Haiyan in the Philippines, which displaced almost 6 million people.1 Hurricanes, floods, landslides, tsunamis, and many other "natural" disasters continue to displace and kill People of the Global Majority worldwide.

By 2050, there may be as many as 200 million climate refugees.2 Perhaps if the wealthier countries in the Global North were more regularly affected by the early rumblings of climate chaos, more financial resources, research, and responsive policies would be directed to the *Climate Justice movement*.

Indigenous people in particular are on the front lines of the impact of fossil fuel extraction. This injustice is part of a legacy of racist colonial practices of land theft and broken treaties. The pattern continues today in places legally recognized as sovereign. A well-known example is the Standing Rock Sioux community in North Dakota, US, who stand to protect their waters and ancestral burial grounds from the Dakota Access Pipe Line (DAPL). Other examples of Indigenous resistance include the Hopi and Navajo/Diné's fight against the Peabody Western Coal Company in Black Mesa, Arizona, US, and the organized resistance to the Keystone XL Pipeline by the Ojibwe/Anishinaabekwe in the White Earth Indian Reservation in Minnesota, US. The battles continue, even after small victories are won.

Zooming out to a global scale, the deleterious causes and effects of climate change persist. According to Project Drawdown, deforestation and degradation of forest ecosystems are responsible for about one-eighth of anthropogenic greenhouse gas emissions today.3 Most of this degraded land has been deforested to turn into livestock feedlots and mono-crop farms, which further increase carbon emissions. According to Consultative Group on International Agricultural Research, one-third of greenhouse gas emissions come from the global food system.4 Draining the water that agribusinesses and other large-scale processing plants require has left 21 of the world's 37 largest aquifers in crisis, and they may soon dry out, according to Canadian author and environmental activist, Maude Barlow. Barlow shared these statistics with us at Omega Institute's Seeds of Change conference in 2015.

When I was in South India on an ecological design fellowship, I heard about the stories of farmers who had gone bankrupt from a combination of climate change-related weather disruptions and debts they owed to predatory corporate agribusinesses. These agri-chemical corporations target vulnerable farmers eager to increase their revenues, selling them expensive patented seed and chemical inputs which they promise will increase yields, but fail to do so. This "failure to yield" has been well documented by expert groups such as the National Academy of Sciences and the Union of Concerned Scientists. At the same time, agribusinesses sue farmers who attempt to save patented seeds. Mass bankruptcy, paired with loss of farmland and climate-related displacement has led to a sharp increase in farmer suicides. According to an article published in 2017 by the National Center for Biotechnology Information, 300,000 farmers have committed suicide in India over the past two decades, a sharp increase compared to previous decades. Scientists writing in the journal *Proceedings of the National Academy of Sciences* have linked these deaths directly to climate change, noting that an increase of 5 degrees on any one day in India was associated with an additional 335 deaths, totaling 60,000 suicides in the agricultural sectors that could be attributed to climate change.

Consider pausing here for ***Reflection and Integration,*** *the central hub of the Regenerative Design Process. Discuss with a Learning Buddy any feelings that arise.*

In areas especially vulnerable to climate disruptions, ecological and economic pressures increase on small farmers. In the case of weather-related disaster, farmers flee their land as climate refugees; or, due to harsh conditions, such as sustained drought, farmers can no longer make a living, go bankrupt, and are forced to sell their land. Many families migrate to the cities in search of work, distraught and divorced from the land and traditions that sustained them for generations.

One of the impacts of this climate-driven socio-economic trend is the increased consolidation of land ownership into corporate hands. Small farms no longer provide their local communities with healthy, affordable, and culturally appropriate food. Instead, private investors turn multigenerational family farms into corporate plantations that produce one or two crops for export. (For a good overview on the issue of food system corporate consolidation and its social effects, see *Rebuilding the Foodshed* by Phillip Ackerman-Leist and *Harvesting Justice* by Tory Field and Beverly Bell). Industrial agriculture degrades local ecosystems with heavy chemical inputs and genetically modified organisms (GMOs). Corporate agribusinesses privatize water for irrigation—limiting water that was once freely available to all as part of the commons—and then discharge polluted runoff into waterways. Alternately, foreigners purchase family farms at low rates, and turn working farms into gated holiday estates for the wealthy.

As a result, regional food security plummets and communities are forced to become dependent on expensive food imports with low nutritional value, greatly altering traditional diets. Globalized capitalism paired with climatic catastrophes leave social injustices and ecological degradation in their wake, all in the name of opening new markets for world trade at the expense of already marginalized people. Farmers with skills, knowledge, land, and a relationship to place become dislocated, jobless, often hungry, and dependent on the capitalist economy for survival. These effects on people and the environment are called "*externalized costs.*"

When we un-numb, we can activate regenerative responses to climate injustice from our love for the world and its people, and our personal passions and skill sets. For example, Climbing PoeTree created a multimedia performance Hurricane Season and eco-justice tour in response to Hurricane Katrina and the state violence committed in its aftermath. They share on their website about the tour, "An integral part of every show is the 'solutions-cipher,' a forum that addresses the impacts of the issues surfaced in *Hurricane Season* on a local level, and illuminates solutions driven by those most impacted, that are already underway. The objective of the 'solutions-ciphers' is to cross-pollinate creative strategies for self-determination and to turn the passion generated in the show into action manifested in the community. Representatives from local grassroots groups that are doing groundbreaking work around the issues brought up in Hurricane Season are featured at the dialogues to garner support for their initiatives and give audience members access into local social justice movements."

Take another pause here for a ***Reflection and Integration*** *Pair/Share: take three to five minutes each to talk about your feelings with your Learning Buddy or another person.*

And the ocean is worth more than gold
And water cannot be held captive
It will reshape even stone
And even when the last tree stands alone
It still makes a sound long after it's fallen
In a forest that lived even if not one saw it
And fed the world it's breath
Whether or not we applauded

One hand clapping sounds a lot like
The rhythms we lost
In generations who sang
Even as they departed
And now we stand at the doorway
In the hallway life brought us
At this crossroads of lost hope and
undeniable promise
Where we choose between paths
Beyond rightness and wrongness
That will lead to the brink of the planet's
exhaustion
Or the age of compassion where the meek
become strongest
And re-inherit the Earth
And re-define progress

– Excerpt from "They Are Selling the Rain," by Climbing PoeTree

Images from Climbing PoeTree's Award Winning Production, Hurricane Season. Art by Alixa Garcia

EXERCISE 18: "I Will Not Turn Away"

In order to focus our hearts and minds on righting injustices and creating new equitable patterns in society, it's important that we be able to face the difficult issues and feel our pain, sadness, and anger about "the mess we're in." When we are not afraid to look at the pain of the world, we become unstoppable in our ability to regenerate change.

I strongly recommend doing this exercise, "I Will Not Turn Away," now and frequently throughout your change-making endeavors. I have had the privilege to learn this practice of squarely facing our pain for the world from Joanna Macy directly. The first time you complete it, please focus your responses on what you have just read in this chapter and what you know about the climate crisis and its injustices.

This exercise is not something to do in isolation or solely with a journal. I encourage you to undertake it with at least one other person, and for each of you to share your responses and actively listen to each other. Take two full minutes to answer each question. Also, you'll want to ask your Wellness Buddy to support you in implementing the next steps you articulate in this exercise.

1. What do you love? The Earth? Nourishing food? Clean water? Justice? Freedom?
2. What pressing issues do you actively avoid looking at that are harming or jeopardizing what you love? If you were to focus your attention on these issues, what would you have to feel? Be brave if you can, and notice any avoidance patterns that may come up in your response.
3. Identify two forms of distraction that keep you numbed out from experiencing your feelings about "the mess we're in." Examples might be overwork, shopping, alcohol, drugs, or media consumption. Would you be willing to give one of these distractions or addictions a break for a period of time that you define? Tell your Wellness Buddy your plan and timeline, and see if they have an addiction they want to release with *your* support, too. Do this together, and on your own terms.
4. Finish the following sentence in three different ways: "I will not turn away from..." Please choose difficult things to look at rather than positive directions you want to commit to. Then reflect on what you notice inside yourself when you complete each sentence.

Please note: Once you begin to remove distractions or addictions in your life, you are likely to feel more grief bubbling up or more hopelessness about the world's situations than you had felt before. Bear with these feelings: they are signs that you are moving in the right direction. Difficult feelings will well up. With the help of resources listed in Consciously Working with Grief and Trauma (see page 66) and Rituals for Release and Renewal (see page 67), we can move through these heavy feelings in a regenerative rather than degenerative spiral.

As we take on this healing process, at times we will slide back into our old habits of comfort and numbness. It's important to recognize when this slipping happens and to take note of what triggered it—and then to be gentle with ourselves. Become familiar with your particular distractions and your Forms of Internal Resistance (see page 70) so you can recognize them quickly as they begin to creep back in. Remember, you're in charge of your thoughts and

EXERCISE 18: Cont.

actions, and you can slow down and make space to choose them consciously so that they serve you on your brave journey. Carol Sanford calls this *internal locus of control.* And know that you are worth it, to do the work needed to honor your pain, and to release it by going into it rather than attempting to bypass it. In facing our pain and anger, we can become free of fear and feel more activated to make change.

● Discussion 3: Environmental Justice ●

Please take time to process with a buddy who has also read about the intersection of racism and environmental degradation in this chapter. Then, discuss the idea of environmental justice. What do you think this concept entails? Do you see that we cannot mend our environmental crisis without ending racism at the same time? If not, place some attention on where your mind hits obstacles in connecting the dots between these two issues.

Go one step further and share equal time (suggested five minutes each) listening to what feelings came up for each of you when reading about environmental and climate injustices. Sadness, grief, anger, despair, and numbness are all legitimate and reasonable responses. What's important is that we have the dedicated space and loving attention of one another to bring these feelings to the surface. When we are able to express our emotions, we gain the ability to think more clearly and flexibly in order to take action.

> *Suppression of our natural responses to disaster is part of the disease of our time. The refusal to acknowledge these responses causes a dangerous splitting. It divorces our mental calculations from our intuitive emotional and biological embeddedness in the matrix of life. That split allows us passively to acquiesce in the preparations for our own demise.*
>
> – R. J. Clifton, quoted in *Braiding Sweetgrass* by Robin Wall Kimmerer

Please see Further Reading related to chapter 5 on page 238.

Social Design Lexicon for Chapter 5

Review the following key terms and write down what they mean to you.

Release and Renewal:

Grief-suppressing Behaviors:

Grief-transformation Practices:

Trauma-informed:

Addictions:

Spiritual Bypass:

Wounded Healer:

Internal Resistance:

Fragmentation of Responsibility:

Culture of Collusion:

Stories of Decline:

Climate Change Reversal:

Frontline Communities:

Global South and Global North:

Climate Justice Movement:

Externalized Costs:

Internal Locus of Control:

Environmental Justice:

CHAPTER 6: BUILDING THE FERTILE SOIL OF OUR RELATIONSHIPS

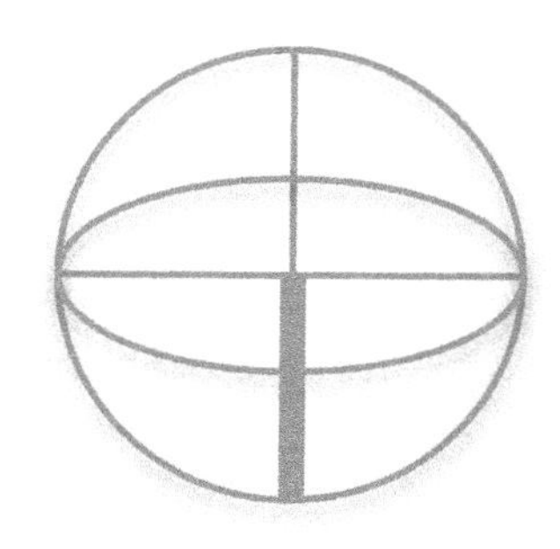

EARTH BELOW: SOIL/RELATIONSHIPS

> *This place where you are right now, God circled on a map for you.*
>
> – Hafiz

The circle that surrounds us might be what Anishinabek scholar and activist Winona LaDuke calls *all our relations*. We are eternally held by an endless circle of interconnected relationships, whether or not we were raised with this worldview or can perceive this truth. We are always in relationship with life, and we can consciously tend our connections just as we tend a garden, enriching the soil so our crop grows taller, stronger, for longer. Soil is the true gold, its richness feeds the world; so too do our relationships. They sparkle and nourish us as the foundation of our survival as social primates.

We can also cultivate relationships with more-than-human relatives. From the plants in the forest to the potted herbs on our stoop, from the water in rivers to the water that flows from the faucet, from the birds that fly outside our windows to the birds that visit us on the beach: there is no place that life cannot reach us.

The more we can lean into this feeling of being held and nested, inside circles that surround us at all times, the more we can feel our inherent belonging. When we have a sense of belonging, we feel kinship with and accountability to the mournful cries and ecstatic triumphs of life, and we long to protect it. *Relational Reality* is a powerful book by Charlene Spretnak that explores interrelatedness as a core principle of life, and details ways to consciously work with this principle in all sectors of our modern world, from education to economics to healthcare. Feeling our connection to all beings is essential to the work of making change.

The l*one wolf archetype* is an echo of past wounds and confused human-generated messages. It is not reasonable, or possible, for one brave soul to carry all the burden. In fact, martyrdom prevents us from realizing our purpose, undercutting us before we succeed. Releasing grief that comes from isolation embedded in this cultural narrative opens up new opportunities to build meaningful support teams. A regenerative model of social change reflects the clear messages of nature—redundancy, diversity, and functional relationships. Isolation, which is the product of modernity's assembly-line mentality and reductionist Paradigm, requires revisioning. Looking to nature as our teacher, we see soil molecules below Earth's surface bond closely together, creating the right conditions—moist, dark, intact—for interrelated transformation to take root and emerge.

Discussion 4: What Creates Isolation?

For millennia, humans have survived as social animals, sustained by networks of kin. We have always been organisms that revere and are interdependent with the lands, waters, animals, plants, and elements around us.

Today, many people are disconnected and isolated from each other, the natural world, traditional customs, and ancestral stories.

Please explore these questions with a partner, taking turns to speak and listen: How have you experienced isolation in your life? What effect has it had on you? What pathways can you see for increasing your experiences of interconnection?

Then zoom out and explore with a group (or with your Learning Buddy): What do you believe is at the root of our modern-day isolation? What will return us collectively to a sense of interconnection?

Nested Wholes and Rings of Influence

When we look to nature, we see that the elements of ecosystems are not self-subsistent. Nor are they reliant on a single relationship or strand of support. Rather, elements of the natural world create many strands of interconnection, so that when one strand is disturbed, other supports are redundantly in place. Whether or not we are conscious of it, we hold in our hands one strand from each web we belong to—we are inherently already interconnected. When we tug on that strand, our influence ripples throughout all the groups and larger systems in our networks. Social permaculture models itself on this web of resilient interconnection.

> *Networks are the only form of organization used by living systems on this planet. These networks result from self-organization, where individuals or species recognize their interdependence and organize in ways that support the diversity and viability of all. Networks create the conditions for emergence, which is how Life changes.*
>
> – Margaret Wheatley and Deborah Frieze, "Lifecycle of Emergence: Using Emergence to Take Social Innovation to Scale"

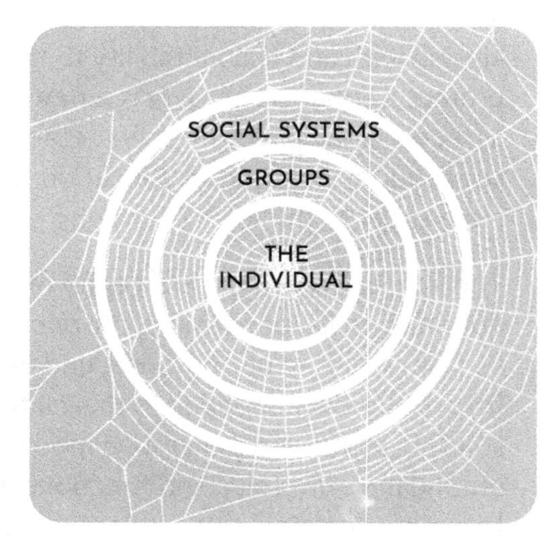

NESTED WHOLES WITH WEB PATTERN

As individuals, we are both whole onto ourselves *and* we are members of various groups—ethnic, religious, political, familial—that comprise a new larger whole. Introduced in the overview of section I, this idea of Nested Wholes, which are also known as "holons," is the focus of the work of systems thinkers, such as Donella Meadows. When we shift our dominant Paradigm from one of reductionist science, where each part is isolated from the whole, and toward an ecological Paradigm, where each part is necessarily interconnected within a larger system, then we begin to remember the true wholeness of life.

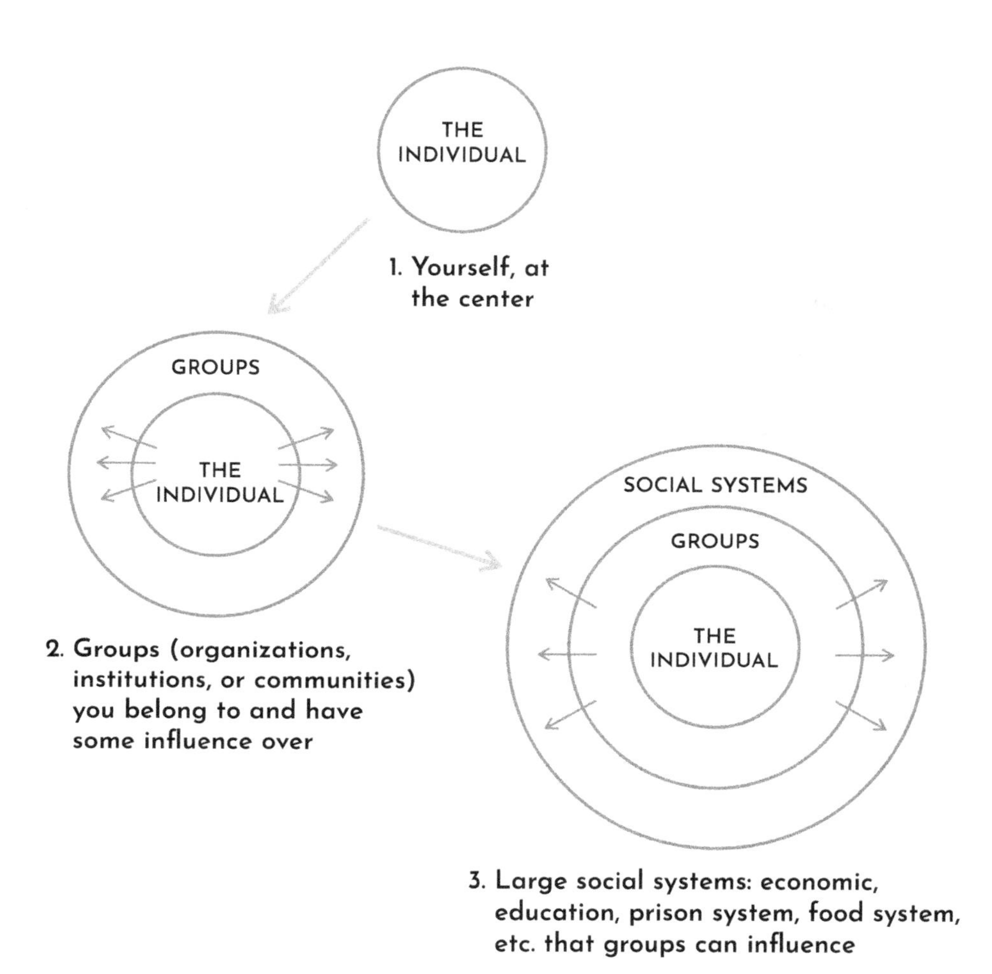

NESTED WHOLES AND RINGS OF INFLUENCE

Like us, each of the groups we belong to are also whole onto themselves and nested within the broader web of their respective social systems. These larger systems are also complete wholes. Let's take, for example, an individual who is an educator that specializes in teaching theater to incarcerated students in prisons. This individual would belong to several networks: community-based educators, academic colleagues, street performers, improv troupes, prison reformers, human rights advocates, and so on. This individual may not have direct influence over the larger social systems they wish to change, but they can exert influence on each of the groups to which they belong. In turn, those groups can create concentric *Rings of Influence* on broader social systems when they work in alliance with other groups on shared goals.

Through proactive coordination and the principle of *positive contagion*, change occurs in social patterns that ripple out and repeat across scales, much like we see in fractals in the natural world. In the example here, one or more of these groups could affect change in the larger social systems of education, the performing arts, or corrections. The more we can coordinate efforts and build *coalitions* with shared affinity groups, the more change we can leverage—shifting the norms, policies, and ultimately, cultures of each system, from a local to an international scale.

> ***At each moment in the emergence of a system, the system tends to go in that direction which intensifies the already existing centers in the wholeness in just such a fashion that the new centers reinforce and intensify the lager configuration or wholeness which existed before.***
>
> – Christopher Alexander, *The Nature of Order*

Humans as Keystone Species in Interrelationship

The reality of interrelatedness becomes even more possible when we start recovering from our collective cultural amnesia and recall that we humans are *keystone species*, one of a handful of species on which other species and natural elements in an ecosystem largely depend. When keystone species, such as wolves or beavers, are extirpated, their surrounding ecosystem changes drastically. (The reintroduction of wolves to Yellowstone National Park in Wyoming, US, is a poignant illustration of this concept.) The regenerative land management of Aboriginal people in Australia is an example of how our species' presence can produce far greater habitat, fertility, and food in a landscape than if not present. That is to say, people have the creative capacity to drastically change any system we are a part of, sometimes for better and sometimes for worse. This is an intrinsic property of being human.

At this point in history, one could argue that the ecosystems around us would change for the better, and naturally regenerate themselves, without human interference. Fortunately or unfortunately, humans may be the only species that can get us out of the crisis we've created; recall that we are the decisive element. Potawatomi professor and author Robin Wall Kimmerer elegantly writes about simple ways we can reclaim this ability to regenerate relationships and land in her bestselling book *Braiding Sweetgrass*. She astutely explores two contrasting Paradigms: human as helper and human as harmer, framed within the context of two very different origin stories that have colored the psyches and behaviors of First Nations Peoples and of Westerners.

It is imperative that we recall the truth of who we are, a fallible yet powerful keystone species. It's horribly irresponsible to shrug our shoulders and just give up. Indigenous Peoples all over the planet have been acting as keystone species for millennia, helping whole new ecosystems come about and thrive. For example, the "wild" landscapes of abundance (fruits, nuts, berries, fish, game, hunting grounds, fertile cropland) that European colonists "discovered" in what today is North America were the result of hundreds of years of active land management. In the Northeast, Native groups stewarded these lands through crop cultivation, systematic fertilization, controlled burns, game population control, and other forms of holistic management. Climate change research in Project Drawdown attests to the brilliance of Indigenous Peoples' land management, finding that in addition to sequestering atmospheric carbon, "[it] conserves biodiversity, maintains a range of ecosystems services, safeguards rich cultures and traditional ways of life, and responds to the needs of the most vulnerable." Many authors have documented this history in their books, including Kat Andersen and Robin Wall Kimmerer (see Further Reading for more).

This fingerprint of humanity has made it possible for life to thrive in new symbiotic ways that may not have been expressed without human intervention. Permaculture urges us to think of ourselves not as invasive species killing the planet, but as necessary partners in the regeneration of life—much like other keystone species that create habitat, fodder, and healthy checks and balances in the ecosystems they shape and inhabit. The film *Inhabit: A Permaculture Perspective* explores this Paradigm of human as helper and related practices further.

Intentional Relationships

In this part of the chapter, we'll take a deep dive into the landscape of human relationships with several exercises. These frameworks can help changemakers authentically build relationships of support and relationships across difference. If we can lift up each other's unique strengths, the more solidarity we can build without getting sidelined by racism or anti-Semitism or classism.

How can we thoughtfully cultivate the types of relationships that move us toward personal and planetary regeneration? As white author and podcaster Tim Ferriss puts it, "You are the average of the five people you spend the most time with." Understanding the nature of each of our relationships and making them explicit, to ourselves and to others, is key to designing resilient social environments.

Here's one approach to cultivating meaningful relationships:

1. Try to see through someone else's lens to imagine their experience of the world.
2. Offer some form of invitation to someone.
3. See what the other person values, then try to nourish that, feeding what the other loves.
4. Give tangible and intangible gifts (based on what you know about what that person values).

One last point here, the stronger that our relationships are in times of loss and grief, the more support we have to feel our deep feelings and then alchemize them into gratitude and praise for the world. Expressing how much we love and cherish life, especially in times of loss, prevents us from getting stuck in our unexpressed grief. In *The Smell of Rain on Dust*, Martín Prechtel writes: "If we do not grieve what we miss, we are not praising what we love. We are not praising the life we have been given in order to love. If we do not praise whom we miss, we are ourselves in some way dead. So grief and praise make us alive." It takes a community to support us to do this powerful and worthy emotional work.

EXERCISE 19: Zones of Relationships and Cycles of Influence

Zones of Use, the permaculture planning tool we explored in chapters 1 and 3, has another social application here. Mapping our relationships onto zones and looking at the vitality of each zone, how frequently it needs tending, what goals and visions we have for it, etc., helps us clarify our orientation toward others. This tool helps us to invest our energy as we cultivate relationships and gather support for our change-making endeavors. Then, we can consider which *Cycles of Influence* effect the health of our relationships and design for those conditions.

This particular diagram is one way to map Zones of Relationships. I've chosen to place the self, Zone 00, at the center. This is not meant to reflect a worldview that privileges individualism and ego over the collective or nature. Rather, this model places the self at the center because we are necessarily nested within all that we are related to. The person at the center, Zone 00, is mobile and traverses all the relationships, tending to each one with varying levels of intensity, much like a bee cross-pollinates across the landscape, but then always returns back to the hive to rest.

Note: You can create another version of this diagram that makes more sense to you if this one does not resonate with your understanding of self and your relationships. You can always rename the zones to better reflect your life circumstances. Take note of alternate arrangements and what they reveal to you about yourself.

Start by reviewing Zone 00 on the right, and work your way outward in the zones, moving counterclockwise. The idea is that you have more frequent contact and stronger relationships with the zones closer to you, at the center. A strong central core means stronger ripples radiate out to those zones that may seem further away or more intangible. Zones 5 and 6, which are unique in that they surround and encompass all the other zones, and their placement here doesn't necessarily reflect the frequency or intimacy of connection you may feel with them.

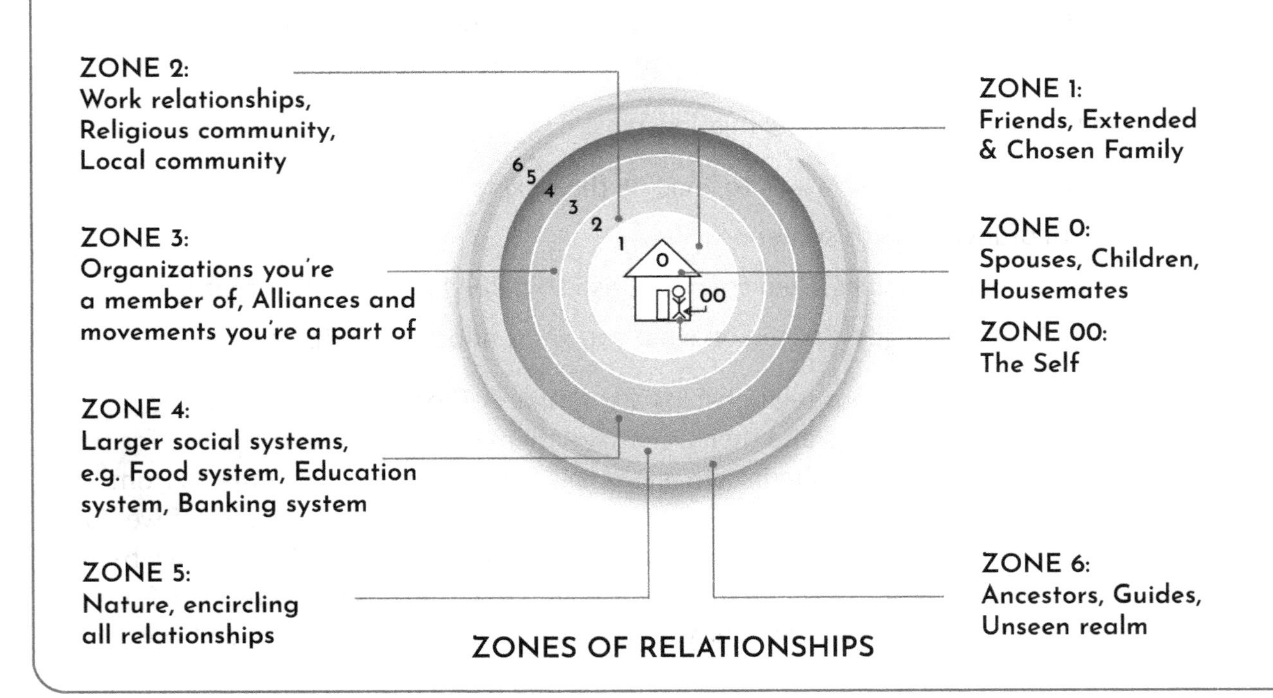

ZONES OF RELATIONSHIPS

EXERCISE 19: Cont.

Draw a Zones of Relationship diagram in your journal, like the one here or your own version. Then draw concentric circles, as is shown here, and label the zones accordingly. Wait to add color! Draw a line to each zone and in the margins, list the specific people, communities, organizations, natural places, and/or unseen forces that constitute each of your relationship zones.

Journal: *Write a short paragraph for each zone (eight total) that describes what each one looks like in your life. Who or what occupies it? What is the current state of health and well-being in these relationships? End with at least one Goal for relationships in that zone, something you can achieve in the next 1 to 3 months.*

For each zone, designate a color. Use colored pencils or crayons (rather than markers) to shade lightly, darkly, or somewhere in between to express how strong your connection to each zone is at this point in time, including Zone 00, yourself.

Journal: *Working with the idea that there exist regular Cycles of Influence, which cycles make it hard to maintain the health of relationships, and which support the tending of these relationships? Start by brainstorming all the Cycles of Influence in your life (e.g., seasonal, hormonal, workflow). Then, see if you can categorize them by their periodicity—how frequently they cycle in and out of your life—on a daily, weekly, monthly, seasonal, or yearly basis. For instance, if you are a college student, your relationship with family members, Zone 1, might suffer during the cycle of the semesters, but thrive during your breaks. Conversely, your relationship to social organizing with student clubs in Zone 3 might flourish when you are on campus, but diminish when you are at home. Spend some time writing about the Cycles of Influence in your life and how they affect each of your Zones of Relationships. In what ways can you visually represent these Cycles of Influence on your diagram?*

EXERCISE 20: Mapping Energy Patterns in Relationships

Now that we have a big-picture map of our Zones of Relationships, we can start zooming in on individual relationships. Observing the dynamics of energy give-and-take in each of our relationships, whether it be with a lover or collaborator, is an important step toward designing the social conditions that support our personal wellness and our broader work.

Here are four types of relationships that we can map through this lens:

- **Extractive relationships:** When one person consistently draws energy and/or resources from the relationship, leaving the other person with diminished reserves after interactions.
- **Consumptive relationships:** They absorb energy from both people, leaving each individual with less energy than before an interaction began; these relationships require continual energy inputs to persist.

Continued on next page

EXERCISE 20: Cont.

- **Restorative relationships:** They occur when two people naturally generate surplus energy when together, and that energy benefits both people equally.
- **Regenerative relationships:** When two people come together and their combined gifts and energy create conditions that serve a greater purpose than just the two individuals' needs; these relationships can be the source energy for a whole effort, movement, or community.

Take a moment to think about various relationships you've had (intimate, social, professional, etc.). Select one person who comes to mind for each of the four types: these will become your reference points. (Note: relationships are not static and can shift across types of relationships. For this exercise, identify what is the current *baseline dynamic* with an individual rather than focusing on the fluctuations.)

Extractive: ______________________ Restorative: ______________________

Consumptive:______________________ Regenerative:______________________

With feeling the effects of these reference relationships, it may become easier to observe and design for the dynamics in your current and future relationships. The more we become literate in relationship patterns, the more we can actively choose the people we want to spend the most time with and for what purposes. We can also try to upgrade an extractive or consumptive relationship with active investment in it, or we can choose to relinquish it.

EXERCISE 21: Anchors and Accomplices

For emotional and spiritual resilience, we can intentionally design relationships with Anchors and with Accomplices (discussed in Chapter 2) to support our personal ecosystem:

Anchors: The term "*Anchors*" comes from Paul Raphael, an Odawa Peacemaker and teacher, from whom I learned a great deal in my early twenties. To me, Anchors are people who are grounding forces in our lives, people who consistently reconnect us to ourselves. In my experience, Anchors have been elders, life mentors, or those with expertise in a particular area that we wish to gain. They can also be family members or friends who are unconditionally devoted to us throughout time, and who know our essence and can remind us of it when we stray too far from our truth. One special quality of Anchors is that they are able to see our hidden gifts and unaware places, and reflect them back to us. This type of relationship is unique and precious.

Accomplices: These are the people who have our back, who witness our day-to-day struggles, and who are willing to stand shoulder-to-shoulder with us in battle when needed. Ideally, we always have Accomplices surrounding us. These can be people with different or shared identities

EXERCISE 21: Cont.

in relation to us, people who will stand up for us, and remember our inherent power and goodness, even when we stumble. Accomplices may come and go in our life. For instance, they may be project- or time period-specific, or some may be lifelong Accomplices.

We can look for opportunities to show up for others in these roles. Those who we show up for may not be the same people who show up for us. With both Anchors and Accomplices, there is a difference between making these relationships *explicit* versus them remaining *implicit*, or unspoken. For instance, you may feel that someone is your Anchor or Accomplice, but why not articulate this or explicitly invite them into this role in your life? Consent and agreements are two building blocks for healthy social ecosystem development.

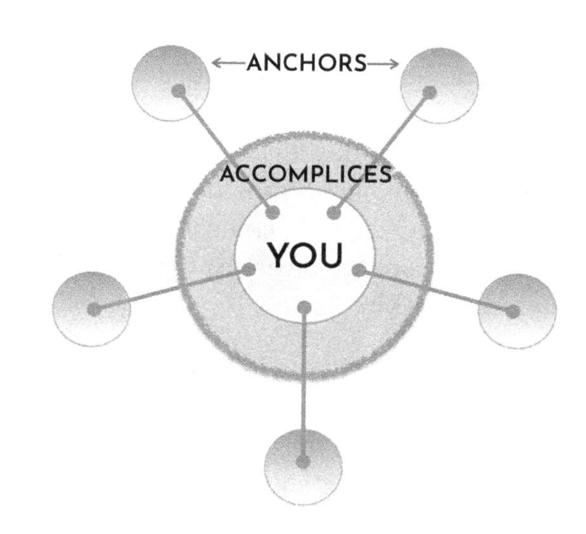

ANCHORS AND ACCOMPLICES

List one or two Accomplices for each of the following Life Sectors. Feel free to add other Life Sectors here that are most relevant to you. Then, note with an "E" or an "I" if these people are explicitly or implicitly your Accomplices. For those with whom you have not yet explicitly requested they show up for you as an Accomplice, consider offering them a gift and inviting one or two of them to support you as such. See how the relationship changes. People often love being asked to step into the role of Accomplice. It's an honor to be trusted in this way.

Family ______________________________ Creative Life ______________________________

Work ______________________________ Change-making Projects ______________________

Other ______________________________ Other ______________________________

In my experience, having about five Anchors at any one time fosters emotional and spiritual resilience for changemakers, especially in turbulent times. Too many Anchors makes it difficult to maintain truly meaningful relationships.

In the diagram, write the name of one of your Anchors next to each Anchor circle. Have you explicitly asked these individuals serve in this role for you? Perhaps the two of you may even want to articulate the agreements and intentions for this special relationship. If grief arises as you consider these relationships or their void in your life, know that feeling is common in this exercise and consider engaging with one of the Rituals for Release and Renewal.

Multiracial Leadership: From Isolation to Alliances Across Race

Social permaculture is about regenerating social systems that are inclusive of our full humanity. Multiracial leadership teams serve as an antidote to the impact of racism on both the oppressed *and* the oppressor. Racist ideology has contaminated relationships between people and capsizes collective efforts to create lasting broad-scale change. Racism, as a social construction, serves to divide people across lines of difference in order to justify the historical and ongoing colonial exploitation of peoples' bodies, labor, and land. Painful outcomes of racism's legacy include segregation, fearful hatred, and state-sanctioned violence. Everyone loses in this equation. The good news is that we can work with a Nested Wholes framework to heal the wounds of mistrust and isolation on the individual level, dismantle structural racism on the institutional level, and create new systems of equity and transformative justice that replace racism on the systemic level. My colleague Yavilah McCoy, CEO of Dimensions Educational Consulting, is a Black Jewish cultural genius who excels at working on diversity, equity, and inclusion across interconnected scales of society, and doing it with loving joy.

As young ones, we come into this world reaching out for connection with everyone. This is natural. Over time, we painfully learn that social conditions do not permit our arms to remain wide open for just anyone. The majority of us across the planet became indoctrinated with racial ideologies, and this conditioning shut down our inherent desire for connection with "the other." This process affects everyone, including people who *benefit from racial privilege* and people *targeted by racism*. Alice Walker coined the term *colorism* in her 1983 book, *In Search of Our Mothers' Gardens*. Colorism describes a form of racism within "racial" groups where light-skinned members receive countless privileges, such as more family resources and better access to education, jobs, and spouses than their darker-skinned relatives. The construction of racism hurts everyone and makes even loved ones turn on each other.

And so, building alliances across difference is a powerful elixir for healing this collective human affliction. The Black Lives Matter movement, a largely queer, woman, and transgender-led movement, recommends that white organizations listen to and take the lead from organizations run by Black, Indigenous, and People of Color. This can look like white people backing organizations led by and for BIPOC and/or giving them resources without strings attached, that is, without attempts to control how those resources are used. It can also look like leveraging individual or collective white privilege to implement government policies or community campaigns proposed by BIPOC-lead organizations. This approach is very different from that of *tokenism*, where one Person of Color is asked to join an all-white board so that organization can get "diversity points," for example. Building multiracial organizing relationships is entirely possible, as we've seen with the climate justice movement, which is predominantly led by BIPOC-run organizations with white organizations backing their leadership.

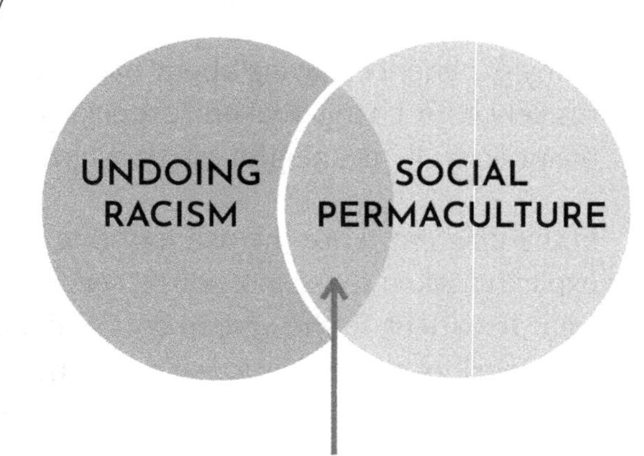

Undoing Racism and Permaculture are Both About **BUILDING RELATIONSHIPS**

Perhaps the next step in this evolution is a proliferation of mixed organizations with BIPOC and white people working side by side. To truly be regenerative and avoid implosion, the dynamics of racism and white privilege need to be explicitly discussed on a regular basis and navigated mindfully. This shift from *monocultural* (single-identity led) *organizations* to multiracial and *polycultural* (multiple identity-led) *organizations* requires courage and perseverance. SoulFire Farm in upstate New York is an example of a Black, Brown, and Sephardic-led nonprofit food justice organization that has invited certain white Accomplices to join their board. Jews for Racial and Economic Justice (JFREJ) is another example of a multiracial organization working to produce intersectional resources, such as *Counting the Omer for Black Lives* and *The Shavuot for Black Lives Guide*, which bring racial justice practices into two Jewish holidays.

Undoing racism and social permaculture both draw their strengths from building relationships. Margaret Wheatley, an African American author and systems thinker, posits this insight in her classic book, *Leadership and the New Science:* The quality of the relationships between individuals within a system will directly reflect the potency and power of that system. Racial justice organizing work offers practices to break down the wedges that reinforce segregation between groups of people.

These practices directly inform my social permaculture approach to leadership development. Here is a twofold path that aids changemakers in mending the web of human relationships:

1. Uprooting the oppressive ideologies we were indoctrinated with: What ideologies have you taken as truths and unintentionally perpetuated in your own behavior? Looking at the racist (or xenophobic or homophobic, etc.) messages inside our minds and bringing them into the light is one way forward. We can speak aloud these confused messages in affinity groups or caucuses with people who have shared privileged identities, or in one-on-one peer listening sessions. There may even be organized discussion groups in your community that have grown out of widespread justice thought leadership, such as Paul Kivel's book, *Uprooting Racism*. Standing Up for Racial Justice (SURJ) is another far-reaching network that may have local chapters in your region. If not, they offer a SURJ Chapter and Affiliate Group Building Toolkit on their website. Growing in self-awareness and self-modulation enables us to think before acting out or saying something that reinforces legacies of oppression. Understanding how we passively collude with injustices is equally important.

Another way to uproot the oppressive ideologies we carry is to learn—through relationships, conversations, books, courses, films, art, music, travel—about the histories of oppressed peoples, their liberation movements, and how injustices continue to play out today. A commitment to learning historical and contemporary struggles helps us recognize how these patterns function in society today and propagate their messaging inside us. The fastest way I've grown personally in this regard is by developing friendships with people across difference, e.g., racial identities, nationality, and religion.

2. Becoming an Accomplice to members of targeted groups: In order to have a positive impact on the world, anti-oppression work needs to go beyond self-awareness and into action. Listen to the personal stories of people who are targeted by oppressions that do not affect you. Listen for what you have in common. What can you do together? It's also very important to tell your personal story, your people's history, etc. This lets others get to know you, which eliminates a common power dynamic where people with privilege ask lots of questions (without sharing back) when speaking to someone with less privilege. This behavior can come across as extractive or transactional, or even as interrogative, to people who are targeted by racism or transphobia, for instance. Sharing our own stories makes us equally vulnerable and builds trust. (At the same time, track intersectional identity patterns here, and assess just how much space it makes sense to take up.)

Becoming an ally also means more than trust-building; becoming an Accomplice means taking action (see chapter 2 on ally vs. Accomplice). This can take the form of interrupting acts of oppression, calling in others' oppressor patterns, and showing up in solidarity at events, such as the Solidarity Vigils held for Sikh Americans who have been the victims of countless hate crimes since 9/11. Equally important is putting your body on the front line to support others. Waving the "ally" flag without meaningful action can be harmful and reinforce mistrust. Other resources for becoming an Accomplice can be found in Further Reading for this chapter.

EXERCISE 22: Obstacles to Building Alliances

Individualistic cultures that privilege competition over cooperation have set up the conditions that keep many of us trying to make change on our own, even if we know it's less effective. When we try to create social change on our own, we get pushback. The Undoing Racism Organizing Collective (UROC) compares this to a jack-in-the-box toy that pops out but then gets pushed back in again. When we build relationships and organize in solidarity with others, our force is much more powerful as an alliance and we cannot be pushed back so easily.

At two of the UROC trainings I attended, we discussed what makes us vulnerable to getting pushed back inside our box again and again, including:

- We try to create change individually, rather than collectively, and harness more power. When we act alone, we are vulnerable on all sides. When we act en masse, we cover more bases and are less likely to be thwarted in our efforts.

  An analogous teaching from nature occurs with nut trees (hickories, pecans, walnuts, etc.). An individual tree would never be able to seed the next generation if it refused to act collectively with others of its species. Through mysterious communication channels (possibly pheromones sent in the wind!), each species conspires to create unpredictable masting years where copious amounts of nuts are produced. The mast outnumbers the feeding needs of the current population of squirrels and other rodents. This coordinated strategy means that some nuts are not eaten, and thus survive and mature into new trees.

- We are socialized, particularly in capitalist economies, to think there's "not enough;" this *scarcity mentality* makes us reluctant to share resources and combine efforts.

  This worldview may be a remnant from the Darwinian "survival of the fittest" theory of evolution. This theory may be the result of "observation bias," where what is perceived in natural phenomena is affected by who is making observations and the lenses they bring. While competition patterns do occur in nature, there are several examples that contrast this theory and its underlying worldview of scarcity. We can observe resource sharing through acts of *reciprocity*, such as trees sharing nutrients with each other through a symbiotic relationship with fungal mycorrhizae underground. Trees offer their starchy sugars to the

EXERCISE 22: Cont.

fungi in exchange for the nutrients that fungi make available to each tree. According to Peter Wohlleben, author of the *Hidden Life of Trees*, nutrients are distributed to sickly trees by the mycorrhizae to ensure the whole of the forest remains healthy.

- Even when the metaphorical jack-in-the-box heroically pops out, the bottom half of its body is still in the box. This metaphor highlights the part of us is still mired in patterns of prejudice and related grievances that keep us isolated from others.

  If we look to animals, there are certainly examples of intraspecies aggression and competition, such as with songbirds. However, once the battle over a mate or territory has subsided, animals literally shake things off and abide side by side. People are different. We hang on to our grudges and struggle with forgiveness. This pattern is intergenerational. We learn prejudice toward people we have been told are inferior to us, based on class, race, religion, etc. We have also learned to fear and avoid people from a group that has oppressed our people historically, such as is the case with ethnicity-based persecution.

Over the generations, these prejudices and fears become deep-seated worldviews about "the other" that we may not even realize are messages we inherited. Being mistrustful or feeling isolated is not just a personal failing; we've actually been trained to stay away from others. If we used our whole bodies, we might be able to access the *full breadth of our intelligence* (emotional, kinesthetic, intuitive, etc.), and choose to reverse the patterns of isolation and start on the path of healing these historical divides.

Popping our heads out but staying halfway in our boxes and the mental constructs that made them still keeps us apart from others, without the chance to heal. One of my nearest and dearest mentors is a Black elder born and raised in rural Mississippi. My mom's side of the family are white folks, also from many generations in rural Mississippi. There is a lot of pain and mistrust from the effects of racism in our families' respective and connected histories. But in present-day Massachusetts, my teacher, a straight Black Protestant woman, and I, a queer white Jew, have taken risks, over and over again, to step toward each other lovingly. In the seven-plus years we've been working together, we continue reaching for connection even amidst the backdrop of historical pain and the messages of mistrust from racism, white supremacy, homophobia, and anti-Semitism.

In your own change-making work, when you've gotten "pushed back in," what stops you from trying again? What fears and discouraging thoughts come up for you? List them here:

____

____

____

____

This might be a good moment to revisit Building Meta-Capacities: An Antidote to Discouragement in chapter 2, page 21.

ID'ing Diversion Tactics

Understanding bureaucratic environments and their constraints to change-making is an important step in strategizing how to flow like water around obstacles. Which of the following tactics have kept you from forming change-making alliances at your work or within organizational or institutional settings? This exercise has been adapted from UROC trainings. Check each box.

- ☐ The board or administration says, "We'd like to, but the policy says..."
- ☐ To appease you or to divert your efforts, the board or administration appoints you to be the head of a special interest "committee," where no one may show up.
- ☐ The board or administration deflects the issues you are raising, by urging you to focus instead on "collecting data" on the issue.
- ☐ You are given a promotion, which results in you being more closely monitored or tempted to stop your change-making work because you have more benefits to lose.
- ☐ There are rules or union contracts that prohibit organizing for change.
- ☐ You internalize the institution's culture, enforcing its rules and limiting your own thinking.
- ☐ You work in a culture of fear—of being fired or ostracized, of scarcity, of not fitting in, of being targeted. Standing out with change-making work means you'll be punished in one of these ways.
- ☐ There is a cultural expectation of overwork, which leaves you with the feeling of not having enough time or resources to make change.

Coalition-Building

Building coalitions for social change will require developing genuine relationships with diverse individuals. Here are some protocols for how to navigate these new and exciting relationships. Being an ally requires a commitment to uprooting our oppressor patterns in the moment, and attending to the impact of our behavior, regardless of our intent. This guideline is widely known as *intent vs. impact*. For example, a common phenomenon in meetings is that cisgender men speak more than people of other genders, and yet believe that they are sharing airtime equally. Men who are committed to being allies to women, nonbinary, and transgender people could address this impact by listening to feedback without defensiveness, validating concerns raised, holding back in group settings, and creating space for other voices to be heard. This topic directly relates to the discussion of calling in vs. calling out raised in Shared Agreements on page 58.

Building a coalition of mutual Accomplices, which goes beyond adopting an ally identity, also means being willing to put yourself and pride on the line—with taking action, taking risks, making mistakes, and communicating vulnerably. Mistakes will always happen, so it's important to embrace them and don't be too hard on yourself. They are opportunities to learn about our unconscious quadrants (see Competence Cycles on page 25) and get closer to one another through ongoing reconciliation efforts. As changemakers, interaction by interaction, we can unlearn the Islamaphobia, ableism, ageism, etc. that has kept us from building coalitions with everyone.

Connection across differences does not, by itself, address systems of power that perpetuate oppression. We must also create coalitions at the group level that enable us to intervene in systems that uphold structural inequities, such as the healthcare, education, and immigration systems. We are most effective when we engage collectively with others in these efforts to move mountains rather than attempting to do so on our own, and instead breaking our backs in isolation.

The work of social permaculturalists will be strengthened by learning from and developing alliances with organizations committed to ending oppression. Please consult Further Reading for a list of resources and anti-oppression organizations that offer trainings, publications, and curricula.

Guidelines for Tending to Impact (vs. Intent)

Often we judge ourselves by our intentions, while we judge others by their actions. Here are some guidelines for remaining accountable to the inevitable *oops/ouch* moments that will arise in our coalition building work. ("Oops" is when we've done something harmful to another without realizing it. "Ouch" is when we feel hurt by others' actions. Assigning this language to these moments of friction helps us more easily identify them and bring them to our awareness.)

- **Be accountable.** Ultimately, it does not matter what our intentions are. What matters is how our actions or words affect a member of an oppressed group. Being accountable for our actions, owning them, and examining them offers a way to shift longstanding power-over dynamics for changemakers committed to justice in the present.
- **Appreciate the opportunity to learn** about where you still need to grow and correct your patterns for next time. The person who generously calls us in and points out the impact of our actions deserves a gracious and heartfelt thank you. When we take ownership of our Unconscious Assumptions that others point out to us, it builds trust and we grow our cultural competencies.
- **Choose to have a "beginner's mind"** when learning about our potentially embarrassing oversights. We can be gentle with ourselves as we humbly learn, and most importantly, bravely continue onward with reaching for others. It's good to share these oops/ouch moments with others, rather than keep them to ourselves. Together, we can create a *community of practice* that gently holds each other accountable in the sacred work of undoing oppression. A community of practice can remind us that no one individual is to blame, and that it is our responsibility to clean up the mess of oppression.
- **Make mistakes.** Patterns of "being careful" often translate into keeping a safe distance, which can come across as racism, transphobia, fatphobia, etc. Mistakes provide opportunities to learn and to build closer relationships as we repair the harms we've done.

None of this is easy work, but it is essential if we want to liberate ourselves from our boxes. Remember that the boxes are not truly ours, but rather socially constructed mental models we've inherited from the societies we're born into. They are designed to uphold systems of power by dividing us from each other. In this big-picture analysis, we can also remember not to feel badly about ourselves if we have one or more privileged identities. White people, heterosexuals, cisgender people, men, Christians, able-bodied, upper-middle-class, and/or owning-class people come into this world as completely good people. These privileged identity groups have been hurt, but often in not so obvious ways, which have left them vulnerable to being coerced into oppressor roles.

Our social change movements cannot leave anyone behind, nor divide one another into good and bad camps. At the same time, we need to be careful to reject assertions such as "All Lives Matter" or concepts such as "color-blindness" regarding racial identities. This artificial leveling the field erases historical and current ways that Black, Indigenous, and People of Color and other targeted groups have been systemically oppressed and exploited. Social attempts to bypass these painful realities and failure to repair the harm that's been done avoids the path needed to create true equity.

Inner growth and interpersonal learning from our mistakes are necessary if we are to become true agents of change in service to creating new systems born of equality and justice. If we don't do this difficult Zone 00 movement from isolation to alliance, and uproot the oppressor patterns we've internalized, we run the risk of unconsciously recapitulating the same harmful power structures in our attempts at new culture-building. We all must do this essential work together, for ourselves and our own liberation from the messages that indoctrinated our minds and obscure our natural impulse to connect with every type of person. Connection is our birthright. We can use our personal agency to reclaim a bigger, whole life and step into reciprocal relationship with all beings.

Please see Further Reading related to chapter 6 on page 239.

Social Design Lexicon for Chapter 6

Review the following key terms and write down what they mean to you.

All Our Relations:

Lone Wolf Archetype:

Rings of Influence:

Positive Contagion:

Coalitions:

Keystone Species:

Cycles of Influence:

Baseline Dynamic:

Anchors:

Explicit vs. Implicit Relationships:

Benefiting from Racial Privilege:

Targeted by Racism:

Colorism:

Tokenism:

Monocultural Organizations vs. Polycultural Organizations:

Scarcity Mentality:

Reciprocity:

Full Breadth of Our Intelligence:

Intent vs. Impact:

Oops/Ouch:

Community of Practice:

CHAPTER 7: SILENCE AT THE CENTER

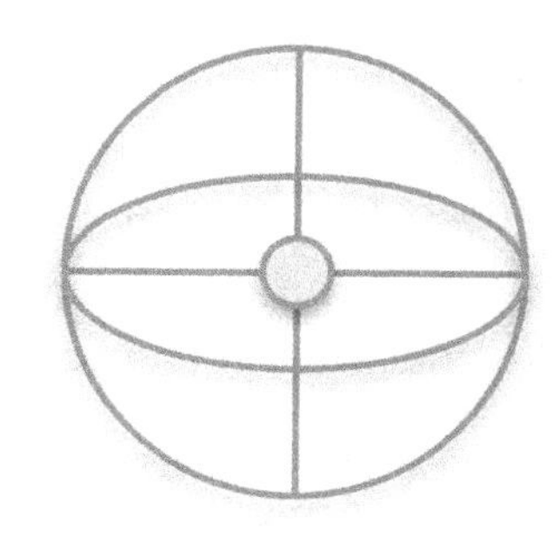

CENTER: PEACE/REFLECTION AND INTEGRATION

Where does your soul go to recharge? Deep inside a rich inner world, eyes tightly closed? At the summit of a mountain, with a panoramic view you can behold? And when you descend from your peak and head homeward again, where on your path do you remember to pause and turn in? In a treehouse close to the birds? Down by the river where white water unfurls? At home in your tub, candles lit low? Or in your bed, asleep and snuggled in close? Oh, where does your soul go for repose?

There is a special magic to the moments and the places where we seek refuge, where we go to integrate, to enter a different state of mind, to meditate, to have one big exhalation. It is natural to visit these places of timelessness again and again, after hard work has been completed. If instead we urgently rush through our exhalation and on to the next activity, we skip an important step in the *cycle of creation and dissolution*. The essential things we've learned on our most recent journey may go astray if we don't take time and space to integrate our experiences. In times of retreat, the road dust falls away, like old skin we've outgrown, so that we can step consciously with fresh eyes into another beginning.

At this juncture, we find the seventh direction: the center. We owe a quiet homage to ourselves, to our past accomplishments, and to our future work. With discipline, we will have to resist the mantra of productivity that we are commanded to march to every day. This act of resistance is not to be taken lightly. Observing a sabbath for our minds, hearts, bodies, and bones is taking a stand for re-humanizing our lives amidst a world gone mechanically astray.

> *Nature does not hurry, yet everything is accomplished.*
>
> – Lao Tzu

Develop Regular Routines of Rest

If we continue with the social permaculture practice of mimicking the intelligence found in nature's rhythms, then we must extend it to the regular periods of rest and dissolution that we observe in the natural world. In latitudes outside the tropics, mammals hibernate annually, amphibians brumate, tree sap drops into underground roots, and compost microbial activity slows. These beings do not wait until they are overextended to contemplate taking a break. Rather, their life rhythms intrinsically slow down on a regular basis. Imagine the consequences in an ecosystem if biotic activity never slowed down for recharge? Even the equatorial tropics are blessed with a steady 12 hours of nightfall, bringing darkness and cooler temperatures every day, affording a daily period of rest and renewal.

Many of the world's religions have a blueprint for a weekly day of rest inscribed in their DNA. The Muslim sabbath is on Friday, the Jewish sabbath is on Saturday, and the Christian sabbath is on Sunday. Collectively, we have a generous three-day weekend! What would our lives would be like if that were the case every week...sigh.

For those of us who are persistent changemakers, community organizers, educators, and/or justice workers on the front lines, it's common to cycle through big pulses of work output. In order to engage in our emotionally and mentally demanding work year after year, decade after decade, we need to proactively build in cycles of rest and retreat for ourselves. Whether we choose to take this downtime in solitude or in communities of *collective care*, it's essential that we do for our personal health and the well-being of our projects. Collective care is a concept that is becoming more popularized through communities of practice, such as Harriet's Apothecary.

Wonderful resources on the importance of collective care and modern adaptive practices for observing a sabbath, whether it's on a Sunday or a Wednesday, are listed in Further Reading. This *sabbatical consciousness* even extends to a fallow period of rest every seven years for the land within the Islamic-Judeo-Christian tradition. From nature's cycles to faith traditions, it's clear that our modern society has much to learn about taking time to rest and recharge. What will your new rhythm of rest and renewal be this year?

Prioritizing Reflection

It can be counterintuitive to slow down and take time to reflect when our overarching goal is change. However, the capitalist programming most of us have received—which values continued economic "growth" over rest and thoughtful contemplation—is quite out of sync with nature's rhythms of down cycles. *Facing death* (our own death, the death of projects, the death of relationships, and so on) allows us to attune ourselves to natural cycles of senescence. When we can incorporate regular periods of rest, reflection, and quiet release into our schedules, intentionally letting go of all that has come before, we make friends with periods of inevitable deaths, as well as make way for the approaching dawn.

A reflection process, which is more about observation of what has occurred rather than active integration of the lessons learned, can occur at any time in the year that makes the most sense for you. Some find it useful to engage in this powerful practice at the Gregorian calendar's New Year of January 1. Others may choose to engage in a yearly review process on the anniversary of starting a new enterprise or on an actual birthday. In the Jewish tradition, the month of *Elul*, which leads up to Rosh Hashanah, and the ten Days of Awe, which fall in between Rosh Hashanah and Yom Kippur, are times that are set aside annually for dedicated reflection and return to spiritual alignment. There is even an auspicious day each month, Yom Kippur *Katan*, just before the new moon, where Jewish mystics traditionally fasted, prayed, and made offerings to release wrongdoings from the last month and to reset before a new lunar cycle began.

No matter the date, adopting this practice has brought profound shifts to entrepreneurs, changemakers, and mystics alike engaged in personal and community regeneration work.

Turning Toward Rituals of Integration

If modern capitalist cultures could be mapped onto the Four Directions (see page 56), they would be stuck in the South direction. The South is a powerful place of growth, action, and learning, but without the other three directions to temper its fire, it turns into an all-consuming monster. We see these patterns of endless growth and nonstop activity ripple through our human ecosystems. Many hardworking people in the US drink coffee in the morning and then again in the afternoon to keep pushing through the day. To wind down in the evenings they drink alcohol, and then take sleeping pills to rest. They start the cycle all over again the next morning. This is a common pattern and perfectly reasonable given the values of the US dominant culture. However, this pattern of turning people into machines, reliant on chemical inputs, has many unintended consequences, such as modern health crises of high blood pressure and heart disease, depression and addiction, and so on.

Integration is an antidote to the go-go-go over-culture. Some people enter their Monday mornings with integration, reviewing their calendar to see what they accomplished the week before. This basic practice helps synthesize the outcomes of last week and mentally prepare for the week to come. In entrepreneurial circles, *co-coaches* fulfill a niche similar to that of an Accountability Buddy. They support each other in taking time to review and integrate what has transpired in the past year. Some communities make bonfires seasonally and invite their friends to reflect on the past three months and share stories from their journeys. This essential function of integration, at the individual and collective level, is how the dissolution cycle regenerates itself and begins the next creation cycle. Without honoring this inflection point with integrative activities, we are undercutting ourselves and our change-making work.

EXERCISE 23: Year in Review Ritual

Slowing Down to Exhale and Review

"Year in Review" is a ritual and meaningful practice that writer, cultural changemaker, and my co-coach, Leora Fridman, and I developed together. As we each left our steady 9-to-5 jobs and began our entrepreneurial endeavors, we found we needed to dedicate time to slow down, much like we do on Shabbat, to integrate our success stories and lessons learned. Feel free to adapt our structure, offered below, so it best suits your needs.

Choose a meaningful date for your Year in Review, and schedule a full day to do this practice in your calendar annually. You'll want to tell someone (an Anchor, perhaps, or an Accountability Buddy) when you are going out to nature on this day for your Year in Review. Ask this person to welcome you back that evening, and listen to what was revealed to you during your solo time. Setting up this storytelling process with a dedicated listener is most essential.

On this day, venture out to a beautiful place in nature by yourself. Consider how you can develop relationships of reciprocity with the more-than-human world. Can you introduce yourself and ask a place for permission to enter it? What is an offering you might start by making? When you feel you have been adequately welcomed in a place (and be open to leaving if you aren't), start by sitting quietly and meditating. Tune into your five senses and see what you perceive in the landscape around you. Notice your body and your aliveness. Speak aloud or to yourself your intentions for being there.

Make sure to take your journal and some delicious food. Unplug from technology during your time away. Spend a minimum of 4 hours there—6-plus hours is ideal. During this time, create a montage in your mind's eye of the phases, trials, successes, and new people who crossed your path. Can you see trends or new understandings that have emerged? Then, thoroughly review (via writing or diagramming) what happened in the year:

- List all the jobs, big and small, paid and unpaid, that you've had this past year. Or if you have one big job, list the projects that make up that job. Developing a website, consulting for a new client, teaching a community-based workshop, babysitting for neighbors down the street are examples.
- List the creative projects and/or nourishing practices that you participated in. For instance, did you read at a poetry festival or attend a meditation retreat?

Then, for each item in your two lists, reflect on:

- Which of your Values aligned with this job or activity? Which were left out?
- Which current skills did you apply? Where did you excel?
- What new capacities did you develop?

EXERCISE 23: Cont.

- What did you learn (about the content or process) during your engagement?
- Did you work solo or with a team? What was good and hard about either?
- Did this job or project feel like it was building up to something? Or was it a one-off commitment?
- Which parts of your whole self did you show people? Where was it safe or unsafe to lead from your identities?
- What consistent patterns in your actions or feelings did you observe across different settings?
- How did each job or activity fit into your schedule? Was the timing of it regenerative or degenerative in relation to your other commitments?
- Were you compensated well and in what form(s) of wealth (e.g., financial, social, material—see Polyculture of Wealth Analysis tool on page 161)? Was it a worthwhile trade for your time and energy?
- What else do you want to include? Generally, what was good? What was not good?

Once you've completed recording your responses to these questions, take some time to sit again quietly and breathe. Let all that you just processed wash over you. Maybe it's a good time for a stretch or a lunch break, something to get your attention focused elsewhere for at least 30 minutes.

When you feel complete with your review and are ready to look forward to the coming year, spend some time envisioning and articulating what is possible. Our words, written or spoken, have the power to shape our future realities.

- **Articulate personal Goals for yourself.** Consider including passions you want to pursue, self-care practices you want to incorporate, and qualities you wish to embody. Please understand that self-care is not a series of one-off activities, but rather a shift in overall priorities. This is an essential teaching for changemakers. Articulate your Goals in present tense active voice (see page 39).
- **Articulate a change-making Purpose for the year.** This could involve your professional or non-professional pursuits in social change. One helpful framework here is what I call the *Changemakers' Recipe*, adapted from words of wisdom shared with me by landscape architect and environmental justice advocate Anne Spirne. (A Japanese version of this framework, *Ikigai*, adds a fourth ring to include what activities you can receive compensation for, which you may want to add based on your Goals).

CHANGEMAKERS' RECIPE

Continued on next page

EXERCISE 23: Cont.

If you want to use this recipe, take some time to make a list for each of the following categories:

- your passions, both personal and professional
- your soft skills (e.g., social, emotional) and hard skills (e.g., physical, technological)
- what that the world needs

From the intersection of these three, craft a one-sentence change-making Purpose for yourself, a map to guide your way in the year to come.

Lastly, spend some time acknowledging your Threshold Guardians (see page 49) who developed in your formative years to protect you. Because change can be scary, the loyal parts of ourselves that try to keep us safe—by repeating the same exact activities and patterns as before—often rear their heads at the moment we envision new possibilities for ourselves, especially if they are outside of our Comfort Zones.

See if you can identify the different Threshold Guardians inside you at this annual threshold, and assign them names. For instance, the protector, the wary skeptic, the perfectionist. From the insights of Internal Family Systems (IFS) work, we know that all of these parts have important messages for you and roles to play. Ask these Guardians what acknowledgment they need or what new roles they would like to fulfill this year. See if they can lay down their agenda to "protect" us, which often results in sabotaging our efforts as we try stepping into the unknown.

When you feel that you have completed your Year in Review Ritual, give a gratitude offering to the spot that held you for the day. This can be in the form of a libation, a piece of your hair, a prayer, a song, etc. A Hebrew song that is a favorite of mine is "*Ha Makom Ha Zeh*," which means "How awesome is this place!"

Returning home can always be a bit shocking after a transformative ritual by oneself out in nature. You've also just time-traveled to the past and future! Being received by your Anchor or Accountability Buddy back in the present helps you to integrate more smoothly, both in terms of what you discovered about yourself and your reengagement with other humans in the built environment. Enjoy telling your story over some hot food with this loving listener. (Note: Telling the *story of the day* is a powerful core routine that many Earth-based communities practice. This regular ritual can help changemakers integrate the trials and successes of our days and weeks. We can offer to do the same for our listening partners.)

EXERCISE 24: "Backcasting" from the End of Your Life

Facing our own death is another regular practice we can cultivate, helping us slow down and integrate the busyness of our lives. This tradition is well established in Buddhist practices and other philosophical traditions. We can use the technique of backcasting: Imagine who you will be at the end of your life and all that you've accomplished. What steps did you take to arrive there?

To begin, immerse yourself in an environment that brings you rest and repose, indoors or out of doors. Mark the beginning of this ritual in some way, such as lighting a candle or drawing a circle in the dirt around where you sit. Imagine you are going on a journey forward in time to the end of your life. Envision the most desirable outcome for your years here on Earth and all that you have achieved. What kind of impact did you have on the world? What kind of relationships filled you up with joy and connection? Which experiences enlivened your being?

Give gratitude for the blessing of your life and make peace with this final moment. Then, by backcasting, think about all of the people, experiences, turns in the road, and crucial elements it took to realize this magnificent ending to your life as you know it.

Journal: *Integrate what you uncovered by writing down what arose in this meditation, without judging or qualifying the messages you receive. Consider reviewing your entry annually during your Year in Review. Perhaps a special journal dedicated to this practice can help keep all of these messages in one place.*

> *All social change comes from the death of old bodies—embodiments of ways of thinking—and the birth of new. In this way, opportunities for liberation are constantly provided.*
>
> – Carol Bridges, *The Medicine Woman Inner Guidebook*

Please see Further Reading related to Chapter 7 on page 241.

Social Design Lexicon for Chapter 7

Review the following key terms and write down what they mean to you.

Cycle of Creation and Dissolution:

Collective Care:

Sabbatical Consciousness:

Facing Death:

Co-coaches:

Changemakers' Recipe:

Gratitude Offering:

Story of the Day:

Backcasting:

Designing for Organizations, Institutions, and Communities: A Recipe for Social Alchemy

SECTION II

Overview

All of the important Zone 00/Self work that you completed in section I has stand-alone value, *and* it serves as the essential groundwork for making changes in our organizations, institutions, and communities. As designers, we are necessarily at the center of our designs, like the heartwood at the center of a tree trunk, growing new rings of creation, radiating out from our core. Thus, becoming conscious and thoughtful about the beliefs, patterns, and Paradigms that we imbue our work with will create more conscious social design projects.

The inspiring message at the heart of permaculture, to reiterate, Penny Livingston's quote—"we are nature, working," with the inherent ability to improve and transform our worlds—can apply equally to the social aspects of our lives as it does to the natural and built environments. The *Regenerative Design Process* is a powerful tool for imagining and designing the structures for new cultural shifts. This process is *iterative*, involving several cycles of refinement, and can be applied to any scale of change-making, from designing one's own life routines to designing a neighborhood-scale project to creating a plan for an international peoples' movement.

I might even argue that the Regenerative Design Process is *liberatory*. It is *nonlinear* and considers multiple perspectives over a protracted period of observation, remaining open to a wide range of outcomes. This flexible yet rigorous process stands in contrast to many strategic planning approaches used in organizing and reform work. Professional organizer and Afro-futurist author adrienne maree brown, in her book *Emergent Strategy*, has observed that many strategic planning approaches tend to be linear, monocultural, and implemented with urgency. She notes that these approaches actually end up short-circuiting the best of intentions and often exhibit the same oppressive tendencies that were the focus of the change-making project in the first place.

The underpinnings of this design process are ecological or context-sensitive, based on deep, thoughtful observation of the environment and whole systems. This process, coupled with design principles derived from nature's wisdom, creates a *holistic approach*. This orientation to making new cultures is essential if our work is to be: truly *regenerative*, rather than *recapitulative* of oppressive dynamics, and *responsive to context*, rather than erasing it—*context erasure* (a common practice in the process of colonization).

When approaching the designing of systems regeneratively, we take into consideration a multiplicity of factors. All beings involved, human and nonhuman, are treated as the Beneficiaries, each with a set of Goals or needs for the designer to incorporate into the Design. To create whole designs, social permaculturalists take an inventory and make Assessments of the ecological and social conditions of any project. This process also guides us in implementing and evaluating our design outcomes systematically. *Ecological design*, where all elements of a system are considered, stands in contrast to what permaculture teacher Dave Jacke calls *ego-logical design*, where a designer makes decisions in a vacuum, apart from any pertinent ecological or social Context. Undertaking a rigorous design process that dives deeply into Context, considers the Goals of numerous Beneficiaries, and develops a critical Analysis and Assessment of existing conditions (including current and historical power structures) is essential for the long-term success of social change projects after they have been implemented.

Why Design?

Why do we slow down to design instead of moving straight into action?

- To make conscious decisions rather than follow reactive impulses
- To have the freedom to engage creativity, rather than defaulting to the status quo
- To inventory contextual conditions and make thoughtful observations
- To consider and weigh multiple possibilities without attachment to a single solution
- To be able to make mistakes "on paper" and question the feasibility of choices before they are implemented

What other reasons can you think of?

Design Process Review

This section introduces new tools for Social Design and incorporates familiar frameworks from section I. Each chapter is dedicated to one of the seven phases of the Regenerative Social Design Process. Here is a review of the phases:

1. Consider the **Context** of the social ecosystems in which our change-making projects occur.
2. Clarify and articulate (to oneself and to the world) the project's **Purpose** and **Goals**.
3. Create an **Analysis** and **Assessment** that reveal unique Opportunities and Constraints.
4. Bring together the Goals, the Analysis, and the Assessment to yield an elegant **Social Design** that is responsive to the Context and realizes the project's Purpose.
5. **Implement** a robust, multistaged plan that moves the Social Design from ideation into action.
6. Determine holistic criteria, tools, and benchmarks to **Evaluate** the project's impact and the degree to which the Social Design achieves the project's Goals.
7. Take the time and space for ourselves, amidst a fast-paced society, to exhale, rest, **Reflect** on, and **Integrate** the work we've created. We do this throughout each phase of the process and when a full cycle of Design feels complete.

Paradoxically, creating a Social Design is a both multiphase process that charts a path for us to follow and something that emerges organically out of our awareness and relationships with the people and places connected to our project. Deep understanding of Context increases with the diligent observation and intuitive insights that we uncover in the Analysis and Assessment phase. However, at every stage in our design journey, we can practice listening deeply and yielding to what's trying to be born!

Do You Consider Yourself a Designer (Yet)?

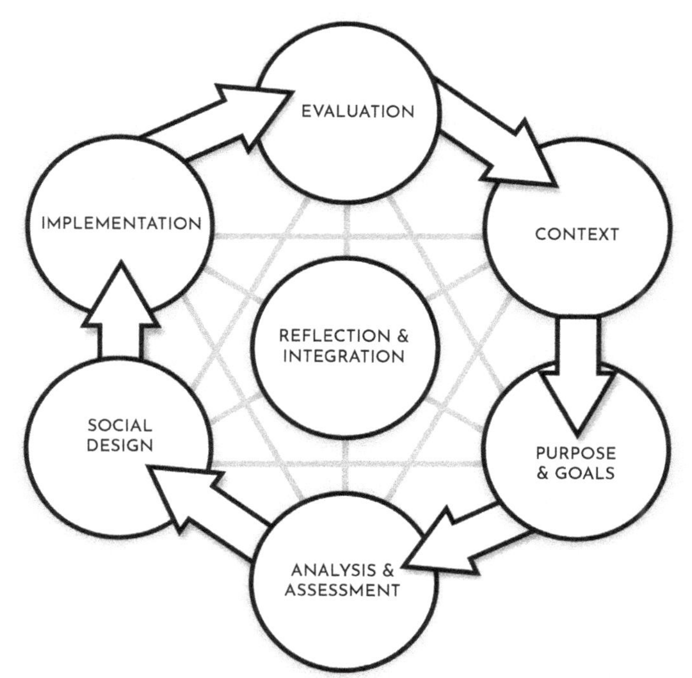

REGENERATIVE SOCIAL DESIGN PROCESS

We may not realize it, but design is woven into our daily lives. We are all naturally designers. For instance, we cycle through the design process every day when we get dressed in the morning, plan our day, and decide what to make for dinner. Here's an example of how we instinctively move through the phases of design when we decide what to wear:

Purpose: Bodily protection and personal expression of the Self.

Context: Understanding our context is second nature to us. We incorporate information about our identities, culture, daily needs, and responsibilities, etc., almost automatically at all moments of decision-making in our day.

Goals: We usually have Goals, whether we are conscious of them or not, when we stand in front of our closet each morning. Perhaps, on this day, you think to yourself, I want to feel comfortable and casual today, but still dress appropriately for my workplace. Also, I want to ride my bicycle rather than take the bus to get some exercise.

Analysis and Assessment: You look outside and observe that the weather is chilly and damp on this morning. Since you are commuting by bicycle today, you assess that it will be important to choose warm, water-resistant clothing to stay dry and avoid getting sick.

Design: Taking into account your Goals and Analysis, you put together a Design in the form of an outfit: flannel-lined jeans, a professional-looking wool sweater, raincoat, rubber boots, and fashionable yet comfortable shoes to change into at work.

Implementation: You get dressed, go outside, and bicycle to work.

Evaluation: You evaluate your Design throughout the day. How well is your outfit fulfilling your Goals and responding to the conditions that you designed for in the morning? Did you observe any changes in the conditions that you did not consider? As you evaluate, you can return to your Goals and see if they are still relevant. Perhaps you decide to go on a spontaneous date in the evening and your appearance Goals have changed. You also notice that the weather is warming up, and you take off some layers. You adapt your Design (outfit), returning to Goals and Analysis, as you gather information through Evaluation.

Reflection and Integration: At the end of your day, or when any cycle comes to completion, you may take time to reflect on your journey and integrate any new information you gathered into your planning for the next cycle. (Note: This seventh phase is not included in other design processes I've seen. I include it as a way to honor the wisdom of cultures that take a Sabbath or a siesta. Amidst the fast-paced constant growth culture of capitalism, these periods of Reflection and Integration seem essential for the conscious incorporation of lessons learned in Design.)

In section II, we unpack the design process, making it accessible, explicit, and conscious. By doing so, we move this intuitive process from the "Don't Know What You Know" (DK) quadrant to the "Know What You Know" (KK) realm of conscious competence. As such, our creations gain power when we are intentional in their Design. When we respond thoughtfully to the conditions that surround us, the impact of our intention multiplies.

Choosing a Project for the "Social Design Lab"

As you move through section II, know that it is a place where you are *safe-to-fail*, a term that I've adapted from Resilience Theory. In other words, this journey can become a low-stakes learning laboratory, a *Social Design Lab*, where you try out new skills and gain facility with what may be an entirely foreign process. You will not be graded on how you perform or the impact of your Design. This is a time to sink in with a Beginner's Mind, to borrow a concept from Buddhist philosophy, and to "trust the process"—a phrase I heard over and over again as I was learning how to design as a graduate student.

In the Social Design Lab portions of this book, you learn to apply the Regenerative Design Process to the development of a new change-making project or to the deepening of an existing project. Before choosing to initiate a project of your own, spend time "observing and interacting" with the social environment that you are passionate about generating change within. Are there existing projects that you could build a relationship with over time and then humbly offer your design thinking to those projects or communities? If there's not already a similar project to the one you're envisioning, dedicate some time to considering what is the specific community or issue you want as the focus of your design project. If you're having a difficult time choosing a project, try coming up with one that addresses issues you feel passionate about, that you have some facility with, and that the world around you needs (refer to Changemakers' Recipe on page 101).

In choosing your project, rather than playing it safe in your Comfort Zone, consider going just slightly beyond the edge of your competencies so that you can increase your skills as you engage with your project. Please note that the first several times you apply the Regenerative Design Process to a real-life project, communicate to others (and yourself!) that you are a student of the process and that you are learning as you go. You are not expected to be a seasoned social designer, so be gentle with yourself. Also, it's important to hold a balance of trying new things and treading lightly with your recommended design interventions. It is possible to create more harm in tenuous social systems with our well-intended design interventions than when we found them. That said, change-making is messy and we evolve systems by trial and error. Don't let fear of making mistakes paralyze you and keep you from engaging in the exciting and dirty work of making social change happen!

If the type of social change project that compels you involves collective, outward-facing change, then your project should serve a clearly defined group, or *specific Beneficiaries*. Referring back to the Zones of Relationships (see page 84) model, figure out which zone or zones you want to influence. Your project could be connected to one or more organization, institution, and/or community within which you long to see change, which generally fall in Zones 2 and 3. The more specific you can be about which groups or individuals will be positively affected by your project, the easier it will be to articulate Goals, Analyze the existing conditions, and create elegant and effect Social Designs!

Alternately, a Zone 00 lifestyle shift is another type of social change project you can choose to undertake. This is especially the case if you realized in section I that you need to strengthen your "heartwood" so that you can offer your gifts more fully without internal collapse. We can apply the Regenerative Design Process to our personal patterns and processes, and create new practices that move us toward regenerative life-affirming patterns and away from destructive harmful ones. In a personal lifestyle shift project, there will also be numerous Beneficiaries; articulate who, in addition to yourself, will benefit from this type of Zone 00 project. A lovingly tended personal Design can yield hopeful new possibilities for yourself and the worlds around you.

If a personal lifestyle shift is in fact your calling for the Social Design Lab (usually one third of Regenerate Change's training participants choose to work on Zone 00 for their projects!), then please translate the prompts in each chapter and orient them around that project Purpose and your personal Context. You'll be answering questions such as: What are the existing conditions of your life that are related to your Goals? Where are your greatest Opportunities and Constraints? Where and how can you design a lifestyle shift to support your health, wholeness, and your wider change-making work?

Know that this first round of learning the design process offered here is not the only opportunity that you will have to design something meaningful; it is only the beginning! So don't worry about getting it perfect or becoming an expert in Social Design by the end of this book. Your first several Designs can be seen as trial runs, wonderful and rare opportunities to take risks.

■ Social Designer Tip: Types of New Project Engagement ■

There are three basic orientations in which social designers engage with new projects. Becoming aware of these orientations helps a designer decide how to mindfully engage with a project going forward:

- **Self-initiated projects:** endeavors that come about from a designer's own will and interest; require outreach to others and who share Values and a common Purpose in order to generate project momentum. (Projects should never be attempted in isolation, even if they are personal lifestyle design projects!)

- **Collaborative projects:** endeavors that a designer co-initiates with one or more parties, who then work together to launch and steward the project. This approach works best when Values and Purpose of the project are clearly articulated at the beginning, as well as shared group agreements, and all parties commit to stewarding the project in service to these commonly held ideas.
- **Client-initiated projects:** paid or pro bono work where another party develops an idea or has an existing project, and then solicits a designer's support to help them develop the project further. In these scenarios, it's prudent to relinquish "outside expert" dynamics that are likely to arise—expectations of the client and/or attitude of the designer. Regenerative design is predicated on solutions emerging not from a single person or system element, such as a designer, but rather from the whole alive system, including a balance among *primary clients* (i.e., those who solicit the designer's help), *invisibilized clients* (i.e., communities who should be represented but aren't invited to the table, so to speak), *more-than-human clients* (i.e., rivers, soil biology, nesting birds), and the designer (whose role is really more of listener and process facilitator than primary decision maker).

All projects should have a defined larger social system that they're ultimately trying to influence, i.e., public housing or international trade. The clearer we are on the system we're attempting to shift, the more change-making success we will achieve. The project Goals should reflect the needs of the specific Beneficiaries. Usually, designers are the ones who articulate project Goals after gathering information from stakeholders about the issues of the people and the place that the project aims to serve. Understanding the true needs of a community from people on the ground, rather than funders or do-gooders in an office far away, is crucial.

Some projects will have clear organizational or institutional partners. Partners can play numerous roles, depending on how the designer engages them and the agreements all parties collectively set forth (see Exercise 28: Identifying Roles in the Project Ecosystem on page 133).

For projects with primary clients who initiate the endeavor, recall the "be relational before transactional" practice for building connection. It reminds us to undo capitalist conditioning of relating to clients as isolated entities for which you, as the designer, are providing "services." Remain open to receiving collaborative input and ideas from clients, while not accepting all their contributions without critical filtering. You'll likely have valuable perspectives as someone less intimately involved with the system. This unique position may require you to honestly deliver viewpoints that may be hard to hear but are essential.

■ Social Designer Tip: Designing Cultural Shifts ■

The first time you design and implement a project, it will create ripples of change in the Context for which you are designing. In order to generate an authentic and lasting cultural shift, however, several aspects of an organization, institution, and/or community will need to be designed for with simultaneous and/or successive design projects. Working as part of a dedicated team of coordinated changemakers, each trained in and applying the Regenerative Social Design Process to a common Purpose, is a more advanced and exciting stage of this work.

A *Social Design Salon* is one way that a team of changemakers can focus on cultural shifting together. Each designer works on a unique angle and specific project that they have autonomy over, yet each endeavor is connected and working in concert with all the other projects their teammates are designing. Their shared Purpose is a clearly articulated culture shift for the entity they wish to transform, while knowing that this larger ripple of change will take time and excellent collaborator communications.

Refining and Designing Your Project

What is and isn't your project about? Become as clear as possible on the *project scope*: what the project does and does not cover; the agreed upon work that needs to be accomplished; and what processes, outputs, or services the designer will deliver (e.g., charette facilitation, design report creation, design presentation delivery, Implementation plan development, etc.).

PROJECT SCOPE

*At its most basic level, the scope is **what** the project involves and... which **outputs** the designer will produce.*

To develop a clearly defined scope, rather than an abstract good idea, you may still need to take big powerful visions and sort them through a refinement sieve. This process is not about restraining or containing good ideas. It's about getting traction. You will return to your in-formation visions, and you will design pathways for implementing them over time. After reading this book and moving through the design process, you'll have the tools to use the process again and again at broader scales of impact. For now, refine the project scope to better engage with the Social Design Lab.

To recap what we've covered so far: articulate the focus of your project in a way that clearly identifies which larger system your project is attempting to change (e.g., energy system, military industrial complex); addresses an area in one or more organizations, institutions, and/or communities that you have some influence over (unless you're focusing on Zone 00); and identifies specific Beneficiaries that the project serves. If you are choosing to design some facet of your life and how it intersects with one of your many social ecosystems, such as your family or your life as a student, stretch to see where you can link it to patterns in communities or identity-based groups that you belong to or are affected by.

The following is an example of taking a big idea and refining it into a workable project. Say you are passionate about eliminating the Great Pacific Garbage Patch (size estimates range somewhere between the size of Texas and Russia), knowing that it's harmful for wildlife and humans alike. For the purpose of choosing a project to design, you decide to scale down a bit, and focus on reducing the waste produced at the institution where you work. You know that your creativity and facilitation skills can make it happen. The Beneficiaries of this project will include the people at the institution and the people, animals, plants, soil, water, and atmosphere downstream of the waste. This project also honors the people and resources that produced the materials that are wasted. You've chosen this project because it embodies your Values (see page 11): reducing consumption, mindfully using resources, honoring those who produce the world's goods, engaging in environmental stewardship and environmental justice (knowing that landfills are frequently placed in poor neighborhoods), etc. Even small-seeming projects can elicit strong willpower from the designer and motivation from others, resulting in unexpected and expansive outcomes.

Some questions about scope that you might wrestle with in this example include: Is your project about changing people's Paradigms related to "throw-away culture"? Or is it focused on changing people's behavior through new systems and related training? Or both? Will the scale of the project start with one wing of the building? Or perhaps just your office suite? Or, alternately, the entire district where you work? Again, reaching for a project that's just beyond your Comfort Zone, but one that's not too ambitious, is important. Consider who might be Anchors and Accomplices (see page 86) for you as an individual changemaker. Who will be project-specific champions within or outside of the institution? Again, for the first time you undergo the design process, I recommend starting with a small- or medium-sized bite (e.g., reducing a measurable amount of waste) and something that could be conceivably achieved (e.g., *not* zero waste) within 6 to 12 months. This helps get traction and avoid discouragement in round one with the process!

Design Lab Outputs

Once you have become clear about your project scope (which may change mid-process), complete each phase of the Regenerative Design Process as laid out in each chapter of section II: Context; Purpose and Goals; Analysis and Assessment; Social Design; Implementation; Evaluation; and Reflection and Integration. Each phase will have one or more *Design Lab Outputs*. When you see this icon, **DESIGN LAB ➡**, it signifies that there is some tangible output, such as writing, diagrams, or drawings, to complete in order to move through the design process.

A note about design work: There are different levels of intensity when engaging in the design process. I've seen experienced designers make a "back of the envelope" Design in literally five minutes, swiftly moving through each phase from years of practice. The other extreme would be taking several years to create and implement a robust Design grounded in long-term observation and incorporation of ongoing feedback, as I do in Social Design consulting work for institutional clients. In the middle of the spectrum, a team of people working on a common project might take a week-long retreat to make a Design.

This book falls somewhere in the medium level of engagement, providing nuanced and robust tools that you can delve into to a greater or lesser degree. I would recommend, at the very minimum, having one month to read section I, complete the exercises, and then another month to move through the first iteration of the design process and complete the Design Lab Outputs, knowing that the actual Implementation and Evaluation will likely take longer. Ideally, you have the time to move through one chapter per week, for fourteen weeks total or the length of a semester. Others may want to read the book and complete exercises over six months. Certainly, some of the exercises can stand alone and be helpful for thinking about things such as the Goals or Implementation of a project, but most exercises are meant to be done as a series and in the order they are presented, building on ones that came before. Once you feel competent with the Regenerative Design Process, then you can modify it and move more quickly through the phases, which will become second nature over time.

A Shared Goal for All Projects

A last word about section II: See if you can allow your Social Design project to become a container for your own personal transformation by designing it to be a loop of reciprocity. With creativity that comes from your heart, you will powerfully leave in your wake more of the type of world you wish to inhabit.

> *All that you touch you change; all that you change, changes you.*
>
> – Octavia Butler, Parable of the Sower

Please see Further Reading related to overview of section II on page 243.

Social Design Lexicon for Overview of Section II

Review the following key terms and write down what they mean to you. Then, reflect on how these concepts relate to your approach as a designer.

Regenerative Design Process:

Iterative:

Liberatory:

Nonlinear:

Holistic Approach:

Regenerative vs. Recapitulative:

Responsive to Context vs. Context Erasure:

Ecological Design vs. Ego-logical Design:

Safe-to-Fail:

Social Design Lab:

Specific Beneficiaries:

Primary Clients vs. Invisibilized Clients vs. More-than-human Clients:

Project Scope:

Design Lab Output:

CHAPTER 8: CONTEXT
IDENTIFYING THE PROBLEMS AND THE POSSIBILITIES

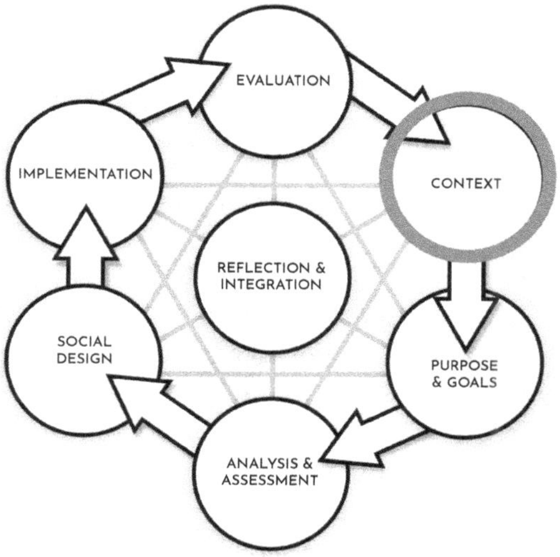

How we perceive a problem often determines the strategies we use to solve it. To understand it fully, we need to locate that problem within its geographic, ecological, economic, cultural, and historical Contexts. These together constitute the *Holistic Context* which provides valuable information for social designers to create whole systems solutions. This Context must also include ourselves—the very vessels through which we perceive life and its challenges. Reviewing our projects' social and ecological conditions through the Nested Wholes framework helps us arrive at a multidimensional understanding of the challenges for which we are designing whole solutions.

> *The most fundamental difficulty today—and the one we are perhaps most fully conscious of in day-to-day events in our bureaucratic society—is the fact that events, actions, processes are not sensitive to context. They are tailored to a standard situation, and fail to pay attention to the wholeness which exists.*
>
> - Christopher Alexander, *The Nature of Order*

Context As Nested Wholes and Rings of Influence

Nested Wholes (discussed in chapter 6) is the framework for how we approach Context, Goals, and Social Design in the Regenerative Design Process used in this book. Exhibiting sensitivity to Context means considering social and ecological conditions across different scales. In the Nested Wholes diagram, each concentric ring is a whole, self-contained system. Each system is nested within and in relationship to the systems or rings that surround it. The larger rings that have smaller rings embedded within them are interdependent with these smaller scale systems. Social systems are made up of the many entities—organizations, institutions, and/or communities—on which their existence depends.

We can take the Nested Wholes framework a step further and conceive of these wholes or circles as Rings of Influence, each one radiating out and influencing the larger circle that surrounds it. As such, designers can:

1. Understand the Context of each of these wholes and how they influence each other.
2. Articulate Goals for each whole.
3. Design social interventions to influence rings that are adjacent to each other.

Here emerges a sense of personal agency to slowly yet systemically affect all levels of society, starting on a smaller scale by consciously choosing the patterns of our own lives, the focus of section I. Then, we can move out and design change-making projects with the intent of influencing the larger systems we seek to transform, the endeavor of section II.

This understanding of influence and adjacency also makes it possible to conceive of our projects as having a beneficial influence *on us*. We can design them to be nourishing loops of reciprocity, rather than draining endeavors. Projects are regenerative when they simultaneously nourish us *and* create a positive impact on the organizations, etc. that surround them. As the cultures and practices of organizations and institutions change, these entities can coordinate to create a movement that sends ripples of influence into the larger social system(s) in which they are embedded (see arrows of influence in diagram below).

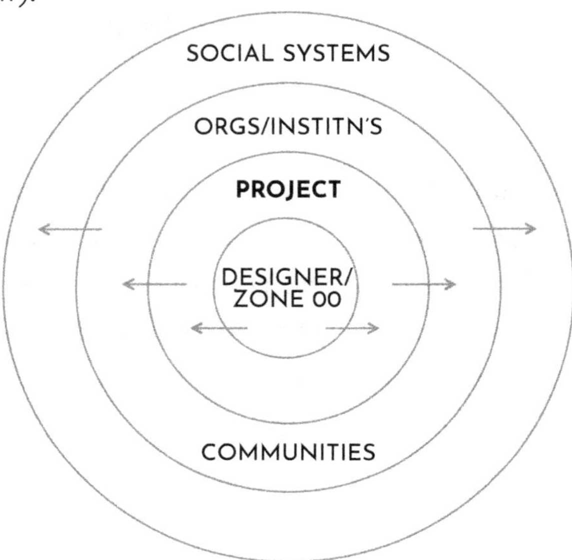

NESTED WHOLES AND RINGS OF INFLUENCE

RINGS OF INFLUENCE

At the center is the designer: creator of the project, directly influencing it.

The project sits in the next concentric ring, embedded in the organizations, institutions, and/or communities it is designed to ripple out and influence.

Collectively, these entities are the building blocks of large social systems and can influence them.

Shared Universal Context: Climate Debt

As we develop our social change-making projects, please note that all projects share a common Context: The Global North is in *climate debt* to the Global South. (Please see page 71 to review Turning to Face the Reality of Climate Change if needed.) If we are creating Designs that address the three ethics of permaculture—Earth Care, People Care, and Resource Share—then the issue of climate debt must be included in the Context of our design process.

The overwhelming majority of climate scientists agree that the wealthy Global North causes the vast majority of carbon emissions. These countries—US, Canada, UK, Japan, and many European nations—have built their wealth by forcibly extracting fossil fuels, along with other forms of resource extraction (in concert with slavery and forced servitude) from countries in the Global South and the Indigenous territories in the Arctic. Such exploitative extraction continues today, especially the pumping of oil in the Middle East, which is done under dangerous working conditions and sometimes forced labor. The Global South and Arctic regions are already experiencing disproportionate damage from climate change. We can recall the example of mass farmer suicides in India, which are plausibly linked to an increase in catastrophic weather events.

The wealthier Global North is indebted to and owes the rest of the world *reparations*. While reparations to Black, Indigenous, and People of Color are an essential ingredient in social and ecological regeneration (see the section on Humans as Keystone Species in Interrelationship on page 82), we cannot rely on financial or land-based reparations to address the root of the climate debt problem. Rather, we need a new narrative or Paradigm, according to Charles Eisenstein in his book *Climate: A New Story*. This Paradigm radiates an evolved consciousness, making unprecedented global actions irresistible, like Western countries engaging in context-specific transformative justice processes and taking leadership from frontline communities on issues of climate change. Without a Paradigm shift that privileges equitable sharing of power and uprooting exploitative economic conditions, humanity will continue pumping carbon emissions and perpetuating injustices, and fail to transform the sources of the climate catastrophe. (See Further Reading for more resources on climate change and climate justice.)

If wealthier countries were located in the tropical areas of the planet, they would be feeling the impacts of climate change more intensely, and they would move faster to do something about it. Naomi Klein, author of *This Changes Everything* and *The Shock Doctrine*, reports that climate change has come in last out of the top 20 issues for US citizens. We all have a heavy burden to carry and need to come to terms with the reality and scale of this planetary crisis. We have the tools to design systemic solutions, from regenerative agriculture to solidarity economics, to reverse the storm already in motion. Again, the book *Drawdown* by Paul Hawken is a resource that combines research from scientists and practitioners from around the world to identify the 100 most effective solutions to mitigate the effects of climate change and draw carbon from the atmosphere.

It is incumbent upon designers of social change to include climate change and climate debt in our Contexts (until their successful resolution!) and to think about these issues in the larger Rings of Influence our projects will generate.

EXERCISE 25: Holistic Context

The Holistic Context of a project centers the Nested Wholes framework and encompasses three interconnected levels of Context: Designer's Context, Group Context, and Systems Context. When zooming out to consider the Holistic Context, we can consciously design each ring to have maximal influence on the rings around it. Oppressive societies train citizens to focus narrowly on their immediate circumstances and abilities as the reason for their status in society, reinforcing the *myth of meritocracy*. This deflects attention from the larger power structures and cultural trends of the social systems, institutions, etc. that influence our access to resources and physical safety in our personal and professional lives. When we wrestle with understanding a project's Holistic Context, we exercise our ability to think systemically.

DESIGN LAB ➡Write a **draft Context document.** This document will evolve over the course of your information gathering. In the end, it should be three to five paragraphs long, two pages maximum. The document objectively describes the social and ecological conditions of the three Contexts your project is surrounded by:

- Designer's Context (Zone 00/you)
- Group Context (about the organization(s), community(ies), etc.)
- Systems Context (larger social systems and patterns)

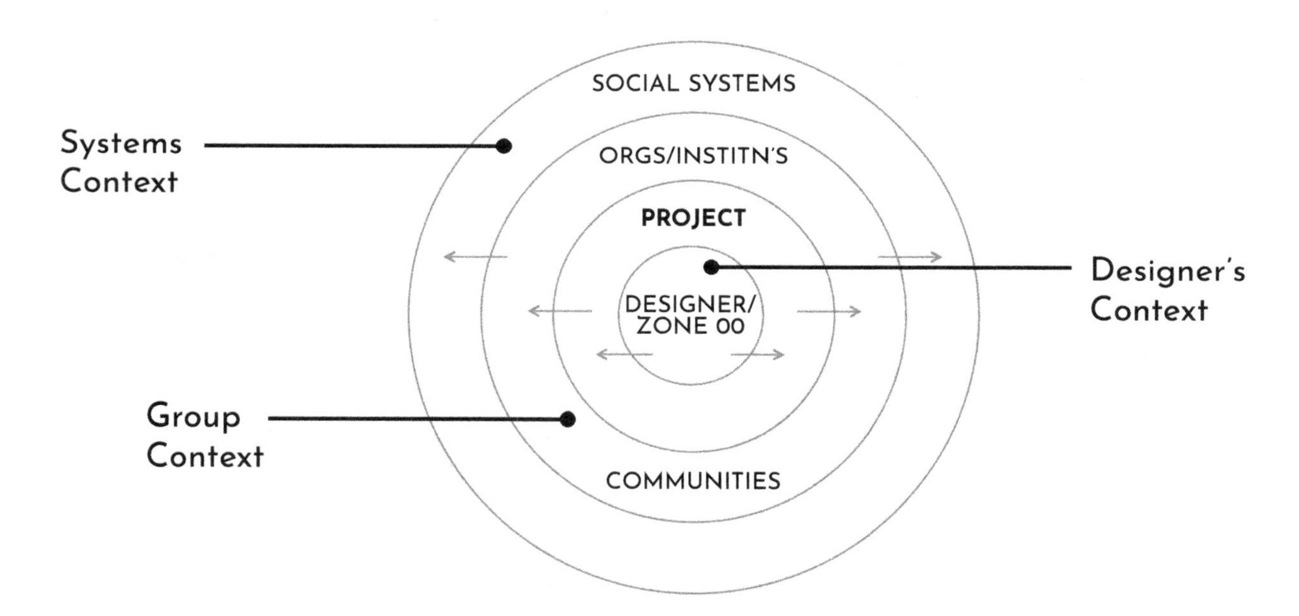

HOLISTIC CONTEXT IN NESTED WHOLES

Note: The aim here is to objectively summarize broad patterns rather than describe specific details or include judgments or Interpretations. Analysis and Assessment is the phase to drill deeper into the details and make Interpretations.

EXERCISE 25: Cont.

1. The Context of any design project necessarily includes the **Designer's Context**. As such, developing awareness of your Context and writing about it is important; you are a key element of the project's ecosystem. Oftentimes we omit the essential practice of *self-reflexivity* in the design process. Who are you as a member of the social ecosystems you're nested within? What are your tendencies or patterns? Describe the existing conditions of where you live on this planet. Are you living in a war zone, under a pandemic, or perhaps remotely out in the wilderness? In what environments do you spend most of your time and with whom? Referring to the location of self series of exercises in section I can help to fill in some blanks. Writing about the identities (see page 12), Values (see page 11), and stories of family and culture (see page 9) that we, as designers, bring to our projects is a good place to start. Then, try to name the unconscious material you might be bringing to this project (see Competency Cycles on page 25), such as saviorism or self-doubt. Where do you get your inspiration for change-making? Is it motivated by creativity or by grief or other? This is an important question posed by James Stark in his Ecology of Leadership program. Additionally, what personal experiences of power (both of domination and subordination) do you carry within you? Remember, your Context description should be concise and relevant to the project Purpose, rather than simply a list of characteristics.
2. Then, describe the **Group Context** of the specific organization(s), institution(s), and/or community(ies) your project is embedded within or aims to serve. Write down a summary of the relevant existing conditions, including the location, environmental characteristics, demographics, etc. What are the typical norms and practices? What are some of the wonderful things and challenging things you observe? What is the weakest link of the system you're designing for? Who are the key players? Refrain from stating Goals or offering solutions here. Simply describe the existing conditions of the Group Context.
3. Lastly, but perhaps most importantly, identify which one to two larger social system(s) you ultimately want to change: this is the **Systems Context**. Are you passionate about the healthcare, economic, or public transportation system, etc.? After you identify the larger social system(s), then go on to describe the broad patterns of those systems that are relevant to your project. They could be big-picture degenerative patterns such as racialized health inequities, environmental degradation, poverty, and/or restorative trends such as the Movement for Black Lives, fossil fuel divestment, re-localizing food systems. If you were working on a food justice project for example, the Systems Context would be the food system. Identifying the patterns related to the project Purpose might include exploitation of migrant farm workers, lack of reliable fresh food access in urban centers, racial segregation in the restaurant industry, and the international food sovereignty movement. Identify *who* currently holds the power in the system. In this case, government officials, financial investors, and corporate agribusinesses. Lastly, what are the *historical structures of power?* Here, we would identify legacies of European colonization, intergenerational accumulation of white wealth from African slavery and Native land theft, and oligarchical rule.

Journal: *What new Reflections and Integrations have emerged for you as a result of paying attention to these three levels of Context?*

The 4 P's: People, Place, Power, and Paradigm

After you have written your first draft of the project Context, comb through your responses and see if any of the 4 P's missing:

- **P**eople
- **P**lace
- **P**ower
- **P**aradigm

Connor Stedman and I developed this framework in the Ecological Literacy Immersion Program that we co-teach at Omega Institute. In social regeneration, we are particularly invested in shaping the Power and Paradigms present in a given system. Embarking on this work, People and Place are wonderful partners and sources of new ideas in how to do so. Deep listening to and observation of People and Place often point the way to innovative, whole solutions much more so than our minds alone could generate.

Of the 4 P's, we've most deeply explored concepts Power so far. In chapter 9, we will delve into specific roles of People in your project ecosystem. For now, think about who are the People involved in the organizations, institutions, and/or communities in which your project is embedded. These may be unique individuals who are key to the development of your project, such as a specific administrator or community elder. And/or, the dimension of People in your Context could encompass collections of individuals. For example, through the lens of your project scope, you might identify People as those who live in a particular neighborhood, an age group within a geographic region, or those across your province or state who share a common vocation.

Understanding the Context of the Place(s) of your project, even if it's a virtual project, is an exciting adventure in itself. Researching the histories of Place is illuminating, especially pre-colonial and colonial histories, as well as narratives told from different perspectives, i.e., narratives from various class backgrounds, from locals vs. transplants, from Indigenous inhabitants vs. settlers, etc. Identify what makes your project Place(s) unique, such as: physio-geographic features, i.e., watersheds and geologic patterns; dominant contemporary cultural practices and subcultures present; land-use histories, i.e., port and fishing industry, agriculture, industrial mill production; patterns of development; food ways; musical traditions, etc. Through this adventure of researching Place, document ideas that emerge about creating *context-sensitive* Social Designs.

Since regenerative social designers are in the business, so to speak, of designing Paradigm shifts, I'll devote a section to the topic and exploration of Paradigms and how they relate to one's project Context.

Seeing and Shifting Paradigms

Identifying a Paradigm—meaning a widely held belief system or cultural template—is a bit trickier then identifying People and Place, and even Power. Paradigms are keenly felt, but not often made explicit. (You may want to revisit the section on Making the Power of Paradigms Visible, in the introduction on page vi.)

Ultimately, the highest leverage point that a Social Design can achieve is the shifting of a Paradigm. This level of influence is much more difficult to obtain than, say, designing structural or policy changes. However, a paradigmatic shift generates the greatest transformation, resulting in a different consciousness, to which all structures, policies, practices, etc. naturally realign. This effect comes about because of the phenomenon of the *self-organization* of complex systems, where all parts of the system work to be in congruence with a new commonly shared Paradigm. Sometimes this can happen as a slow evolution over time, as we have seen in the LBGT rights movement—which has expanded to include queer, intersex, asexual, and other sexualities and genders (LGBTQIA)—and the reformation of policies related to same-sex marriage, insurance benefits, adoption, etc. Other times, a disturbance to the system creates a sudden change in Paradigm and policies. This change can be positive, or it can be reactionary and degenerative. An example of this type of Paradigm change was the political shift in the US from a "prosperity" Paradigm to a "security" Paradigm immediately after 9/11.

Shifting Paradigms toward societal transformation is what is called for in these times, as Donella Meadows correctly asserts. My colleagues and I are not just trying to grow prison gardens as a project, for instance; we're implementing prison gardens in service of shifting dominant Paradigms and related practices in the prison industrial complex and the food system. Gardens are wonderful, but gardens are not the point. They are an instrument for transformation, for dismantling oppression, food apartheid, and "criminal justice."

This book explores five Paradigms, moving from *exploitation* (e.g., oppression and extraction) to *sustainability* (e.g., salvaging and protecting what we still have) to *charity* (e.g., incremental change; end of tail pipe solutions, often with power-over dynamics) to *solidarity* (e.g., reciprocity and mutual support among people, and between people and land), and, ultimately, to *regeneration* (e.g., creating systems that evolve their capacities for justice and environmental repair, build supportive reciprocal relationships, and self-regulate over time). The way that I think about Paradigms as evolving from one to another is inspired by my teacher Carol Sanford's book *The Responsible Entrepreneur.*

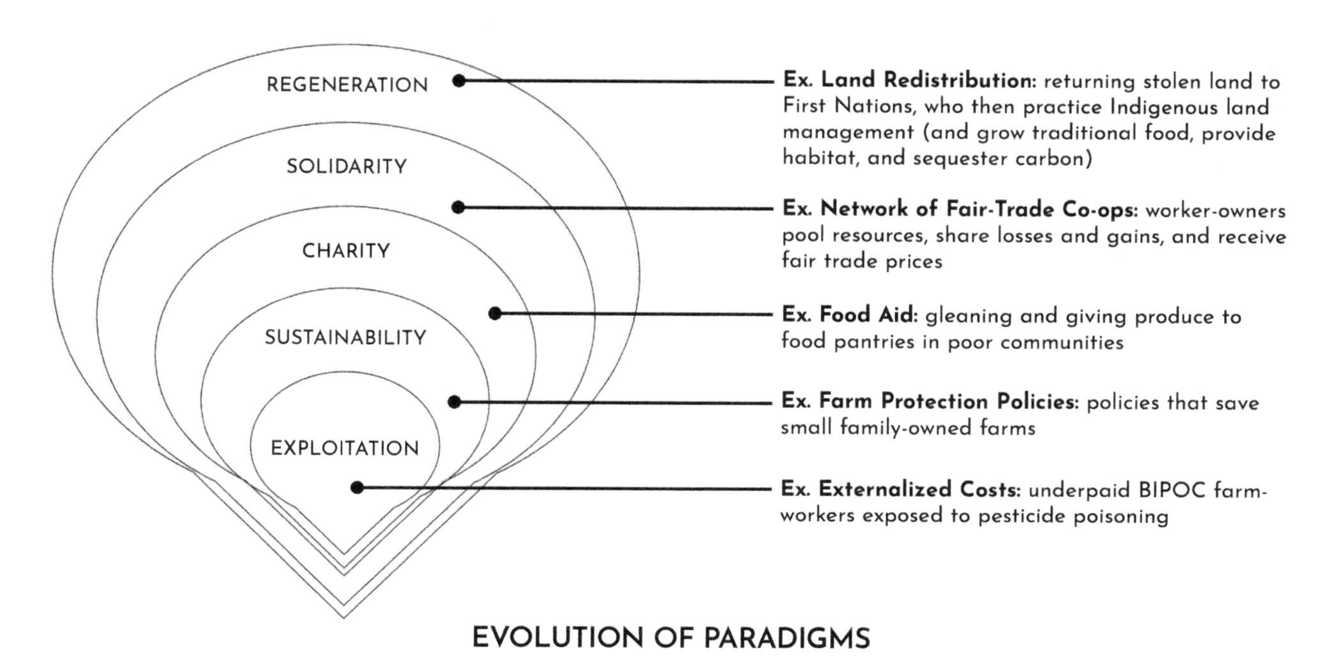

EVOLUTION OF PARADIGMS

Regeneration is about external considering of whole systems, whereas the other end of the paradigmatic spectrum is characterized by personal greed, the motivating force of exploitation. There are an infinite number of more subtle Paradigms within these larger paradigmatic trends. Let these five Paradigms be a structural map for you to plot more specific Paradigms onto; "constant growth and productivity," for example, might fall under the exploitative Paradigm, while the idea that "decentralized mutual aid is a core solution" might go under the solidarity Paradigm.

Paradigms can be as ubiquitous and unquestioned as water is to aquatic life, and thus exist in the Unconscious Quadrants (see page 25) of our awareness. Patriarchy and white supremacy are examples of widespread systemic Paradigms. adrienne maree brown elegantly brings to light how the white supremacy Paradigm functions when she writes in *Emergent Strategy*, "Trayvon Martin and Mike Brown and Renisha McBride and so many others are dead because, in some white imagination, they were dangerous. And that imagination is so respected that those who kill, based on an imagined, racialized fear of Black people, are rarely held accountable.... Imagination turns Brown bombers into terrorists and white bombers into mentally ill victims."

How do we respond to such ingrained and flagrantly unquestioned Paradigms (by those in power), rooted in hate and social inequity? What is a regenerative response to outdated and degenerative Paradigms? What are *positivist solutions*, rather than reactive oppositions, that will allow us to shift current Paradigms of oppression?

Social permaculture is a positivist approach to life that focuses on designing solutions. Rather than holding cynical attitudes or spending our energy on opposing what we don't want, this emergent field is about creating cultural Paradigm shifts toward what we do want. Our human creativity, paired with a positive attitude and an intentional design process, equips us with the ability to replace traumatized colonial, misguided ways of approaching life and evolving new ways that facilitate societal transformation. Grace Lee Boggs proposes that there is a much-needed Paradigm shift from the cultural emphasis on "critical mass" to a focus on "critical connections." Small, slow, steady, decentralized patterns succeed everywhere in nature and are resilient in the face of disturbances, while patterns that embody the idea of critical mass are vulnerable to large-scale disturbances and tend toward unlimited, dangerous expansion, as with overfishing of the oceans or cancer cell proliferation.

Emergent cultural conditions that come about from intentional design, based on the permaculture ethics of Earth Care, People Care, and Resource Share, can support regenerative structures and systems and create a positive feedback loop. The newly developed structures and systems can then guide concrete practices at every scale of society that reinforce the evolution of our collectively held Values, shifting us from the dominant Paradigm of exploitation to a Paradigm of regeneration.

EXPLOITATION PARADIGM		REGENERATIVE PARADIGM
POWER OVER	→	RECIPROCITY
PROGRESS	→	EVOLUTION
PROFIT	→	UNIVERSAL ABUNDANCE
PRODUCT	→	PROCESS
TRANSACTION	→	RELATIONSHIP

PARADIGM *SHIFT*: From Exploitation to Regeneration

EXERCISE 26: Paradigms at Work

DESIGN LAB ➡ See if you can identify some of the central Paradigms for the three Contexts that surround your project: Designer, Group, and Systems. This exercise is a meta-cognition task, asking you to reflect on the worldviews that you are personally bringing to the table and that surround your project. Try to objectively observe and report these Paradigms rather than writing about your feelings or judgments about them.

Journal: *Write your responses to the following questions:*

Designer Paradigms: *List the Paradigms that you, as Designer, are bringing to the project. Which of these Paradigms are ones that you have consciously chosen because they align with your Values? E.g., people are fundamentally good. Can you identify any unexamined or unquestioned Paradigms that you harbor? E.g., people with financial and material wealth are smarter/better/more deserving than people with less. Lastly, what deeply held perspectives do individuals who are your collaborators/partners bring to the project? E.g., tithing and charity are our responsibility as upright citizens.*

Organizational/Institutional/Community Paradigms: *Which Paradigms operate most strongly in the organization(s), institution(s), or community(ies) you're working with? E.g., white staff make better/ smarter/strategic decisions than staff of Color. Can you identify historical events or trends that brought about these Paradigms? And how, if any, are the thinking and worldviews in these entities changing?*

Social System Paradigms: *What Paradigms dominate the system(s) you are designing to influence, and from which influential groups of People do they emanate? E.g., public security is possible because of a police state and carceral systems. What worldviews have captivated and colored our* collective imagination *of what's real and what's not?*

After completing this exercise, go through your responses and look for two types of personal patterns we explored in section I: patterns of agency and patterns of disempowerment. Which of these Paradigms express a regenerative worldview of can-do proactivity, self-determination, and/or ability to exert influence? And which of these Paradigms express degenerative attitudes of reactivity, scarcity, and/or passivity?

White Supremacy Paradigm, Characteristics, and Their Antidotes

As we've been exploring, making Paradigms visible and identifying the practices that uphold them is not an easy task. The more that we can move unconscious yet widely accepted Paradigms into our awareness, the more we can consciously live into new Paradigms that reflect ethics of justice, equity, and respect for the planet.

Here are some common characteristics (and their regenerative antidotes!) that reinforce a Paradigm of white supremacy—the belief that white people are the superior human race, and should therefore dominate society. These practices and antidotes come from *Dismantling Racism*, a workbook by Kenneth Jones and Tema Okun. *Cultural norms*, such as these, are often implicit and unquestioned in Western societies. When we name them and make them visible, they can become mutable and democratically determined. Without critical investigation, they continue on, functioning as instruments of power and upholding Paradigms that perpetuate inequality.

- **Perfectionism:** focusing on inadequacies and/or mistakes in others' work; seeing mistakes as personal failures; showing little appreciation for the work that others do; **Regenerative Antidotes:** creating a culture of appreciation; designing learning organizations with clear feedback loops; being safe to make mistakes and reevaluating what could be different next time; noticing what went well; making specific suggestions of how to change things to go better next time.
- **Sense of Urgency:** moving at such a fast pace that makes it difficult to be inclusive; focusing on quick or highly visible results, often sacrificing relationships and partnerships along the way; pandering to funders who expect rapid outcomes; **Regenerative Antidotes:** slowing down to prioritize inclusivity and diversity; writing realistic funding proposals with feasible time frames; developing plans for thorough decision-making in atmospheres of urgency; encouraging democratic processes even if they will take more time.
- **Quantity Over Quality:** directing resources toward the production of measurable Goals; valuing quantifiable outcomes more highly than processes and qualitative effects; expressing discomfort with emotions; **Regenerative Antidotes:** including the development of qualitative Goals when planning; identifying and publicizing organizational values; making time for group process and for people to share their feelings.
- **Paternalism:** decision-making is clear to those with power and opaque to those without it; those with power are making decisions in the interest of those without power; disregarding others' viewpoints; **Regenerative Antidotes**: making decision-making processes transparent, and giving an opportunity for input and feedback; including, listening to, and respecting people who are affected by decisions in the process.
- **Right to Comfort:** believing that those with power have more of a right to emotional and psychological comfort; scapegoating those who "cause" or trigger discomfort; equating individual acts of unfairness against white people with racism, and characterizing such as "reverse racism"; **Regenerative Antidotes:** welcoming discomfort and acknowledging that it brings growth; increasing one's political analysis of racism and oppression; not taking things personally.

This is a good time to process your thoughts and feelings with a Learning Buddy. Share equal time listening to each other about what you just read and how you feel about it. When you are finished sharing, please return to Exercise 26: Paradigms at Work and see if there are any new insights or practices you want to add to your Context that may have been missing from what you originally identified.

■ Social Designer Tip: Understand the Essence of the Context ■

Part of understanding a system and its Context involves understanding its *essence*. Regenerative business consultant Carol Sanford discusses the concept of essence in her book *The Responsible Entrepreneur*. She asks her students to identify the essence of an organization, institution, or business, discerning the energetics and Values that went into its formation. How is this essence, embedded in the DNA of an entity's origins, continually expressed throughout the life of the entity? Identifying the essence of a group can shed light on the difficulty or ease with which it can transition into a new expression of itself. For instance, if the essence of a business is to create an opportunistic structure to make money, evolving its Purpose to a more socially conscious expression will likely be frustrating and difficult to achieve. However, if the essence of a business is to serve the community, the form of it services can change over time, but its essence will remain.

Learning to look at whole systems, to identify essences, and to integrate these contextual understandings will prepare you to work with any entity that has solicited your design expertise. With this lens, you can discern early in the process how successful design interventions might be in making long-lasting change. Without taking the time to observe different angles of the Context, it's easy to miss valuable information that can help us decide in which directions we choose to take a project.

● Discussion 5: Cleaning Up "The Mess We're In" ●

What do you think should be the role of the Global North in taking responsibility for the current state of the world or "the mess we're in"? What is the role of reparations and transformative justice, involving white wealthy families and communities of People of Color impacted by a white supremacy Paradigm? What feelings arise when you discuss these topics?

Topics to consider in your discussion:

- legacies of colonization, genocide, and slavery
- globalization, Westernization, and the erasure of traditional cultures
- consolidation and privatization of the world's wealth
- climate change and the climate refugee crisis

Please see Further Reading related to chapter 8 on page 244.

Social Design Lexicon for Chapter 8

Review the following key terms and write down what they mean to you. Then, reflect on how these concepts relate to your project's Context.

Holistic Context:

Climate Debt:

Myth of Meritocracy:

Self-Reflexivity:

Historical Structures of Power:

Context-sensitive:

Self-Organization:

Exploitation Paradigm:

Sustainability Paradigm:

Charity Paradigm

Solidarity Paradigm

Regeneration Paradigm:

Positivist Solutions:

Emergent Cultural Conditions:

Cultural Norms:

Collective Imagination:

Essence:

CHAPTER 9: PURPOSE AND GOALS
WORKING WITH VISION AND PRAGMATISM

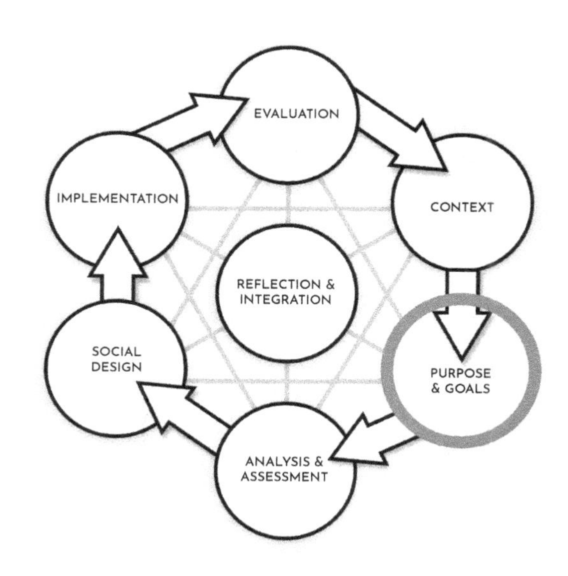

After thorough consideration of the Holistic Context and the related social and ecological conditions of a project, we enter the next phase in the design process and discern both *Purpose* and *Goals*. Here, we dream aloud and imagine "the more beautiful world our hearts know is possible," to quote the title of Charles Eisenstein's book on Paradigm shifting.

Although widely used by nonprofit organizations and in grassroots organizing work and some design processes, the word "mission" derives from colonial histories and current practices of coerced Westernization. Christian missionaries believed it was their obligation or mission to convert Native Peoples who held non-monotheistic belief systems to Christianity. Instead of "mission," I use the word "Purpose" as a linguistic act of decolonization, knowing that our language shapes the ways we perceive the world and which stories we imbibe as truth. When I hear the word "mission," I feel anxiety and urgency, perhaps just as Christian missionaries might have felt in their roles. To me, the word "Purpose" feels calmer, confident, and unwavering from the source of one's internal blueprint.

Purpose Statement

A Purpose Statement is *the big idea*, what a project is about, distilled into one sentence. It's a small collection of words strung together that reflects our heart's yearnings as it rises in our chest with conviction and passion. And this tender Purpose is bolstered with support: Goals reinforce the project's Purpose by describing the desired conditions that will come about as a result of the Design having been Implemented. When the project achieves its Goals, we can rest assured that our Purpose is coming to fruition. For example, the Purpose Statement of the Urban Farming Institute in Boston, MA, one host site of the Regenerative Design for Changemakers training, is: "to develop and promote urban farming as a commercial sector that creates green collar jobs for residents; and to engage urban communities in building a healthier and more locally based food system." Their Goals that support this Purpose include:

- Train residents from Massachusetts' urban areas to become successful urban farmers.
- Acquire and prepare land for farming.
- Educate community, city, and state stakeholders in support of appropriate policy changes in regards to land-use and urban farming practices.
- Through research and development, document and map the urban farming industry and its impact on social, economic, and health outcomes for both practitioners and the industry as a whole in order to create a new Paradigm.

This phase in the design process of developing a Purpose Statement nicely complements the work of *Afrofuturism*, the essence of which is the collective imagining of liberatory post-racist narratives. In her book *Emergent Strategy*, adrienne maree brown writes about *collaborative ideation*, in which the more people who collaborate on the process of articulating new stories for the world, the more people who will be served by the resulting world(s) that emerge.

What are the ideas that, through the realization of your Design, will bring the greatest amount of liberation for and connection among all beings? This is an important question to be asking yourself as you articulate your Purpose and Goals. "We are in an imagination battle," echoes Brown, referencing the work of poet Claudia Rankine and Intelligent Mischief founder Terry Marshall.

One more thing to consider at this stage in the process is your Values. They fill the basin in which your Purpose rises to the top. This is a good time to revisit the Values, Values, Values exercise on page 11. Also, you can add any new Values that may have surfaced since you completed the exercise. Be open to questioning and re-evaluating some of them! The person that you are now may hold different Values from the person that you were then...

Getting Clear on Your Purpose

There are endless project ideas and an infinite number of Purposes that one could pursue...so how do you choose to invest your finite time, attention, and energy? Consider the following questions applied to the Changemakers' Recipe.

1. What are you passionate about and what do you value?
2. What is your skill set, or Conscious Competencies (see page 25)?
3. What do you observe that the world (of your Project Context or beyond) needs (see page 118)?
4. And finally, what activities, goods, and services is the world of your Project Context willing to pay for?

The intersection of these spheres may give you enough fodder to move forward in articulating your draft Purpose Statement. If there is not a clear overlap of these spheres, then that's valuable information. Perhaps this suggests you first step back and undertake a personal development project to build your skill set. Or, maybe you need to tune in to the social ecosystems around you a bit more and focus on understanding the needs of those communities. If your passions, skills, and the needs of the world all intersect, but you determine there is no one willing to pay for the work, now you know you need to keep your day job and focus on change-making as an avocation.

CHANGEMAKERS' RECIPE

Once you feel clear about one or more places of intersection in the Changemakers' Recipe, then you can hone the project's Purpose. If your intention is to start a social-impact enterprise or generate financial compensation as an outcome of your project, you'll also want to incorporate a fourth ring. This ring, at the intersection of the three spheres, names the various services that you believe the current economy—considering all its numerous subcultures—would be willing to pay for. Even though capitalism is one of the key underlying systems that has led to the exploitation of life on the planet and we may not want to participate in it, we are still (mostly) operating in a capitalist economy. We need to obtain a personal livelihood so that we, our families, and our social change work, can be supported. As such, we can find ways to earn a living, either through our change-making projects or with other employment that subsidizes our commitment to social change work.

Another approach for getting clear on the Purpose is to observe social and ecological conditions that pertain to yourself. If your Zone 00 is not vital and resilient, consider designing for and strengthening this central zone first before turning to other zones. One of my consulting clients runs a family business focused on healing practices. The business was growing so fast that she and her family could not keep up with the pace. They hired me to help them design a new branch of the business. After I spent some time understanding their Context, Values, and Identities, my recommendation was to spend the next year centering the wellness of each (overextended) family member, rather than reaching for more growth in the business. They are now using the design process to support the Purpose of strong personal resilience nested within a culture of family wellness.

Time is another element to consider when choosing a project Purpose. Ask yourself, What resources, opportunities, or influence might I have right now that may change as my circumstances change in the future? For instance, a program participant at Omega Institute was in her junior year of college. As she was wrestling with her project Purpose, I asked her some questions about her current Context, the Designer Context. She realized that she had the privilege of being in college for one more year, during which she had access to research facilities and faculty mentoring. This temporal understanding of her Context and resources therein helped her to sift through the project options she was considering. She chose to focus on a Purpose nested within her academic program, where she could leverage available short-term resources in a way that could influence conditions beyond the college's walls and after the moment of her graduation.

The project scope, that we discussed in chapter 8, comes into play in a Purpose Statement. What ground will your project cover? Your scope might include: the specific Beneficiary group (community/organization/institution) or groups the project seeks to impact; the geographic location, such as region, city, town, or neighborhood; the larger social system the project aims to shift; and the general means or approaches to be used in change-making. For instance, the current draft Purpose Statement of this book is: "This social permaculture guide teaches changemakers, especially those working at the intersection of land and justice, regenerative design tools for cultivating personal resilience and developing culture-shift projects."

The Power of Unconscious Patterns to Obstruct Change

The same power of influence and principle of positive contagion that we explored in chapters 6 and 8 also applies to projects with unconscious patterns, that when left in the shadows, can obstruct intentions of change-making. The existing Unconscious Assumptions, Values, and cultural norms of organizations and institutions will influence the projects, programs, or initiatives with which they engage. For instance, a historically white conference center that caters to upper-middle-class visitors will necessarily exhibit tendencies associated with race and class privilege. If the conference center wants to create a new program whose Purpose and Goals are to reach more racially and economically diverse audiences, then the whole organization has to undergo a cultural shift. Otherwise, it may inadvertently undermine the changes envisioned because of the influence exerted by its dominant cultural practices.

A cultural shift in an institution can be very difficult to achieve if there are no precedents, and members or staff of that institution may not be able to detect the messages of their own institutional culture. Well-meaning white decision makers may articulate a Purpose to create more equitable and accessible programming, but focusing solely on programming in a vacuum is not enough. In order for a new program to truly reach more racially and economically diverse audiences, and sustain this new Purpose over the long term, the culture of the organization necessarily needs to transform. This shift includes a wide range of changes, from examining unspoken race and class assumptions held within individual staff and leaders, to shifting who holds power in the organization into the hands of leaders of Color and/or working-class leaders, to remaking the cultural cues of the physical spaces, and to modifying the language, messaging, and marketing for programs.

Systemic change takes time. Center for Whole Communities, another host organization for the Regenerative Design for Changemakers trainings, serves as a case study of an institutional shift that successfully made its patterns conscious. Over the course of two significant organizational evolutions, they deeply reflected on their Values and actions, and seeing how well they aligned. After this internal organizational work, they shifted toward serving a more racially diverse constituency and becoming a multicultural organization that prioritizes issues of land, race, class, gender, power, and privilege.

Reinventing Organizations by Frederic Laloux uses Ken Wilber's Integral Theory on Development Stages of Consciousness to explain group dynamics and systems change. The book shares a good deal of theory and practical steps for evolving the culture and practices of organizations from stagnant pattern replication toward regenerative Purposes.

The permaculture principle *observe and interact* reminds us to first come to understand the patterns and principles of a system. And only then, are we encouraged to slowly introduce design interventions to thoughtfully shift all of the Nested Wholes of a system. Without this slow due diligence, we fall prey to skipping over deep-seated patterns—that when left to their own devices, will always result in pattern reproduction and sabotage stated Purposes of change-making. As regenerative designers, it is our responsibility to diligently and lovingly help bring these deeply ingrained patterns to the surface, make them and their impacts visible to others, and intentionally help transform these patterns across all expressions of a given social system to align with a project's Purpose.

EXERCISE 27: Articulating a Draft Purpose Statement

A Purpose Statement may not be finalized until the very end of the design process. For some, it may be revealed sooner than later, even right at the start. For others, it will evolve over time. When we more fully understand the Holistic Context of our work, the necessity of a certain project Purpose may rise to the surface in response to the needs of a community or place.

DESIGN LAB ➡ If you haven't already, revisit the Values, Values, Values exercise (see page 11). Again, you can add any new Values that may have surfaced since you completed the exercise. Then, create a one-sentence draft of the Purpose Statement that explains what your project is about. Articulate it in present tense active voice (see page 39), with a clear subject and active rather than passive verbs. See if you can resist getting attached to this first draft, trying to finesse it to death. Keep moving, keep writing, and then come back. Remember, the design process is nonlinear and therefore flexible and forgiving.

Exercises later in the chapter focus on Goals Articulation. Once you have developed project Goals, then return to your draft Purpose Statement and amend it so that the main components of the Goals are reflected in the Purpose Statement. This relatedness creates internal project cohesion, helping you to focus your design thinking. It also sends a message of integrity when telling the story of your project to those you're hoping to engage in the process.

Goals Articulation Overview

Here, we continue to apply the Nested Wholes framework to the creative act of *Holistic Goals Articulation*. As we explored in section I, each of us is part of several Nested Wholes. These systems include our communities, larger social systems, the whole web of life, and the unseen realms. As designers, we bring all of ourselves to our projects—our identities, Values, and life experiences, as well as our strengths, gifts, and Unconscious Assumptions. The complex composite being that we are in this moment is going to influence our projects from the center. This is not an egoistic orientation; rather, it's an acknowledgment of our interconnectedness and the principle of positive contagion. Here, we can claim our ability to influence all that we touch. We can bring intentional artistry and power by slowing down to articulate our project Goals consciously and rigorously from a place of self-literacy (the focus of our work in section I).

How can we generate Goals that do not just face outward, toward our projects or clients, but also nourish us, the changemaker-designers? In turn, when we create conditions where our projects feed us, we are then able to show up and more fully give to our projects over the long run. I refer to this ideal condition as a loop of reciprocity (introduced in chapter 3). It is regenerative by Design.

Conscientiously Gathering Input for Project Goals

Goals are a pragmatic way of articulating our Values, intentions, dreams, and longings. We arrange these gems into a coherent string of words that, when realized through thoughtful Design, expand the meaning of our lives and the evolution of our world-mending work.

In addition to the Goals that we, as designers, have for a project, we must ensure we are meeting the needs of the organization(s), institution(s), and/or community(ies) for which we are designing. A common oversight for enthusiastic novice designers is to forget that the Design should to respond to the requests of the people they are designing for. As designers, we can and should bring in our own Goals, especially for ourselves and for larger social systems. However, we must refrain from allowing our Goals to eclipse those of the people involved in the day-to-day project circumstances.

We can gather information about these needs through a stakeholder interview and/or community forum, also known as a *charette*. A charette is particularly useful in creating community buy-in for a project. When people feel a sense of ownership in the creation of a project, they are more likely to stay involved and see it through. Also, the collective intelligence of a group brings about new possibilities for directions forward that are often overlooked by interviewing one or two individual clients. Most importantly, if we're working with communities of which we are not a member, we want to honor the adage of "nothing about me without me." In other words, charettes, community forums, interviews, and surveys help ensure that fair representation from communities distinctive from our own are incorporated into project Goals. And even if our change-making projects are in service to communities or organizations of which we are a member, it's still prudent to increase the data points of diverse needs into your project Goals. One person should never speak for their entire community because all in-groups comprise heterogeneous individuals. (See Appendix, page 223 for Interview Questions that you can use and adapt for your project; see chapter 9 Further Reading for resources on facilitating charettes and other community-engaged events.)

If your project is a new initiative that you're creating, then you can "interview" yourself as its representative. You can also interview stakeholders from existing groups that your project aims to collaborate with and/or serve.

If your project is already underway, then select at least two people as representatives of the organization, institution, or community you are working with. Ideally, the people you choose have the capacity to see the big picture *and* have decision-making power or influence in their group(s).

There are several roles (i.e., elements) that encompass the complex ecosystem(s) of your project. For example, those who play the role of *gatekeeper* and who share your Values can become *project champions* and help you to achieve your Goals, especially after soliciting their input early in the design process. However, it is also prudent to identify and build relationships with other *stakeholders* who do not share your Values and get to understand their perspectives in relation to your project Purpose and Goals. Interviewing gatekeepers who you may have seen as *adversaries* or obstacles helps begin the process of building relationships across difference, and hopefully trust, too. Understanding the diverse political and power dynamics of the system(s) you're working within will yield a more robust and thorough Social Design that works to address the three permaculture ethics.

EXERCISE 28: Identifying Roles in the Project Ecosystem

Making visible the various roles (and the unique individuals behind those roles) early on in the design process increases your facility with your project's social layers. In so doing, we can consciously tend to each type of relationship with nuance and intention. In turn, the impact of our design work and base of support increases.

In this exercise, you are asked to think about which of these roles are relevant to your project. Which People (of the 4 P's) or entities (organizations, institutions, businesses, communities) do you want to gather information from in the process of articulating Goals? Will any of your Goals be about relationship development with and/or amongst any of the People or entities in these roles?

Here are numerous possible roles you may encounter in your project. There may be several roles suggested below that are not applicable to your project and/or perhaps there are others you'd like to add. Please develop roles of the project ecosystem that reflect you and your project.

Designer:

Collaborator:

Primary Client:

Invisibilized Clients:

More-than-human Clients:

Project Partner:

Stakeholder:

Beneficiary:

Negatively Impacted Party:

Champion:

Gatekeeper:

Adversary:

Project Manager:

Implementation Team:

Project Evaluator/Evaluation Team:

Continued on next page

EXERCISE 28: Cont.

Journal: *Please write your responses to the following questions as they are relevant to your project.*

Write down what you understand each of these roles to be in a Social Design project (next to them above or in your journal). Which People or entities in your project might play which of these roles? Write their names next to each role and a statement of intent for how you would like to engage with each person or entity.

Are there any clear next steps in cultivating the type of relationship you want to have with them for the sake of the project? If so, write those out as well.

Lastly, draw a mind map (see page 148) in your journal that illustrates the types of relationships amongst the key players, power dynamics, communication channels or lack there of, etc. Consider making a legend! Then step back: what patterns do you observe in this social ecosystem?

Reflection and Integration: Take a moment here for Reflection and Integration. What did you learn from this exercise? What roles had you not previously thought of? Who is already involved in the project that now you can perceive a specific role for? Any other Integration that you'll carry forward into thinking about project Goals and roles?

■ Social Designer Tip: Look for Commonly Held Values ■

Can you identify the Values each of the key players in your project ecosystem hold? In particular, what might be commonly held Values—such as public health or open space—that you share with adversaries and/or gatekeepers? Appealing to underlying Values and finding points of connection can help you design pathways for turning project opponents into champions.

EXERCISE 29: "Best Day of My Life" Visioning Exercise

This exercise stimulates ideas for your own contribution to the Goals Articulation and is fun to do in a group. It is an adaptation of different visioning exercises from organizational coach Robert Gass, many of which can be found in *The Art of Leadership: Participant Workbook II*, published by the Rockwood Leadership Institute.

In the spirit of Dr. Martin Luther King, Jr.'s timeless speech, "I Have a Dream," allow yourself to dream aloud three times, to a different listener each time. In order to do this exercise, you'll need a way to keep time and six or more people (even numbers only). If you're alone, try it with three different mirrors (much less fun, but doable).

Provide a chair or cushion for each person (you can also sit on the floor). Place two seats facing each other, with just a little space from the next pair of seats facing each other, and so on. Have everyone sit in one of the seats.

Then, designate who in each pair will go first; for example, you could say: "Everyone who is facing the door will be Group A, everyone facing the wall will be Group B." Each person will have the chance to dream aloud three times while being listened to by three different "best

EXERCISE 29: Cont.

friends" (listeners) that they are meeting up with at a "coffee shop" (imagined setting).

Before the timekeeper sets the timer, they say to the room, specifically addressing Group A:

> You're meeting up with your best friend who you haven't seen in a long time. You're at a coffee shop five years in the future... When you see them, you say, "**It's been so long!!...And it's been the Best Day of My Life!**...Everything is working out, for me personally, for my loved ones and communities, and for all beings on the planet." Then, describe to your best friend how you feel, what you've accomplished, and what you observe in the world around you.

ALL BEINGS
YOUR LOVED ONES
YOU
& COMMUNITIES
ON THE PLANET

HOLISTIC VISION FOR THE FUTURE

Once the timekeeper reads the prompt and then sets the timer for two minutes, people in Group A share their dream of the future with the person in front of them.

When the two minutes are over, the timekeeper asks Group A to stand up and find a new seat in front of a new "best friend," (someone in Group B). Then, the timekeeper rereads the part of the prompt in bold. After the second sharing is complete, repeat the process for a third and final time.

Once Group A has shared three times with three different "best friends," then Group A stays in their seats and it is now Group B's turn. At this point, the timekeeper rereads the prompt for round one of Group B. Continue on as Group A did, so that Group B gets to dream aloud three times with three different listeners for two minutes each time. Reread the bolded part of the prompt for rounds two and three.

If you don't have access to an even-numbered group of six or more, then see if there are three mirrors in your house and use them as your "listeners." If not, you can always move to three different locations in your home or outside, or call three different friends on the phone for your dreaming aloud sessions. Be creative rather than skipping this exercise if you don't have a group to do it with!

As soon as you or everyone has spoken three times, move to the next part of the activity. Everyone stays where they are, and takes out a journal and a pen.

Journal: *Each person writes down what they heard themselves say in their dreaming aloud, and captures this precious fresh material in a journal. Then everyone circles key words or phrases that feel powerful to them and aligned with their inner Purpose.*

People can reflect on what repetitions emerged in their three stories? What in their descriptions evolved over the course of the exercise? Once everyone has written down all that they can remember, go back and see if there are any omissions and fill in anything they forgot to write down, concerning their dreams:

- *for oneself personally*
- *for one's loved ones and communities*
- *for all beings on the planet*

Identify Specific Beneficiaries

As you develop ideas for your Goals Articulation, be deliberate in identifying the specific Beneficiaries of your project. The more defined the cross-section of the population or community you can specify, the higher the likelihood that your Social Design will respond uniquely to their needs and be most effective in its endeavors.

It's also easier to gain design traction when we know our "market," to borrow language from the business world. If you can identify a clear niche or group of people that you want to engage, the easier it will be to design the project deliverables.

For instance, I recently lead a Regenerative Design for Changemakers training for librarians across the northeast US focused on issues of climate change. This cross-section of participants, in itself, represents a specific group of Beneficiaries (or participants in this case). As such, it was very easy to adapt the training curriculum to meet their interests and social positions! Moreover, I pushed them in their Social Design projects to clearly define a small sector of the public that they wanted to engage. Generally, their project Goals centered around leveraging the resources and role of their library in their respective communities to help with disaster preparedness and climate change education.

As the Social Design Lab components of the training unfolded, participants became clearer and clearer on the specific Beneficiaries related to their Goals. One participant started out working with youth, and eventually she narrowed it down to engaging high school students in low-income neighborhoods living near the flood-prone coastline. Another participant was focused on working with vacationing families who visited her library on Cape Cod. She settled on her project's Beneficiaries being all of the library's Instagram followers who could stay in touch throughout the year. The Design recommendations involved ways to connect Instagram-savvy millennials with a new app about understanding their respective home region's vulnerability ratings for different forms of natural disasters and ways to monitor incoming threats of disturbance. This refinement process used to identify specific Beneficiaries helped participants develop nuanced Social Designs that matched their Values and broader project Purpose.

If you are feeling stuck in identifying specific Beneficiaries for your project, you can revisit Exercise 2: Mapping Personal Identities and Histories on page 12. Run through each of the identity categories and see if you can articulate three or more specific identities that your ideal project Beneficiaries hold. For instance, say your design project Goals include organizing your Jewish student group on campus toward dissolving patterns of insularity and instead building solidarity with other communities. As such, perhaps the specific Beneficiaries of your relationship-building project could be young Muslim women and Jewish women on campus.

This scope of Beneficiaries makes it very clear who the project is designed to affect. You could get even more specific, if it made sense based on your Context and project Goals, and narrow down your Beneficiaries to Muslim and Jewish women who are immigrants and/or first-generation college students. Again, holding a specific group(s) in mind for which you are designing helps clarify the directions of your project and makes you more effective in achieving your Purpose and Goals.

The How-To of Goals Articulation

The Nested Wholes approach is one way to articulate Holistic Goals. In Exercise 30: Holistic Goals Articulation, you will be asked to articulate one to three Goals for each of the Nested Wholes:

- yourself, as creator of the social change project
- the organization(s)/institution(s)/community(ies) that the project is situated within
- the larger social system(s) that your project aims to influence

We hold the potential to design each ring so that it receives resources that nourish it. Magically, when one ring is supported, that ring radiates out and influences the larger ring that surrounds it. A loop of reciprocity between the project and ourselves should be designed from the beginning. Over time, this loop develops the capacities and resilience of the project and designer in an intimate act of co-regeneration. Ashara Ekundayo Gallery, an arts venue in Oakland, CA, that showcases the work of Black women in the African diaspora is a powerful illustration of this concept. Ekundayo, a Regenerative Design for Changemakers training alumna, employs the permaculture principles and design tools to structure her life and her change-making projects so that they mutually support each other's well-being and resilience.

How we phrase our Goals creates an image in our minds and in the minds of others. We can play with language as a means to bring our projects into manifestation. As mentioned in the opening to this book, *Abra K'adabra*, a well-known Aramaic saying for casting magic spells, translates to "I create as I speak." The perennial wisdom of this phrase guides us in calling forth our envisioned future, as if it is already occurring. It treats time as if it is the only thing between us and our vision.

Practically speaking, the format we'll use for writing each Goal is one complete sentence. Each Goal should support an aspect of the project Purpose. A full set of Goals, when realized, brings the Purpose into fruition. Ideally, a project has two to four Goals for each of the three Contexts (Designer, Group, Systems). Each Goal has its own set of *Objectives* that support it. Goals are more general and qualitative, whereas Objectives are specific and concrete. Objectives point to particular outcomes that you want to realize through the Implementation of your project.

Here are four example Goals for the Group Context, which is the institutional level, of the Jail-to-Farm-to-College and Employment Program that I co-developed with a former visionary food systems student, Joshua Freund, at the Franklin County Jail in Greenfield, MA. After a community charette and a few interviews, we developed the following Goals, which represent a synthesis of ideas from incarcerated residents, jail administrators, community educators, Joshua, and myself:

Goal 1: The program engages incarcerated individuals in a variety of vocational skills-building experiences relevant to the regional economy.

Goal 2: Therapeutic horticulture develops participants' ecological literacy and sense of belonging to the natural world.

Goal 3: Mindfulness-based activities encourage participants to recognize their capacity to take positive action and cultivate healthy personal habits.

Goal 4: Community mentors volunteer to teach incarcerated students, reducing recidivism rates by building pro-social networks to support their reentry.

GOALS & OBJECTIVES

Goals: general & qualitative

Objectives: specific & concrete

Notice that these Goals do not prescribe *how* they will be achieved. Oftentimes there is a tendency to present a Design solution within the Goals. Refrain from rushing ahead. Again, Goals are qualitative and more general. Objectives support the Goals with concrete parameters, but still do not go into definitive directions. Once the Analysis and Assessment phases of the process are complete, then we can develop the details of the Design. The Design is the outcome, or the sacred marriage so to speak, of joining the Goals and Analysis. The Goals are like a lens, helping determine what we focus on in the Analysis, so that we don't stagnate in analyzing the project conditions endlessly!

To continue on with the Goals from the Franklin County Jail, the following are example Objectives intended to support Goal 1: "The program engages incarcerated individuals in a variety of vocational skills-building experiences relevant to the regional economy."

> Objective: Vegetable planting and harvesting in recreation areas increase participants' vocational skills, confidence, and connection to the outdoors.
>
> Objective: Greenhouse management training builds vocational skills for a growing sector of the surrounding rural agricultural economy.
>
> Objective: Cooking, food preservation, and food handling classes increase individuals' food security and prepare them with culinary skills.

These Objectives strike a good balance between being concrete and not too specific. Notice they do not detail *how* they will be implemented. In contrast, if the first Objective described the schedule of classes, how many participants would attend, content of the curriculum, etc., that would be jumping to the outcome of the Design prematurely. At this juncture, we still want to keep options open.

When you arrive at the Evaluation phase in the process, you will design ways to measure your Objectives. You can create criteria that will let you know that you've fulfilled an Objective. For instance, you can determine the criteria for specific planting skills, such as knowing how to plant seeds for six species directly in the ground (direct seeding) and how to grow (start) six other species as transplants.

Another example of criteria is determining the number of participants who you want to learn these skills. You may have tools in mind, such as interviews or surveys, for how you will measure outcomes, such as participants' increased confidence in and connection to the outdoors.

The phase of articulating Goals and Objectives is a very good time to develop a proposed Evaluation approach, outlining which project outcomes you want to measure, as you go or after a milestone has been reached, and which tools you want to use to do so. Once you have begun the Implementation phase of the project, revisit these ideas and amend them as needed. They may still be on point, or some things may have shifted and you can modify your approach to the Evaluation.

■ Social Designer Tip: Flag Unrealistic Expectations Early and Often ■

As designers working with established organizations and institutions, it's important to flag situations that pin hope on one champion project or lone wolf leader. Expectations of a silver bullet that can transform an organization is an expression of a monocultural approach. This situation can set up unrealistic Goals where designers *overpromise and underdeliver*. Flag this pitfall when you see it coming. Also, be careful to avoid being used as "the talent" who, it is imagined, can whisk away longstanding organizational gridlock or other forms of stagnation—a colonial "coming in and fixing" pattern. Use your creativity to set up the conditions where the system will thrive in your absence.

ADDITIONAL SOCIAL DESIGNER HAZARDS

- being entrapped by a particular stakeholder's agenda
- holding an attitude of superiority
- following colonial patterns of "coming in and fixing"
- sinking into disempowerment

Helping the organization or institution you are working with to articulate feasible and open-ended Goals avoids overpromising and underdelivering. Let them know that undertaking a holistic design process will create space for adaptive solutions to arise, resulting in change that sustains over time. The Goals can support this approach when they involve dynamic processes that respond to the Context. If we continue on with the earlier example of the historically white conference center, dynamic and open-ended Goals might include such actions as: developing ongoing anti-oppression staff trainings that respond to changing issues; designing non-extractive, reciprocal relationships with other organizations; and redesigning existing projects to better align with new organizational priorities. Refrain from Goals that dictate defined formulas or set of best practices to follow—these are necessarily not context-sensitive. With porous Goals that can breathe, we create responsive design solutions that go beyond a face-lift. With a deeper understanding of social Contexts, designers can help organizations, institutions, and communities to truly regenerate themselves from the inside by articulating thoughtful, capacious Goals.

EXERCISE 30: Holistic Goals Articulation

This exercise is an adaptation of a planning process from Holistic Management International, an organization that advocates for holistic strategies to regenerate degraded landscapes while producing a yield in the forms of dairy, meat, soil fertility, etc. Here, this approach is adapted for Goals related to designing holistic social change projects.

Articulating Goals can sometimes be difficult. You can source raw material that can create the Goals from client interview(s) (see Appendix on page 223), community charettes, and previous exercises if you get stuck:

- Your Holistic Context document (see page 118): What are the key issues your project aims to transform? What is the weakest link in the system(s) you are designing for? Through your understanding of the Context and the three permaculture ethics (Earth Care, People Care, and Resource Share), consider what some project Goals might be.
- Values, Values, Values (see page 11): What do you value? How can your Values become the basin from which your Purpose and Goals source their essence?
- Writing from the "Best Day of My Life" exercise (see page 134): Which words did you circle? What themes repeated themselves? Mix these ingredients into the elixir of your Goals.

DESIGN LAB ➡ Keeping in mind that resources flow where attention goes, please articulate one to three Goals in present tense active voice sentences (review on page 39) for each of the following Contexts. Then, add at least two Objectives under each Goal. Focus your writing on the function of the Goal, rather than describing the superficial form it could take. Remember, Goals are qualitative and open-ended so that they give the project direction without being so specific that they dictate a premature solution. Objectives are specific and concrete, and they support the Goals they fall under.

NESTED WHOLES AND RINGS OF INFLUENCE

Yourself/Designer – how do you want to feel as a changemaker, and what qualities will you exude through the realization of this project? How will this project feed you, personally, and what new capacities will you develop?

(Consider connecting your personal Goals to your Life Sector Analysis [see page 42]. How can these Goals embody the permaculture principle of multiple functions, helping you increase the vitality of the sectors you want to strengthen, while simultaneously serving your project? For instance, to increase the health of my friendship sector, I engage certain friends as project partners so that our friendship evolves from a Restorative Relationship to a Regenerative Relationship.)

Organizations/Institutions/Communities – who are your specific Beneficiaries? What overall impact and systems-level change will your project have on the entity(ies) it is designed to influence? Information that you've gathered from your meetings and interviews with project stakeholders, including Beneficiaries, gatekeepers, etc., determines much of the content for the Goals at this level.

EXERCISE 30: Cont.

Larger Social Systems – what larger social system (choose one to two) does your project aim to shift? Examples: healthcare system, political lobbying system, mental health system, etc. Describe, in general terms, the Goals you have for how this system will undergo a culture shift because of your project, even if over decades.

Please articulate Goals in present tense active voice, as if the desired outcome of the project is already happening. With present tense, we are calling the future into being, imagining in our minds and in the minds of our listeners that the project is already underway. This differs from articulating Goals in future tense, such as "The workshop will inspire teenagers..." or in conditional tense, such as "Fresh vegetables could feed immigrant families..." These tenses pronounce a future we may never get to. Also, avoid verbs such as "hope," "intend," or "would."

Active voice, rather than passive voice, lets you know who the agent of change is and who or what is responsible for realizing the Goals of your project. Always state who is the subject/doer. Choose active verbs, such as "deliver" or "engage" or "heal," rather than passive or helper verbs such as "is" or "are" or "have." Your Goals should follow the format of subject then verb. Once you have gone through this process, read your Goals aloud...can you feel the vision land in your body?

Humans have the power to bring ideas into the world, to manifest them through our words and how we wield them—not only in spoken words but also in written and visual communications. As the phrase *Abra K'adabra* suggests, we are the creative speaking ones, with beautiful human languages that have the ability to cast magic upon the world with our beloved voices. With the help of these gifts, our Purpose and Goals emerge.

> *You have the power to shape words into a combination that will release energy as you go forth. You have been given many words (which are concepts) by the dominant culture. Some of them may no longer be useful for you. They may be interfering with your good now, whereas previously they may have helped you to survive your particular situation. You are at a point of taking charge... Now is the time to contemplate just what the words you hold in your mind are doing for you and others. What meaning are you giving your life as you articulate your experience to yourself?*
>
> – Carol Bridges, *The Medicine Woman Inner Guidebook*

Please see Further Reading related to chapter 9 on page 245.

Social Design Lexicon for Chapter 9

Review the following key terms and write down what they mean to you. Then, reflect on how these concepts might relate to your Purpose and Goals.

Purpose:

Goals:

The Big Idea:

Afrofuturism:

Collaborative Ideation:

Observe and Interact:

Holistic Goals Articulation:

Charette:

Gatekeepers:

Project Champions:

Stakeholders:

Adversaries:

Objectives:

Overpromise and Underdeliver:

Multiple Functions:

CHAPTER 10: ANALYSIS AND ASSESSMENT
THE ESSENTIAL "WHAT?" AND "SO WHAT?"

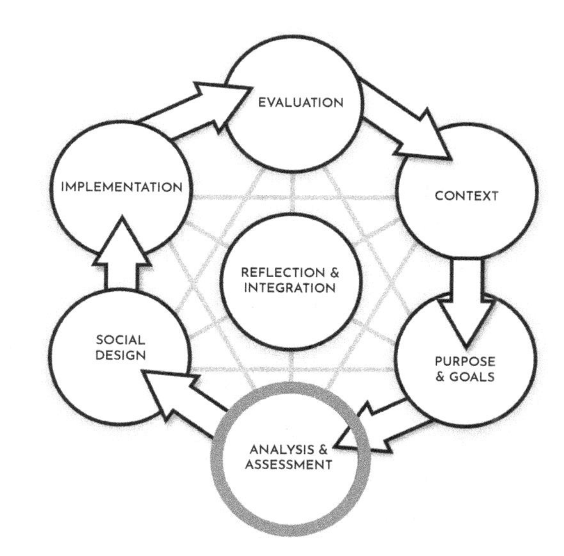

The Analysis and Assessment phase in the design process separates and simplifies the layers of complex systems. Critical thinking applied to social landscapes is one of the most accessible tools we have for intervening in systems and redirecting them toward justice and healing. Passionate changemakers in Rwanda who have been successfully rebuilding the country since the 1994 genocide voice a central message: critical thinking has the power to deconstruct and divert troubling conditions before a genocide takes place. Critical thinking skills, paired with active bystandership—physical and verbal interventions that prevent harm and promote the welfare of individuals and groups—are integral tools now taught in nearly every sector of Rwandan society.

In this chapter, we will explore a systematic approach to conducting Analyses and Assessments that promotes critical thinking applied to your own country, community, and day-to-day life. The analytical tools discussed can provide different pathways to help you understand the *existing conditions* of your project more deeply and the web of challenges it seeks to address. Remembering that the design process is not linear, you may find yourself revisiting your description of Context and rearticulating Goals as you discover more about the existing conditions that surround and shape your project.

As we continue to cultivate our understanding of the relationship between Zone 00 (ourselves as changemakers) and our outer change-making projects, we can engage in reflexive practices. This process helps us to create projects that respond to the conditions and needs of the world as it is, not the mental model of the world we hold through our beliefs. Recalling the idea of Unconscious Assumptions from chapter 2, we must ask ourselves two important questions: What are my worldviews and habitual thought patterns? How might they impact my project and its Design? We want to make sure that we don't see only what we're looking to see in our Assessments. These questions, which we are wise to revisit repeatedly, require us to make Observations about ourselves, first and foremost, and then to make Interpretations about what we've observed and how it might be influencing our project.

This cycle of inquiry with *Observations* and *Interpretations* embodies the Analysis and Assessment phase in the design process. With a Nested Wholes framework, we can make social Analysis inquiries, and then apply them across Contexts. What are the observable patterns and cultural norms I carry? Of the organizations, institutions, and communities I want to transform? Of the larger social systems I aim to shift? How do these social conditions pose *Opportunities* and *Constraints* for Social Design and Implementation? Engaging in social Analysis for design projects has been beautifully modeled by Starhawk, founder of the Earth Activist Training, and my colleague Lisa DePiano, founder of the Permaculture f.e.a.s.t. (for ecological and social transformation) course in Western Massachusetts.

The How-To of Analysis and Assessment

The underpinnings of permaculture and the Regenerative Design Process are based on what permaculture co-founder Bill Mollison calls "protracted, thoughtful observation" and whole systems Assessment. Designers can explore any social environment the same way we would approach a multispecies ecosystem: making Observations and Interpretations of a dynamic web of elements, each performing specialized functions in relation to others and the whole. Think of an extended family system or a community governance system as examples of a complex social web.

Analysis and Assessment tools help landscape designers to understand the current and historical conditions of a defined physical location known as the project site. With Social Design, the site can certainly include a physical location, such as a region, city, or neighborhood. The breadth of the Analysis in Social Design, however, allows us to focus on the Contexts of People, Place, Power, and Paradigm. Through these lenses, we can zoom in and assess the complex relationships that the project is nested within—among individuals, groups, and social systems, and between beings and places, including land, animals, waterways, cultural elements, etc.

ANALYSIS = OBSERVATIONS
ASSESSMENT = INTERPRETATIONS

Observations: the "What?" What patterns do you observe about the conditions within and surrounding your project?

Interpretations: the "So What?" Why are the patterns you observe relevant to the project Purpose and Goals? What is their impact?

When we analyze and assess social systems ecologically, we consider what conditions are found in the project's Holistic Context. Through the lens of our Goals, we can sift through infinite bits of information to focus on what may be most relevant.

We start by making objective Observations of social and ecological phenomena. Observations are patterns that we can recognize with our senses or other instruments for measuring: what we see, hear, feel with our skin, and sense through other organs. Observations need be separated out from our judgments or Interpretations. Observations are simply the "What?" while Interpretations are the "So what?" explaining how a pattern you observe relates to the issues you are designing for.

Interpretations are how we make Assessments; they are translations that our brain performs almost automatically to process the information we take in. We make Interpretations through the combined *personal filters* of our cultural norms, belief systems, learned world history, personal history, identities, and even passing moods. We will go over an example of Observations and Interpretations related to the global food system later on in this chapter on page 151.

"The Beach"

In the Regenerative Design Process, we make space to consider design challenges from a multiplicity of angles (a *polycultural approach*) rather than a single point of view. This helps us avoid getting attached to one immediate solution (a *monocultural approach*). Excellent ideas will come to you as you move through the design process. These ideas are important! However, it's easy to become attached to these solutions prematurely. And so, I encourage you to create an area in your journal or sketchbook that is designated as *The Beach*, a place to hold intriguing ideas.

Many designers and organizational planners call this place the Parking Lot, where they "park" ideas. I prefer an ecological analog and a more pleasant place to visit: The Beach, where your ideas can mellow in the golden sun and sea breeze, rather than baking and withering on asphalt. Further along in your design journey, you can return to your early ideas and evaluate if they still make sense for the direction your project is headed.

Our initial solutions may be brilliant, but they may not consider the whole system, and can divert our attention before we've had a chance to gather and digest information. When we rigorously work our way through each phase of the design process, we avoid defaulting to our well-worn neural networks. Instead of us simply applying solutions from familiar mental models, new ways of approaching challenges receive the space they need to evolve. The Regenerative Design Process assists our inherent brilliance in birthing emergent ideas, ones that were previously unavailable to our conscious mind.

Place your emergent design ideas on a dedicated open page in your journal, and label the top of the page "The Beach," and revisit them once you reach the Social Design phase of the process.

■ Social Designer Tip: Pitfalls ■

Getting attached to early ideas rather than taking possible solutions to The Beach is but one of the pitfalls in the design process. Another common pitfall is confusing Assessment with Design Directions (detailed in the next chapter). Design Directions are generalized actions about how the project will be carried out. The design process is clarified when you slow down and keep these separate from Assessment. To avoid conflating these two phases, remember that Analysis tools assess the current conditions that surround a project. Their function is *not* to paint a picture of what things will look like in the future once the Design has been implemented.

Analysis can and should include expressions of past conditions that surface in the present, such as policies that arose in response to events from decades ago. But generally speaking, Analysis focuses on the details of the present-day conditions, which are summarized in the Holistic Context. See the sample Observations and Interpretations of the global food system on pages 151 to better understand what makes each of these distinct.

Choosing What to Analyze

Selecting Analysis tools that will provide the most relevant assessment for your project requires creativity and rigor. With your Goals in mind, consider what facets of the project's ecological and social conditions each Analysis tool might reveal. Consider working with a polyculture of tools rather than choosing only one or two that may not reveal a full picture. The more facets we analyze and assess, the more information about Opportunities and Constraints we gain with which we can equip ourselves. (Note: The first time you undergo the design process, consider applying most or all of the Analysis tools presented in this chapter, remembering that this inaugural journey is a kind of laboratory for familiarizing yourself with new instruments and gaining diverse skills.)

If your project is a **new initiative**, you'll focus your Analysis and Assessment on:

- the project's Holistic Context
- conditions of case studies similar to your project
- prospective project partners

If your project is **already established**, then you'll analyze and assess:

- the project's Holistic Context
- the current state of the project
- patterns of the organization(s), institution(s), or community(ies) it's embedded within

In this chapter, you'll have an opportunity to review and adapt frameworks from section I and then learn new Analysis tools. At the end of this chapter, you will be asked to complete two Design Lab outputs in Exercise 35: Analysis and Assessment Synthesis on page 163. You'll be asked to choose different types of analysis tools, apply them to your project, and develop Observations, Interpretations, a Summary Synthesis, Opportunities, and Constraints. (Please look over the exercise if you would like more details about where we'll be going.)

Adapting Zone 00 Tools for Project-Scale Analysis

In addition to the Analysis tools presented later in this chapter, you can also apply many of the tools found in section I, which focused on the Zone 00/Self, to your project analysis. Consider pausing to breathe or take a break between each one as you read through them, as there is a lot to consider using!

- **Review Personal Identity Map** (see page 12)—Analyze how your personal identities relate to and impact the project. What worldviews or Unconscious Assumptions do you bring to the design process and the particular project you are working on?
- **Identity Mapping of a Project Element** (see page 12 and adapt it)—What are the identities of one element of your project, such as a key program, neighborhood, farm, community, or cultural center your project is a part of? What socio-economic class is it in? Is it different from the class it serves? What ethnic identities are involved? Is there a dominant gender? You could also choose to map the identities of: people on your Advisory Board or Board of Trustees; people you are serving; your key collaborators; your funders; Gatekeepers, etc. In this Analysis, clearly state whose identity you are mapping, and also consider mapping the identity of more than one element in your project.

- **Institutional or Organizational Niche Analysis** (see page 17)—Here, we apply the concept of the Social Niche Analysis and scale it up from the individual to the collective. A Niche Analysis can help you decipher the role and function of an institution, organization, or community more holistically. If you are working with an existing project, what is the niche of the project itself? If your project is new and in the ideation stage, what is the niche of the institution(s), organization(s), or program(s) that the project will partner with or be housed within? If you're working on a community-based project, consider analyzing the niche of organizers or a hub within that community. Be explicit about which entity you're analyzing. The example diagram is focused on the Hunger Artists, a project of a former social permaculture student at University of Massachusetts-Amherst.

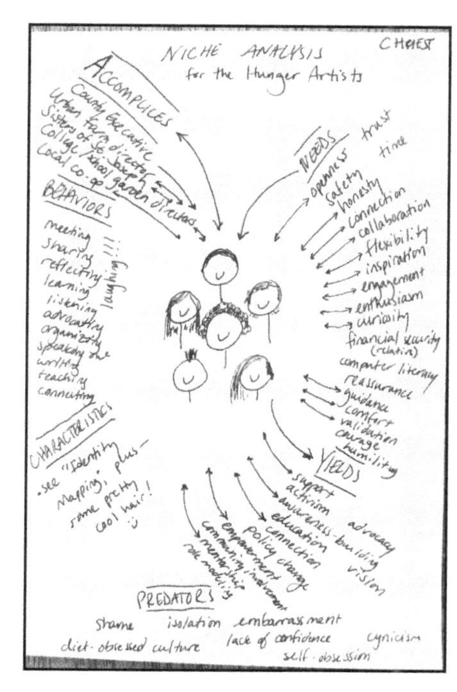

Organizational Niche Analysis

Drawing by Katie Chriest

- **Project Financial Flows and Pools** (see page 47)—Instead of personal finances, consider creating a Flows and Pools Analysis to observe the financial picture of your project. What do you notice that was not obvious before? Note: this exercise works best with existing projects.
- **Sector Analysis** (see page 42)—Be creative and identify six to ten pertinent sectors that you believe make up a whole thriving project. Then, see if there are any sectors you've missed by asking others on the project team to add any you may have overlooked. Perhaps there is a sector for public relations and another for multicultural leadership and another for artistic engagement. Develop sectors that you want to analyze based on your project Goals and the three permaculture ethics of Earth Care, People Care, and Resource Share. Then, complete this exercise.
- **Barriers and Launchpads** (see page 49)—What project Barriers continue presenting themselves? These could be social, physical, or environmental. Perhaps unconscious and oppressive dynamics, such as ageism or language oppression, continue to thwart progress? Does a lack of physical resources, such as a classroom space or van, stunt project growth? Do environmental constraints, such as loud noise from a neighboring business or toxins in the soil, cause persistent challenges? Then consider the Launchpads, meaning the conditions, places, and/or relationships that can support the project's success (or that have supported other similar projects). How can this Analysis help you see how problems could be solutions?
- **Zones of Relationships** (see page 84)—If your project is already established, how healthy are the various Zones of Relationships that your project has with its Beneficiaries, staff or volunteers, neighbors or community members, the local government, larger social systems that affect it, the natural world, ancestors, etc.? If it's a new project, what relationships do you, the Designer, on behalf of the project, have to bring to the table? Consider completing the Zones of Relationships Analysis for the community or group the project will be anchored.
- **Cycles of Influence** (see page 84)—What influences flow into the project's conditions on a regular basis, whether it be daily, weekly, seasonally, yearly, or other? First, make Observations about the effects of these cycles and their periodicity. Then make Interpretations as to whether they are supportive, hindering, or both to the project Goals.

- **Relationship Analysis**—Drawing on two exercises, Mapping Energy Patterns in Relationships (see page 85) and Anchors and Accomplices (see page 86), consider thinking critically about the quality of and energetics in the project's relationships with individuals and groups. What types of relationships does your project have with other groups? What is the baseline dynamic of each of these relationships: Extractive, Consumptive, Restorative, or Regenerative? Which specific organizations, institutions, and/or leaders are you collaborating with? How can you build stronger, more explicit Anchor and Accomplice relationships with project partners within the community that your project is designed to influence? (This Analysis, paired with a commitment to relationship development based on reciprocity, is valuable because it moves the project away from a charity Paradigm, in which an outsider to a social ecosystem gives handouts without sharing vulnerably or building relationships. Instead, when we genuinely connect, share in the struggle, take direction from those most impacted, and respond to their stated requests, we move towards a solidarity Paradigm. Make some Observations and then assess "which Paradigm am I coming from today?")
- **Project Ecosystem Analysis**—Revisit Exercise 28: Identifying Roles in the Project Ecosystem, and consider making each role type or individual a certain shape or color and mapping out the system on a large piece of paper. Draw lines among the players to illustrate the current state of power and relationships in the project ecosystem. Then, make some Observations and Interpretations about the ways in which current players and roles are negatively or positively impacting your stated project Purpose and Goals. What patterns can you see playing out? Which Design Directions may be emerging for ways to design key relationships among various people and their roles in the project ecosystem?

Reflection and Integration: For each of the above tools, it's important to zoom out and look at the patterns that emerge rather than nitty gritty details. Then, summarize these patterns in a few sentences; this is an important Integration moment. Make Observations and Interpretations. What is the weakest link? Where is the project well resourced? Lastly, go on to identify Opportunities and Constraints that move toward project Goals. Which of the conditions are Constraints, providing valuable information and structural limits for the Design? Which Constraints can be turned into resources?

Mind Mapping Tool for Systems Thinking

What would happen if we focused only on a single issue of a system, a point amidst a wider web, that we want to transform? We would eventually see that the system persists, even when one of its issues improves. In contrast, when we address a whole system in which different problems are interconnected, we create holistic solutions that respond to the systemic level.

A *mind map* is a visual tool that designers use to depict complex relationships within a system. To gain a whole systems perspective on your project and its interrelated ecological and social conditions, you can develop a simple version of a mind map. Circles around issues that your project seeks to transform represent *elements* in the current system. Lines that connect the circles represent *relationships* among the elements.

To illustrate how to use this Analysis tool, we'll look at a large-scale project whose Purpose is to transform the global food system. The Goals focus on environmental regeneration, justice for food-system workers, and eliminating fossil fuel inputs. Grasping for a whole systems perspective on a massive project such as this one, we can begin by mapping elements of the global food system and their relationships as part of the Systems Context. Alternately, if we only considered one aspect of the existing conditions, such as the proliferation of genetically modified organisms (GMOs), but ignored how the food system exploits farm workers and depletes topsoil, we would miss understanding the interconnectedness of these problems. A project that aims to influence a large societal system necessarily needs to design for multiple interconnected solutions to address a complex web of issues. We start a mind map with a random assembly of current social and ecological conditions, as we have here of the global food system.

ELEMENTS OF THE GLOBAL FOOD SYSTEM

Once we have identified the key elements in the Context, we can start mapping their relationships. For example, "land grabs and landless workers" connects to "exploitation of undocumented workers." Land grabbing in Latin America, by wealthy individuals and opportunistic corporations, creates landless workers who then seek other employment for their livelihoods. This condition has led to a pattern where vulnerable migrants seek jobs in the US. Some gain minimal protection from migrant worker programs, but many do not. Corporations and agribusinesses in the US, perhaps some of the very same businesses appropriating people's farmlands, take advantage of undocumented workers. Unprotected by labor laws and afraid of deportation, landless workers can easily be exploited. They often receive poor pay and work in hazardous conditions.

In this mind map below, lines symbolize existing relationships between elements. This exercise teaches us to think systemically rather than myopically. More complex mind maps might include lines with arrows to represent causation or directionality or use dotted lines to represent tenuous or potential relationships. All of these variations can be communicated in a key or legend included with the mind map. For now, we will start with a simple mind map with circles and solid lines.

MIND MAPS

Circles represent the elements and characteristics in the system.

Lines represent the relationships among the elements.

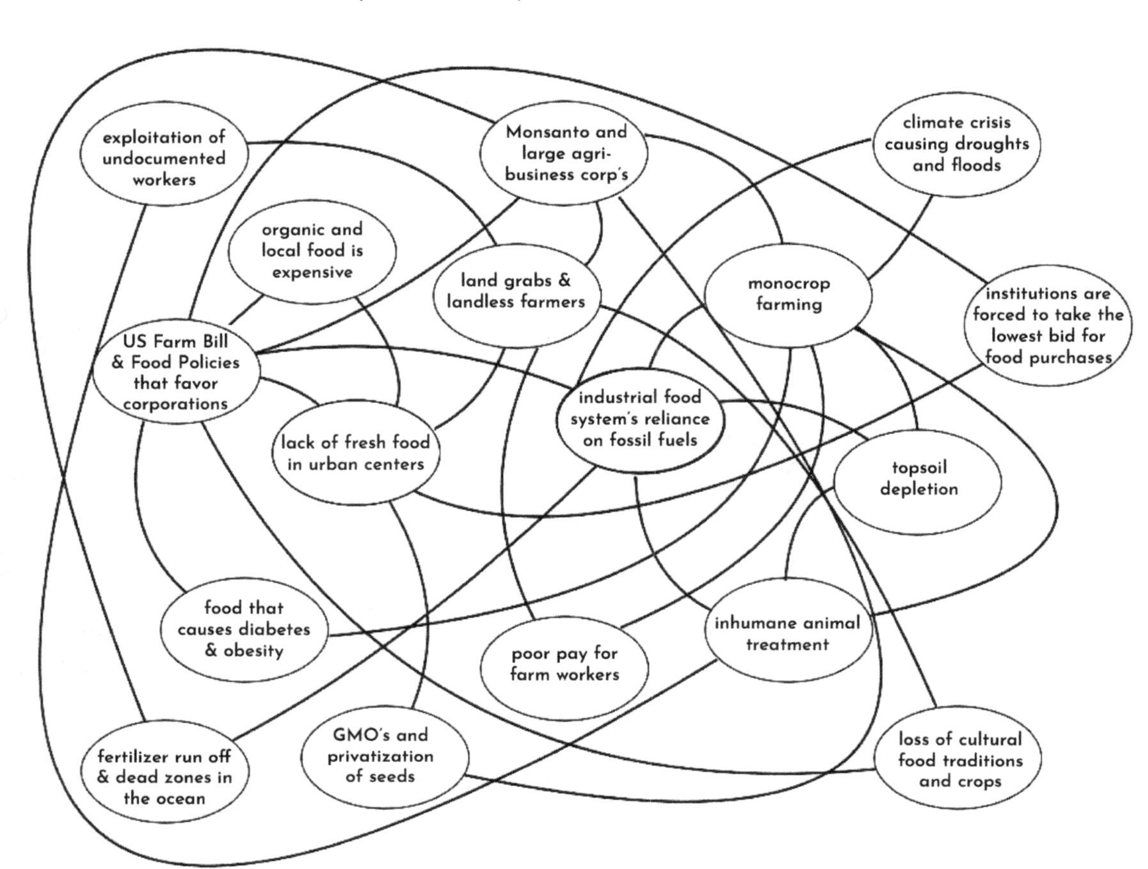

MIND MAP OF GLOBAL FOOD SYSTEM ELEMENTS

A core skill in regenerative design is pattern recognition. When we become literate in the myriad *pattern languages* found in nature and understand their functions, we can apply them to designing social systems. The form of a mind map reminds us of a web pattern. The pattern language of the web provides the same functions no matter where it shows up: capturing and distributing resources, exchanging information, and using redundancy to strengthen and reinforce the well-being of each element it connects. The global food system certainly benefits from these functions of the web pattern.

In response, can we, too, create designs that benefit from the web pattern? Rather than finding this mind map overwhelming or discouraging, how can we replace degenerative elements with regenerative ones, and exploitative relationships with reciprocal ones? From mapping the "problem," we learn that the more connections each element has in the web, the stronger the system's resilience. We can turn the problems into solutions, a permaculture principle, by mimicking the inherent intelligence of the web pattern in our own designs. Can you think of other hidden Opportunities revealed here?

Sample Observations and Interpretations

From the global food systems mind map, we can make Observations about this system and generate Interpretations. Completing these sometimes laborious but essential steps eventually brings us to a tipping point in our process, Design Directions, which we will discuss in more detail in the next chapter.

Before reading on, take a minute to make some overall Observations about the existing conditions of the global food system. What patterns do you observe? And then, what Interpretations (based on the project Goals of environmental regeneration, justice for food system workers, and eliminating fossil fuel inputs) might emerge from each Observation?

Journal: *Pause here first to write your own Observations and Interpretations. And then go on to read the following examples of them and see how yours align or not. There are no right answers, just perceptions.*

- *Observation 1: Power is concentrated in the hands of few*

  → *Interpretation: Mobilizing change will not be effective if done only by individuals or a handful of organizations.*

  → *Interpretation: There are only a few key people and corporations that the project would need to influence to make some amount of change*

  → *Interpretation: At times, changemakers will likely get discouraged or feel paralyzed to make change when looking at the concentration of power*

- *Observation 2: The global food system impacts every scale of community and ecosystem*

  → *Interpretation: The global food system is devastating the very resource base that provides food for people and animals*

  → *Interpretation: We all are in trouble unless we intervene in the system*

  → *Interpretation: People everywhere, from small remote villages to wealthy Westerners, are hurt by this food system. This includes loss of personal livelihoods for small-holding farmers and fisherpeople, and the onset of diabetes, heart disease, and obesity in financially well-off communities*

Summary Synthesis *of the global food system: decisions made by a few powerful companies focused on profit, resulting in exploitation of people and land*

EXERCISE 31: Mind Map Analysis and Assessment

Choose one of your project's Contexts, either a Systems or Group Context, that you would like to have a better whole systems understanding of. You can create a sketch of this exercise in your journal, and then transfer your final map onto a big piece of unlined paper to share with others at the end of the design process.

DESIGN LAB ➡ Create a mind map and written Analysis and Assessment. Start by brainstorming all of the elements (the current social and ecological conditions) and then plot and circle each one on your paper. Look for the relationships between them. Draw lines to visually link elements that have a connection. You can use simple lines, as in the food system mind map, or you can create your own lexicon of lines and/or symbols that show nuanced relationships. Remember to include a key so that if someone else looked at your mind map, they would be able to follow your systems thinking.

Note: Something magical happens for our internal processing when we use our motor skills to draw, pencil on paper. However, there are several excellent digital tools for mind mapping, such as Coggle, Imindq, MindMaple, and Sketchboard.

Journal: *When you have completed the mind map, take out your journal. What is your Analysis and Assessment of your map? Write your Observations and Interpretations, including at least three Observations and three or more Interpretations for each Observation. Finally, identify Opportunities and Constraints related to the Goals that have surfaced through this process. Review the related descriptions and examples earlier in the chapter if you get stuck. Repeat this visual and analytical process for as many Contexts as you would like to assess.*

Analyzing Oppression in Societal Systems

Institutions, organizations, and communities have structural oppression embedded in their policies, practices, and, sometimes, their mission. This social phenomena is not any one entity's fault. Oppression is systemic and ubiquitous, and we all inherited mechanisms that have been built into societies to serve the dominant groups, which in most of the world is comprised of European-heritage, owning-class people. Understanding and analyzing the interrelation between racism and economic oppression is important for any change-making project that seeks to transform systems.

Take a moment to reflect on all you know about racism and classism. Let this understanding in your body and mind arise from personal experience and all that you've learned through various relationships, experiences, trainings, classes, films, etc. Many of us have to decolonize our minds purposefully (and our nervous systems! according to Dr. Michael Yellow Bird and Resmaa Manakem) and decide to actively unlearn the fearful, hateful messages that try to compel us to dominate and extract from others. We absorbed this mentality towards the "other" from the colonial Paradigm and practices in one or more cultures around us.

When people develop alternative systems as a strategy for resisting capitalist exploitative systems (e.g., housing cooperatives, community medical clinics) without analyzing and addressing structural racism and classism, these alternatives do not dissolve structural inequities. Instead, they reproduce them by creating exclusive subcultures of which only a small minority can access these resources. Creating small enclaves of radical alternatives also diverts the attention of brilliant changemakers who might otherwise work to transform dominant systems of the over-culture. This situation creates a brain drain of sorts, leaving the public systems with fewer resources than before critical thinkers left to create alternative systems. Think about radical parents leaving PTA boards and taking their children out of public school and sending them to private institutions or homeschooling, and the impact on the schools for those who can't afford to buy their way out of an under-resourced system.

If we aim to design truly regenerative systems and cultures, we must attend to structural inequities in our projects' Analyses, Assessments, and Designs. If readers and students use only self-serving aspects of regenerative design to create future realities that exclude people of different races and socio-economic classes, my heart will be sunken. And even worse, we will end up with the same "mess we're in" now, but with less precious time to resolve these issues, in the face of planetary climate chaos and increasing social divisive violence.

Let's take an example of how we can engage this process to assess historical conditions that have contributed to structural racism in the US. In the aftermath of the Great Depression, the federal government created the Federal Housing Administration (FHA) as part of the New Deal to promote homeownership, a worthy goal that helped launch many US citizens into the middle class. Black, Indigenous, and People of Color were largely denied access to FHA resources through a discriminatory practice of redlining, where they refused mortgages to people in certain neighborhoods (often neighborhoods of Color). Between 1930 and 1950, the FHA financed three out of five homes purchased in the US, yet only 2% of FHA mortgages were made available to BIPOC applicants.[1] One Observation is that the New Deal disproportionately benefited white people. One Interpretation is that the new American middle class deliberately excluded BIPOC citizens.

To continue with our Analysis of oppression in societal systems, we can observe a recurring pattern about the intersection of racism and economic oppression in the US. The 1935 Social Security Act excluded domestic and farm workers (combined, these jobs constituted approximately 65% of the Black workforce).[2] Only in 1950 were domestic workers added, followed by agricultural workers in 1954. This 15-to-20-year period after the Act was ratified prevented the accumulation of familial wealth for nearly a generation. An eerie echo of slavery and sharecropping, still today there is no minimum wage for farm workers. We can observe that this absurd lack of minimum wage impacts mostly poor migrant farm workers from Latin America and African Americans. One Interpretation of this situation is that the institution of slavery finds new strategies and expressions to continue even after the Emancipation Proclamation of 1863.

These issues are hard to look at, and may make us feel angry, uncomfortable, and even paralyzed. But in the process of assessing a whole social ecology, we create more enlightened and comprehensive Designs. Analyzing structural inequities gives us clues as to where to best intervene in the system in order to catalyze systemic change. We get to do this difficult yet rewarding work together—with our Learning Buddies, Accomplices, and various project collaborators.

Journal: *Write down your response to the question, Why does an Analysis of race and class matter for regenerative design projects?*

EXERCISE 32: Analyzing Structural Oppression

This exercise is adapted from an exercise used in the Undoing Racism Organizing Collective (UROC) training. Here is how I've adapted it in the Social Permaculture for Food Justice course I teach at the University of Massachusetts-Amherst.

Take a moment to revisit your Holistic Context and Holistic Goals. Then complete two iterations of this exercise for two of the scales you're working on:

Scale 1. The larger social system(s) your project aims to shift

Scale 2. The organization(s), institution(s), or community(ies) in which your project is nested

DESIGN LAB ➡ *Journal:* *For scale 1, first make Observations about how the social system(s) in your* ***Systems Context treats, exploits, and/or denies access to BIPOC and/or poor people.*** *Can you see how system conditions replicate dynamics of domination/subordination? How are your answers connected to the 4 P's—People, Place, Power, and Paradigm—that you identified in the Context phase?*

Answer the same questions for Scale 2, this time focusing on how the organization, institution, and/or community in your ***Group Context treats, exploits, and/or denies access to BIPOC and/or poor people.*** *Again, how are your answers at this scale connected to the 4 P's you identified in the Holistic Context?*

Finally, zoom out and create a Summary Synthesis of both scales of systems. It is prudent to consider both:

- *the treatment of BIPOC and/or poor people who work in the system*
- *the treatment of BIPOC and/or poor people who are recipients of the system*

(To gain more insight if you are not a Black, Indigenous, or Person of Color, ask a friend who is BIPOC what experiences they've had with these systems and organizations, etc. Likewise, if you are not a poor person or were not raised poor, ask a friend who is poor what their perspective is on these Contexts. We may not be able to see forms of structural oppression if we benefit from them and/or are not directly impacted by them. Listening to another's perspective, a guiding direction from dismantling our mental boxes in chapter 2, is one way to make visible the lens of our own perceptions and may reveal important pieces we may have missed.)

Once you have considered these systems as wholes, see if you can list the primary elements of each system, like we did with the global food system. Then generate Observations for elements you choose to analyze, based on your Goals.

The example on the next page analyzes structural oppression of key elements (particularly in the US) of the global food system (scale 1): cultivation, processing, distribution, and waste management. You can choose to review this example before generating your own race and class Analysis or you can review this example afterwards to glean ideas.

EXERCISE 32: Cont.

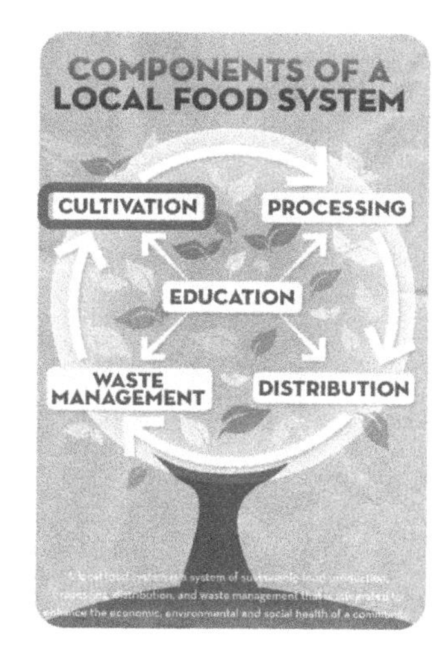

Cultivation

- *Land theft from Indigenous Peoples, followed by displacement and/or slavery, in Turtle Island/the Americas by European colonizers for farming and grazing*
- *Slavery and deportation of Indigenous Africans for Europe's and its colonies' labor needs, orchestrated by white slave traders; farm slavery continuation in the form of sharecropping and convict leasing*
- *Discriminatory practices of the USDA toward farmers of Color regarding loan acquisition and disaster aid;[3] mass decline in Black-owned farms*
- *Low wages and bad working conditions for farm workers in the US—more than one million men and women, mainly from Mexico, Central America, and West Indian villages[4]*

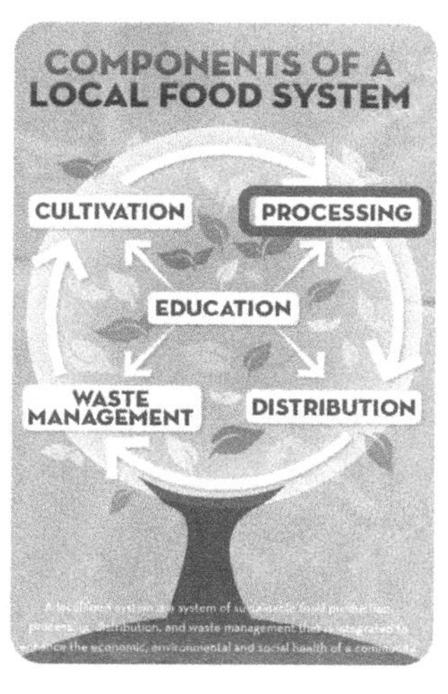

Processing

- *Food processing plants employ a majority of non-white immigrant labor and Black workers in low-wage jobs*
- *Meatpacking (predominantly staffed by immigrants of Color) is one of the most dangerous jobs in the US. The meatpacking industry has the highest rates of injury and illness of any manufacturing job[5]*

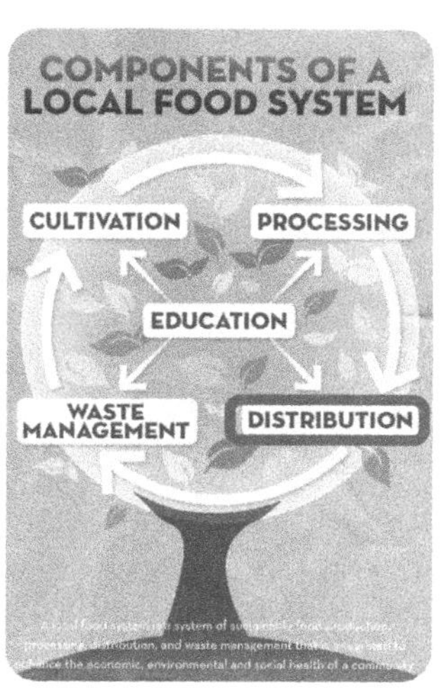

Distribution

- *The average grocery store is smaller in poor neighborhoods, and many of the products sold there are more expensive than in white, middle- and high-income neighborhoods[6]*
- *"Food redlining" is a common practice, in which supermarkets avoid opening stores in low-income urban communities, which are often predominantly inhabited by Black, Indigenous, and People of Color[7]*
- *In poor rural areas, unless a family has access to farm produce and season extension, then convenience stores are typically the only food options*
- *Diabetes and obesity are disproportionately high among BIPOC (only 7% for white people, versus 12% for Black and Latinx people and 15% for American Indians[8])—in part a result of lack of access to fresh foods*

Continued on next page

EXERCISE 32: Cont.

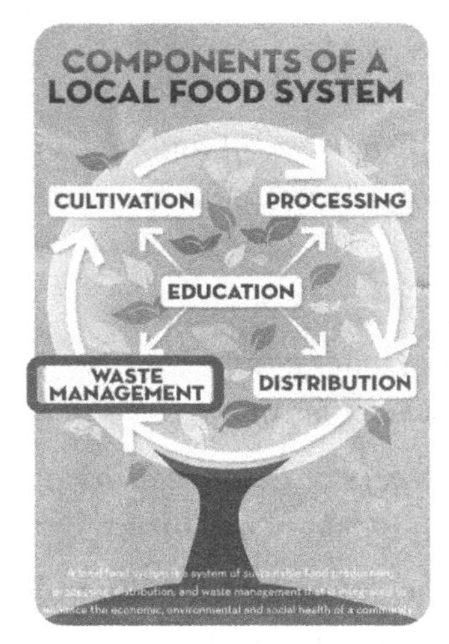

Credit: *Feed Northampton Food Security Plan*

Waste Management

- *Landfills and sewage treatment plants are often located in poor communities of Color*[9]
- *Methane emissions—partly caused by the anaerobic digestion of organic waste in landfills—contribute to climate change. BIPOC communities are on the frontlines of climate disruptions*[10]
- *In the Global South and elsewhere, it's often BIPOC and poor people who sift through household and corporate waste for items that can be reused or recycled; this dangerous work is one of the few ways for many to earn money*

Summary Synthesis *of structural oppression in the global food system: Workers in BIPOC and poor communities are adversely affected and targeted by an exploitative food system that is designed to serve white elite profiteers.*

Valuing Non-Financial Forms of Wealth

Through a permaculture perspective, we can see that capitalism, a system that solely values Financial Wealth, is not much different from a monoculture or plantation, where only one crop is valued and cultivated in a large swath of land. Monoculture-based agriculture and a monocultural economic system run counter to the intelligent diversity and redundancy of ecosystems. A monoculture mentality has detrimental effects, leaving both our food system and our financial system vulnerable to disturbances.

a limited, exploitative, and vulnerable financial system

a democratic, pluralistic, and regenerative economy, based on reciprocal relationships

The economy, run by banks and defended by tanks, has only one valued form of wealth: financial capital. To continue with the metaphor of agriculture, regeneration of depleted land happens only through diversifying plant, bacterial, and fungal communities. Similarly, we can regenerate our financial systems by valuing resilient *polycultures of wealth*, and reject exploitative *monoculture of money* models focused solely on financial capital. The Justice and Ecology project from Movement Generation, an eco-social justice organization based in Oakland, CA, offers an excellent strategic framework booklet on this topic, entitled "From Banks and Tanks to Cooperation and Caring: A Strategic Framework for a Just Transition."

The perceived and often real need to earn increasing amounts of money to survive in a capitalist society can create difficult choices for changemakers. Sometimes, it seems as if our eco-social Purposes are in conflict with our personal survival. Transitioning away from a solely money-based economy can be a subversive, empowering, and difficult act of cultural regeneration. At the same time, we can acknowledge that the current trade system is based on financial capital and that we still need money for many reasons. With this acceptance, we can begin to move our money around to develop additional systems. For example, we can invest our money in land, work less to invest time in our mutually supportive relationships, or exchange money for skills, training, or experiences. It is sobering to realize we can't eat gold to nurture us in times of sickness or rely on our investments to protect us during a long stock market collapse.

Shifting our perception of wealth can liberate our minds from compulsively thinking about our value being based on volatile and vulnerable financial earnings and savings. A true understanding of security arises from beyond the conditioning of *upward mobility*. "Your network is equal to your net worth," a common adage in the business world, attributed to white author and business executive Tim Sanders.

Perhaps you are already engaging in solidarity economics, enacted through non-exploitative ways of trading value. If so, see how you can apply design thinking to diversifying and reinforcing these systems. If these practices are new to you, then let your creativity be unleashed in this new landscape! Take account of all the ways you are rich, including areas of value that you had not yet considered as wealth. Or try conducting transactions in forms of wealth other than money, and see how economics change. Valuing multiple forms of wealth, at least as highly as we value money, is another tool for changemakers in building a more just, ethical, and ecological economy.

The Eight Forms of Capital and Eight Forms of Currency frameworks provide a map of different types of capital and wealth, expanding our view of capital from only financial capital to a diversity of forms. Ethan Roland and Gregory Landua, my friends and colleagues who lead financial permaculture workshops and wrote the book *Regenerative Enterprise*, developed these frameworks. This diagram shows their original thinking and language, and it comes directly from the Regenerative Enterprise Institute.

CAPITAL	CURRENCY	COMPLEXING TO...
Social Capital	Connections	Influence, relationships
Material Capital	Materials; "natural" resources	Tools, building, infrastructure
Financial Capital	Money	Financial instruments & securities
Living Capital	Carbon, Nitrogen, Water	Soil, living organisms, land, ecosystem services
Intellectual Capital	Ideas, Knowledge	Words, images, "intellectual property"
Experiential Capital	Action	Embodied experience, wisdom
Spiritual Capital	Prayer, Intention; Faith, Karma	Spiritual attainment
Cultural Capital	Song, Story, Ritual	Community

Credit: Regenerative Enterprise Institute

EIGHT FORMS OF CURRENCY

I choose to modify their language, changing "capital" to "wealth." I make this distinction for two important reasons. When we view spiritual customs or living beings, for instance, as capital, we can easily repeat our conditioning to commodify these precious facets of life. This unintended outcome ends up reinforcing the same capitalist Paradigm we want to evolve. Secondly, capital connotes ownership: we focus on *whose* capital or investment. Rather than viewing a spiritual practice as intellectual property, for instance, or seeing livestock as our private stock, can we see ourselves as wealthy because we are in reciprocal relationship with these gifts? Can we see the wealth in relationships where we honor the ancestors who bestowed spiritual customs to us or praise the animals by raising them with humane care, and in turn, they nourish us?

In a similar vein, Cultural Wealth can't be bought. We can only can participate in the growth of it; it is not a product. This form of wealth is one of the only forms that cannot be gained on one's own; it requires community to generate this collectively held richness. It is both rare and undervalued in Westernized countries, and it is threatened in rapidly modernizing places.

I've also modified Roland and Landua's framework by adding an additional form of wealth, Temporal Wealth. Incorporating this form of wealth acknowledges that surplus time, time available beyond income-producing work hours, can be an *Asset* or a *Void*. Temporal Wealth frees up possibilities for how individuals choose to invest it. For some, having extra time to spend developing other forms of wealth is scarce. Economic constraints limit the Temporal Wealth of poor and working-class people who often work two or three jobs to make ends meet. When we fail to acknowledge this precious resource, we make assumptions that people can easily invest in other forms of wealth beyond their necessities for survival.

The related exercise, Polyculture of Wealth Analysis Tool, leads you through this Analysis for your project. In thinking about designing your own life, you can map and analyze forms of wealth with the focus on Zone 00. Through the lens of personal Goals, this exercise can reveal where to invest, exchange, and withdraw forms of wealth to increase resilience in your personal resources.

EXERCISE 33: Polyculture of Wealth Analysis Tool

This tool helps social designers analyze the forms of wealth that are in abundance and that are lacking in the conditions that surround a project.

Step 1. Please look over this diagram and the examples given for each form of wealth. Are there other examples you'd like to add? Then proceed to the next steps.

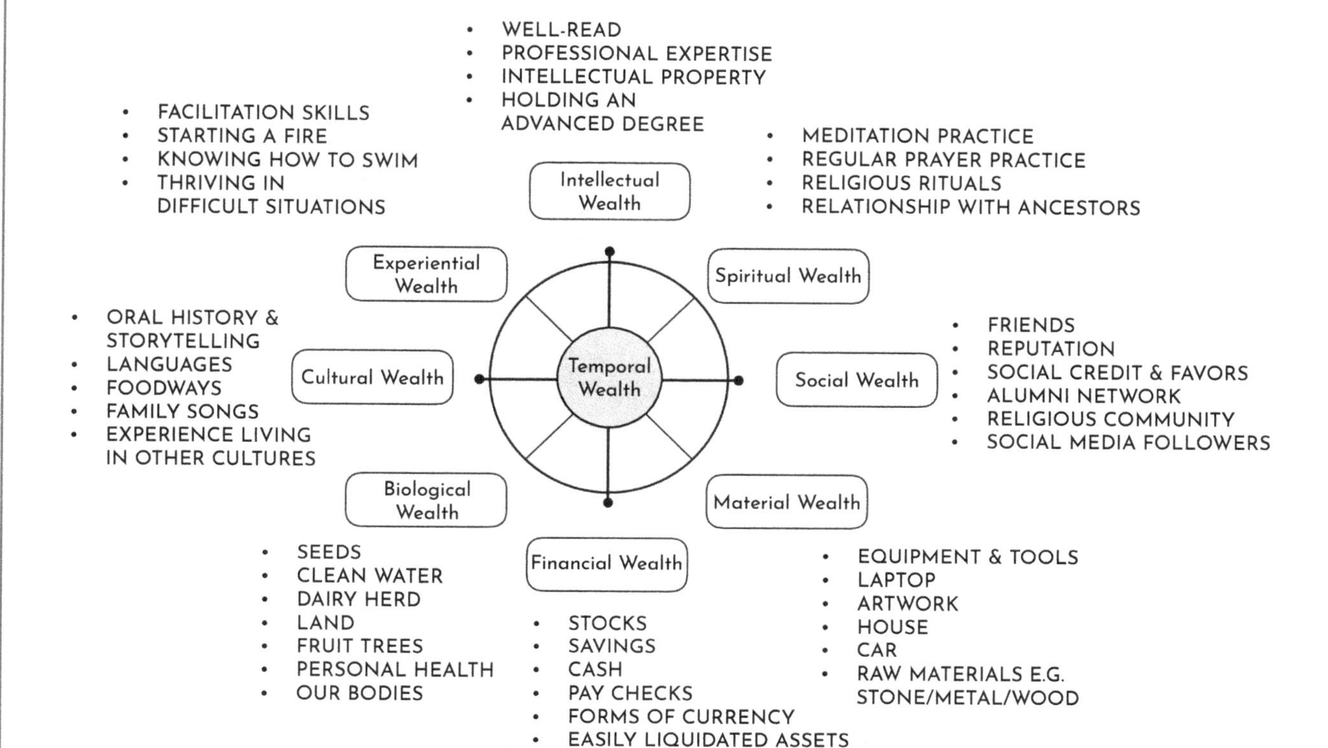

EXAMPLE FORMS OF WEALTH

Credit: graphic and examples from Abrah Dresdale; concept from Regenerative Enterprise

Step 2. If you are working on a new project, create a list of Assets (the existing forms of wealth that your project has access to) and a list of Voids (forms of wealth that your project lacks) under each of the wealth categories on the following page. These lists should be generated based on your project Goals. For an urban food justice project, for instance, you may list a toolshed as a Void in Material Wealth. For Assets, you might list community members who know how to grow traditional foods. If you are redesigning an established project, you can list Assets and Voids for the project as it stands currently. Please list at least five Assets and five Voids for each form of wealth.

Note: Though it may be tempting to use this tool to illustrate the forms of wealth you hope your project will yield after you design it, remain in the Analysis phase and focus on existing conditions.

Continued on next page

EXERCISE 33: Cont.

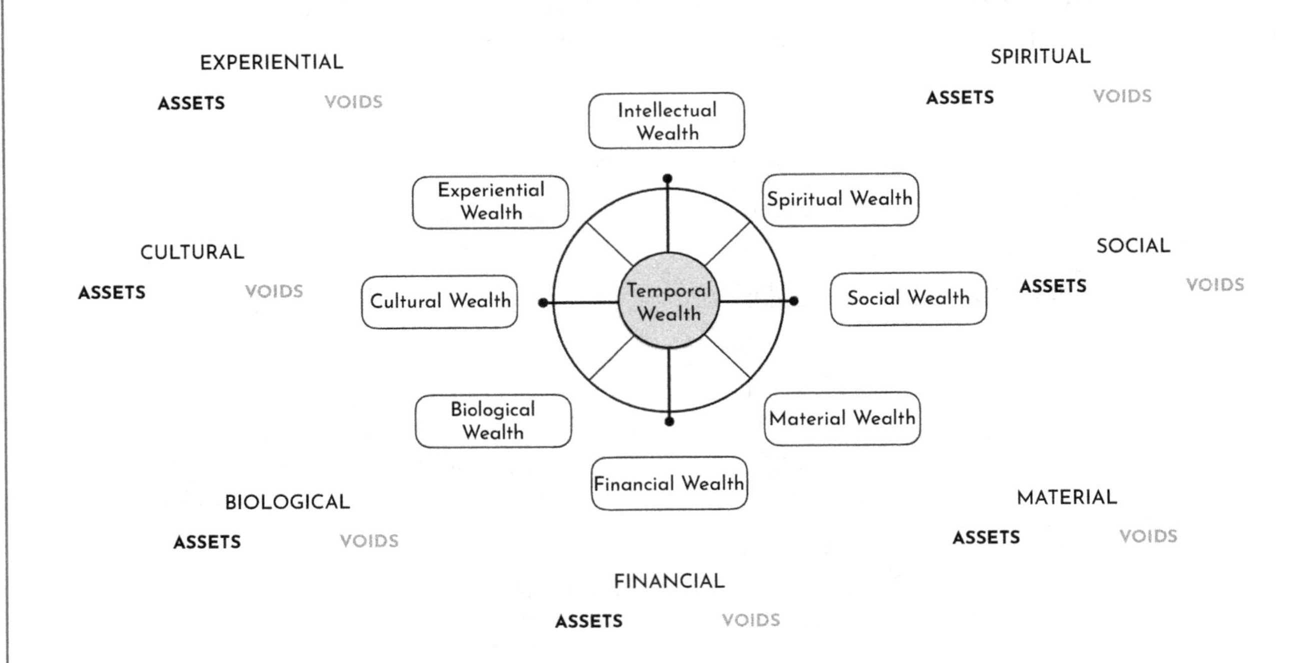

ASSETS AND VOIDS ANALYSIS

Credit: graphic and examples to Abrah Dresdale; concept from Regenerative Enterprise Institute

Step 3. When you have listed the Assets and Voids, shade in each corresponding wedge of the next pie chart to create a visual Analysis. Shade in the wedges proportionally based on your Assessment of the wealth of each form. Shade in 100% of a wedge for a form of wealth in which the project conditions are very rich. Shade in only 10% or 20% of a wedge that has many voids, and so forth.

Start shading in each wedge at the center, working out toward the circle's edge. Shade the inner Temporal Wealth ring darker or lighter, depending on your Assessment of how much time free time the people involved in the project have collectively.

When you finish, take a step back and observe the pattern.

EXERCISE 33: Cont.

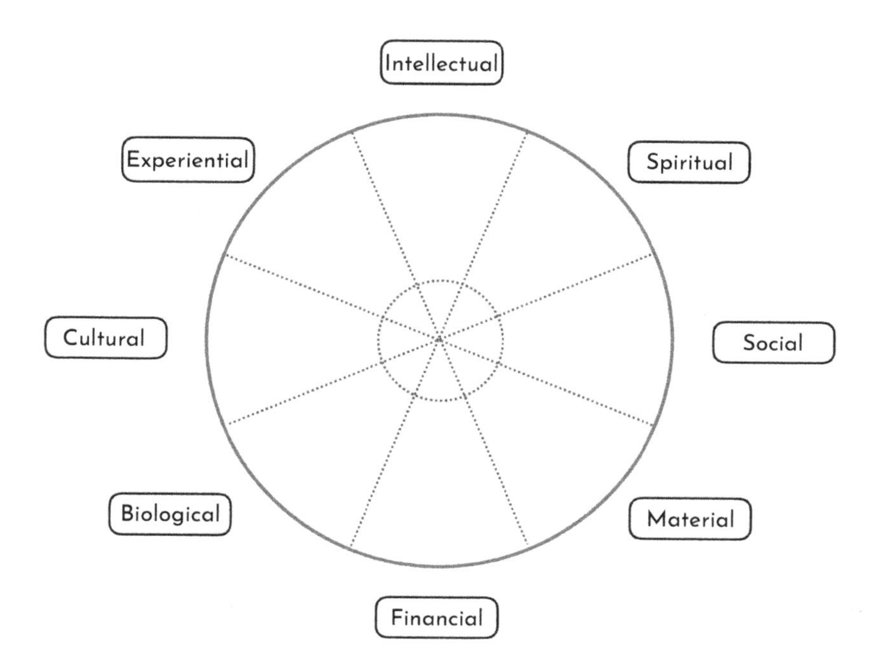

POLYCULTURE OF WEALTH VISUAL ANALYSIS

Journal: *Please respond to these Analysis and Assessment questions:*

- *Can you observe diverse resources as a polyculture of wealth now rather than a monoculture of money, an economic worldview that comes from a monoculture mentality? How has your Interpretation of wealth and capital shifted for you personally? For your orientation to your project?*
- *Which forms of wealth is your project strongest in? Weakest in? How is Temporal Wealth related to your answers? What did you learn about its availability that you had not realized before?*
- *How you might exchange wealth in one area for growing forms of wealth in other areas? For example, can your project use its Assets in Experiential Wealth to grow forms of Financial Wealth by offering workshops? Or can your project call on the network of its founders, part of its Social Wealth, to attain a rent-free lease on land, a form of Biological Wealth, that your project lacks?*
- *What Assets do project partners or other groups in your network have that could help your project achieve its Goals? What do these individuals or groups lack that your project can offer to them in exchange?*
- *Lastly, revisit the reflexive questions from the beginning of the chapter: What are my dominant habits and worldviews? And how might they impact the process of creating this Analysis for my project?*

EXERCISE 34: Pre-Mortem List

Balancing hopeful vision with grounded pragmatism is a fine line to walk. The permaculture principle of edge effect reminds us that this area is the most fertile soil for growth. Our project growth is sustainable when we can realistically acknowledge constraints and prepare ways to adaptively respond to them, grounding our plans with a Pre-Mortem List.

Reflection and Integration: Please take at least five minutes to reflect on all of the design outputs of your project so far: Context, Goals, Analysis and Assessment. [Note: You may want to complete Exercise 35 Analysis and Assessment Synthesis before you create your pre-mortem list.] Once you can clearly image these dynamic and related pieces of the design process, take out your magnifying glass, so to speak...

Journal: *Make a list of all the places where you can see weaknesses in the project. Where might it fail, and what would be the cause(s)? Think about your understanding of oppression and internalized oppression. Is there a way that unconscious classism, for instance, is constraining the types of outreach and marketing channels I plan to use for publicity? Will internalized oppression keep me from taking risks and making the project vibrant and visible?*

Consider the various forms of wealth. You might ask yourself: Are my time constraints (Temporal Wealth) going to limit the quality of what I can offer the project? Is my network (Social Wealth) not well developed, restricting the project's reach?

Once you create a Pre-Mortem List, then incorporate this material into your design thinking in the next chapter. You may want to go back through your Analyses and Assessments with these new insights, and represent them there, as well.

EXERCISE 35: Analysis and Assessment Synthesis

After reading this chapter and completing the exercises, complete the following Analysis and Assessment Design Lab Outputs.

DESIGN LAB ➡ For your project, choose and create a minimum of four kinds of Analyses (from the list of adapted Zone 00 Analysis tools, on page 146, and the additional exercises presented in this chapter). These Analyses can include analytical diagrams, drawings, and/or writing. For each kind of Analysis, generate:

- Three to five Observations (the "What?": What patterns do you objectively observe?)
- A minimum of three Interpretations for each Observation (the "So what?": What is the impact of the patterns and how are they relevant to the project Purpose and Goals?)

Remember to include a bullet before each Observation and a small arrow before each Interpretation (see Sample Observations and Interpretations on page 151).

DESIGN LAB ➡ Once you have completed your Analyses and Assessments, zoom out and review all of them together. Look at the whole picture: what is the overall pattern language, the contours and general trends of what you have uncovered?

In one or two sentences, write a Summary Synthesis of your Analysis and Assessment (see sample on page 156). This synthesis helps us practice the Reflection and Integration touchstone of the design process.

From this synthesis create a list of at least five Opportunities and at least five Constraints related to your project Goals. These should be short sentences or bullets.

Please see Further Reading related to chapter 10 on page 247.

Social Design Lexicon for Chapter 10

Review the following key terms and write down what they mean to you. Then, reflect on how each of these concepts relates to your Analyses and Assessments.

Existing Conditions:

Observations:

Interpretations:

Opportunities:

Constraints:

Personal Filters:

Polycultural Approach vs. Monocultural Approach:

The Beach:

Mind Map:

Elements and Relationships:

Pattern Language:

Polyculture of Wealth vs. Monoculture of Money:

Upward Mobility:

Assets & Voids:

CHAPTER 11: SOCIAL DESIGN CONSCIOUSLY WEDDING GOALS TO ANALYSIS

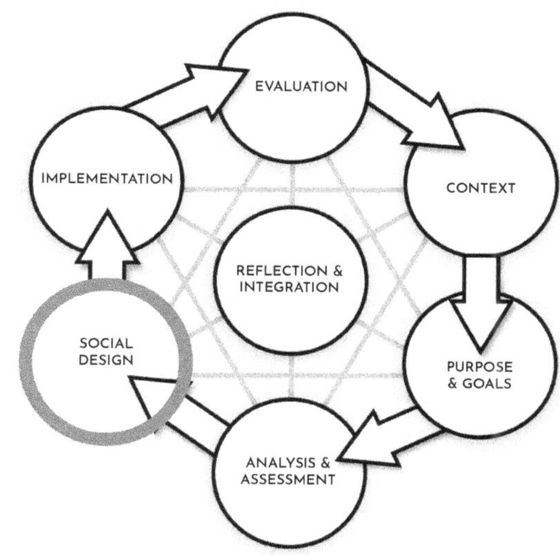

All humans are inherently designers. By our very nature, we are creative beings. We can generate infinite solutions to any one problem. The Regenerative Design Process provides a structure with which designers can create elegant and capacious solutions that respond holistically to a number of problems simultaneously.

In permaculture, we approach "design" as a verb, not as a noun. "To design" something is an imaginative living process. Alternately, "the design," when used viewed as a noun, reduces design down to a static product, a thing that can be easily mass produced or commodified. The living approach to design used in this book reflects a Paradigm of *solution emergence*, whereby innovative responses reflect the unique conditions of each project. This Paradigm stands in contrast to the that of *mechanized production*, often disguised as "best practices," which can result in formulaic solutions and cookie-cutter outcomes. These predetermined "solutions" generally end up rehearsing the same patterns of degradation and mindless hurt we aim to transform. Additionally, in this book's particular approach to regenerative design, emphasis is placed on the creativity of the changemaker, the designer, because designers are integral to the process of Social Design, not anonymous workers, separate from their creations.

My friend Alixa Garcia, cultural creative from Climbing PoeTree, eloquently echoed this point on the *Laura Flanders Show*:

> I don't believe in revolutions, I believe in solutions. This is a *solutionary* time, and we need solutionaries to come to the front. Revolutions tend to revolve the door of hurt. When those at the bottom try to neutralize the violence inflicted by those on top, historically speaking, these efforts tend to be violent ones...Hurt people hurt people. Yet, this is a critical time when we really need healed people to heal people and creativity does that, solutions do that. So how do we create a platform of imagination to really propel us forward? (comment amended by Alixa Garcia, July 13, 2018)

In response to Garcia's poignant question, regenerative design may be one of those *platforms of imagination* that serves as a catalyst for social transformation.

Design as an Iterative Process

The design process is an adaptive system that builds on itself over time. Developing a practice of inquiry and soliciting different ways of learning about a project's Context is fundamental. New information can change our original thinking about the Purpose. As the diagram of the design process illustrates, it is a nonlinear cycle. More accurately, the process resembles a spiral in motion, much like the unfurling of a flower bud or fiddlehead fern. We build our knowledge and insight as we traverse through several iterations, moving from a broad Design that is *conceptual* to one that is *schematic* or sketchy to a *detailed design* with specific recommendations.

Once we develop design ideas, it's important to travel around the spiral once again, reflecting further on the connection between your project's Goals and its social and ecological conditions. Each turn takes us to a higher level, affording us a better view and opportunity to integrate new information. As we do so, we can inquire: How well do our Design recommendations respond to the project Purpose and Goals, or do we want to evolve them? How can we hone the Design to better align with a holistic understanding of the Context? Does it address findings from the Analysis and Assessment of the project's conditions? How can it create a loop of reciprocity and nourish ourselves, the designers? We will revisit the current draft of project Goals and Purpose at the end of this chapter to see what may have shifted in the process.

Social Design Is Born

Regenerative designers are midwives; we attend to the crowning of a new creation. We deliver a living Social Design that is a product of a sacred marriage, a wedding of the Goals to the Analysis.

"Our goals guide the site analysis and assessment; the site analysis and assessment discovers the design," echoes Dave Jacke and Eric Toensmeier in *Edible Forest Gardens, Volume II.*

Jacke's advocacy of ecological design over ego-logical design is worth mentioning again here. In ecological design, designers deeply consider the Context—the social and ecological conditions of a project. Intrinsic to ecological design is thinking about the entire ecosystem. This means considering potential project Beneficiaries whose voices are not at the table and that often go unheard. Ego-logical design, in contrast, occurs when a lone wolf designer assumes a directorial role. They impose a design that comes from the isolated ego, without considering the Context or the social and ecological implications of implementing a Design in a vacuum.

Changemakers' Commitment to Regenerative Design and Paradigm Shifting

As changemakers, we commit to the rigor required to create Context-sensitive designs that are full of integrity. Our regenerative solutions have the power to transform current and historical legacies of domination and degradation in the communities and places where they are situated. We also commit to designing systems that are adaptive in the face of unpredictable future scenarios. This means including proactive innovations to climate chaos and its related crises (human displacement, resource scarcity, species extinction, etc.). Thinking about the future also means making our

Designs flexible, so that they can incorporate emergent strategies for social change as conditions shift over time. We cannot know what the future holds. As such, this nonlinear and adaptive design process will be an essential tool in our open-source library for collective liberation as we push forward to face unforeseen challenges.

When we aim to work on the level of cultural regeneration, we have the exquisite opportunity to shift the Paradigms of the larger social systems within which our projects are nested. Three dimensions of the Great Turning, according to Joanna Macy, are: holding actions; structural changes; and shifts in consciousness. She posits that all three dimensions are necessary for a just transition away from *late-stage capitalism* predicated on an exploitation Paradigm. What we are headed for is still in the imaginal realm. And in that liminal space, a Social Design tool box not only positions changemakers to create structural changes, i.e., solidarity economics or universal healthcare, but most critically we are positioned to design the third dimension—shifts in consciousness. When we set our sights on the widest horizon of Paradigm shifts and employ systematic design thinking there, we have the opportunity to influence all policies, practices, and organizing principles; everything snaps into alignment with an overarching Paradigm. As changemakers, we commit to true cultural regeneration at the source, at the paradigmatic level. Designing this third dimension of the Great Turning is necessary if we are to shift dominant patterns of global exploitation toward justice and planetary healing.

Guiding Principles for Social Design

Working with principles found in the natural world sets apart regenerative design from other manners of designing. Enacting these principles in our solutions, *and* in our process for arriving at those solutions, means that our designs are backed by the intelligent patterns expressed by this beautiful planet. Keen observers of the natural world have authored the following principles, which I hope will guide your change-making work.

The permaculture principles and their social examples (see introduction, page iii) derive from long, thoughtful observation of nature. They suggest how humans can mimic nature's patterns and processes in the design of landscapes, built environments, and social systems.

In the Introduction to Permaculture course that Lisa DePiano and I developed at the University of Massachusetts-Amherst, she explains that two of the core principles she works with in Design are *least change, greatest effect* and observe and interact. In one of her lectures, she shares that this second principle "echoes how I intend to engage in an initiative. We'll prioritize listening and getting to know the people and issues in a place, and sharing what we observe so we may determine how to be most effective." She continues to explain her design approach, "Once you understand the natural system of that community, its needs, assets, and organizing principles, you decide to lend your ideas and skills." She aims to observe and support what's already working well within an organization, institution, or community, and then develop Designs that build on its strengths—a slow and thoughtful eco-logical vs ego-logical design approach.

An effective Social Design contains a strategy for meeting its Goals. At the same time, it remains flexible enough to incorporate new properties that emerge beyond the pattern of the strategy. We refer to this approach as the *50/50 principle*. In curriculum planning for nature-based education, for example, this principle calls for planning 100% of a curriculum outline and anticipating that only about 50% of it will happen. This principle advises that we refrain from adhering too strictly to our "strategy." We need to expect and make space for emergent learning opportunities and unexpected needs that arise in the moment.

Social alchemy is part of our tagline at my organization Regenerate Change and a core principle with which we regularly work. Understanding the psychology and perspectives of the people in your project ecosystem (see Roles in the Project Ecosystem page 133) can provide great insight into the directions your Designs can take. Turning adversaries and gatekeepers into project champions can be done with careful social alchemy. Finding common ground between your project Goals and the underlying values of these key people can dissolve barriers to change. Building relationships and trust over time, which often come with practices of repeated reciprocity, humanizes us in others' eyes. Opponents' perspectives of us can shift; we once were pesky changemakers creating disruption but have become whole people who want the best for the wider community. Folks who assume roles of gatekeeper or oppressor are undoubtedly serving as middle agents and enacting the will of the larger power structures at the expense of their own humanity. Through personalized attention, care, and trust-building, walls crumble and new alliances form in service to the highest good. From the work of Systemic Constellations, I've learned that, ultimately, the larger system is always seeking energetic balance, and if you can illuminate ways to restore that balance, the elements of that system will follow you.

Additional principles that can be helpful guideposts in Social Design include some of the *emergent principles* outlined by adrienne maree brown in *Emergent Strategy*. They include adaptation, interdependence, decentralization, resilience, and fractal awareness. All of these principles are patterns that repeat over and over again in nature:

- Animals adapt to their surroundings. Coyotes and crows are powerful beings who are adept in *adaptation*, surviving in rural to urban regions and everywhere in between.
- Lichens are a true symbiotic expression of *interdependence* between algae and fungus.
- Squirrels spread their buried caches of nuts in a *decentralized* pattern throughout a landscape, which brings more *resilience* to their stored food supply. At the same time, reciprocity is the outcome because squirrels store more than they can eat and plant the seeds of trees to come on behalf of the parent trees.
- *Fractal awareness* lets us see that fractals abound everywhere in nature, from fern fronds to watersheds. Their ability to transfer energy and information through the most efficient geometric forms means that the same geometry—an elegant synthesis of many factors—will be repeated across different scales.

How can you consciously incorporate one or more of these emergent principles into your design work? I find it helpful to choose three core principles and post them up around my work space to guide my design decisions. Which principles here, in addition to the ones given in the introduction, most resonate with you?

Identifying the Desired Function of Your Design

As you delve deeper into the Social Design phase, consider which of the three dimensions of the Great Turning you intend to influence. Making this decision centers around the underlying *function*—what result you're trying to achieve. Are you focused on designing a well-thought-out holding action, such as a campaign to resist gentrification or a direct action to protest a new pipeline? The underlying function here is to obstruct more harm from being done. Consider how this action can be in service to a larger Paradigm shift. Alternately, your focus might be designing a structural change, such as a community land trust or mutual aid network. In this case, the function is about creating alternatives to the status quo, new structures that engage enough people toward a tipping point where fringe endeavors become mainstream. Again, how can you link these structural changes to a shift in consciousness? Or, are you up for the head-on challenge of cultural regeneration, positioning your work to intentionally create a Paradigm shift in the systems that have impacted your community? For example, if your family members have experienced incarceration in prison, you might decide to work with others to create a shift in consciousness from the dominant Paradigm in the US of "security and retributive justice" towards "repair of harm and transformative justice."

Once you are clear about which dimension of the Great Turning you're working on, you can apply the Regenerative Design process to projects at any scale. It's effective at the personal scale to the scale of organizations and institutions and even to larger national or global systems.

The Shift from Analysis and Assessment: Design Directions

It's common for both green and well-seasoned designers to linger awhile in the Analysis and Assessment phase of the design process. Often referred to as *analysis paralysis*, it can be tempting to dig deeper and deeper into the details of a project's ecosystems. Design Directions help us make a faith-full leap onward to the Social Design phase in the process.

In review, we identify the Context, and make analytical Observations and Interpretations about it through the lens of the Goals. Observations are things we can objectively observe with our senses, answering the question of "What?" Interpretations are the Assessments that our mental filters determine from our Observations, and they answer the question of "So what?" The last question in this threefold progression that moves us into Design is: "Now What?" Answering this question yields Design Directions. We write Design Directions as imperative statements.

"WHAT?" ⟶ "SO WHAT?" ⟶ "NOW WHAT?"
(Observations) (Interpretations) (Design Directions)

Design Directions do not prescribe the specific *form* the Social Design will take. Form, as used here, describes how exactly the Goals will be reached or which permutation the designer will choose. Rather, Design Directions point to the underlying functions (broadly speaking: holding actions, structural changes, and/or shifts in consciousness) that are needed, essential services or roles necessary to meet the Goals and respond to the Context without prescribing the form. We begin working with the form of the Design once we conceive of Design Alternatives, different ways of meeting the essential functions, before committing to a final Design.

Recalling the example of Goals from the Franklin County Jail in chapter 9—a project aimed at structural changes—we continue here with example Analysis, Assessment, and Design Directions. (Notice the omission of the terms "inmates," "criminals," or "prisoners." These are dehumanizing terms that whittle down full people, citizens having an experience of incarceration, into individuals who have a single, disparaging identity.)

Here we will focus on only two of the four Goals from the program in order to simplify:

Goal 1: The program engages incarcerated individuals in a variety of vocational skills-building experiences relevant to the regional economy.

Goal 4: Community mentors volunteer to teach incarcerated students, reducing recidivism rates by building pro-social networks to support their reentry.

"What?" (Analysis/Observations—complete sentences with subject and verb)

- Unemployment and job scarcity in the region have increased since factories closed down.
- The Franklin County Jail has a 45% recidivism rate.
- The jail is in a rural, agricultural region of Massachusetts with a burgeoning local food system.
- There is a culture of volunteerism and strong movement for social justice in the region.

"So What?" (Assessment/Interpretations—complete sentences with subject and verb)

→ A lack of economic opportunity leads people to pursue illegal means of acquiring money.

→ Arrest and incarceration rates would likely decrease if there were more job opportunities.

→ There will be increasing employment in food systems work and increased need for agricultural technical assistance for farmers as the local food movement grows.

→ Food justice advocates and non-profit farm organizations may be interested in developing relationships with and leading workshops for jail residents.

Here we are at the tipping point, moving to the Social Design phase in the design process. Remember, the Design Directions emerge from marrying the Goals to the Analysis and Assessment! With this in mind, please read on...

"Now What?" (Shift to Design/Design Directions—imperative sentences)

- Provide incarcerated participants training in agricultural sectors that are growing in the region: organic farming, greenhouse management, food processing, and commercial composting.
- Develop a clear pathway for job placement and entrepreneurship opportunities in farm and food systems as part of people's reentry plans.
- Invite key advocates, educators, and leaders from the farm and food justice community to visit the jail and lead workshops inside. Explain to these prospective mentors the many benefits of making these connections inside the walls.
- Incorporate these organizations and mentors into the reentry plans of program graduates.
- Develop ways to tell the story of this project so that people on the inside and outside will want to become involved, making the system more resilient and well-resourced so that there is program continuity if project champions leave.

EXERCISE 36: Generating Design Directions

Take a moment to review two of the Design Lab outputs you've created thus far. Refer back to your Goals from Exercise 30: Holistic Goals Articulation on page 130) and the Observations, Interpretations, and the Summary Synthesis you generated in Exercise 35: Analysis and Assessment Synthesis.

DESIGN LAB ➡ Then, develop at least three Design Directions coming out of each Analysis tool you chose (a minimum of four tools the first time you go through the Social Design Lab). Remember, Design Directions point to underlying functions that move the project toward how it can best achieve its Goals. (If you're struggling with what is a "function," you can look at the list of example functions in the Key Elements and Essential Functions section later in the chapter on page 175). Recall that we write Design Directions as imperative statements that provide a general rather than specific direction for the Social Design. Wait until we arrive at the Design Alternatives to get into the details of the "How?"

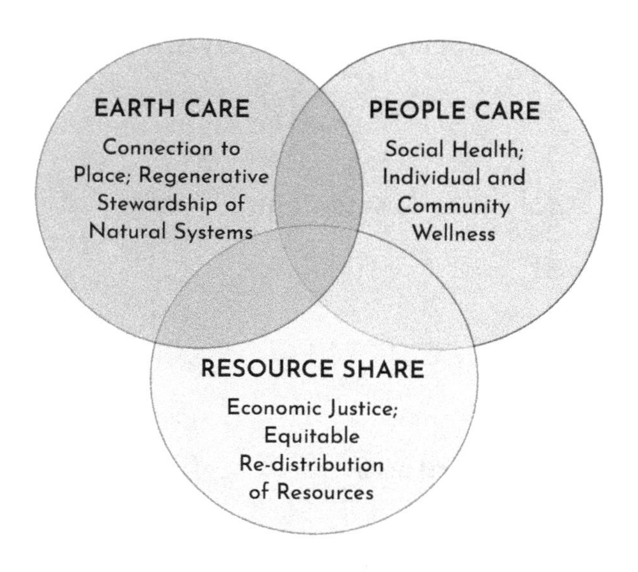

PERMACULTURE ETHICS

As you generate Design Directions, revisit the three permaculture ethics of Earth Care, People Care, and Resource Share. See if you can cover all ethics in how you conceive of your Design Directions. A powerful (mixed) metaphor for this moment in the design process is to intentionally plan when we are still high up in the watershed, rather than scrambling to create ethical outcomes or end of the tailpipe solutions once we've begun a project's Implementation.

Design Alternatives and Design Criteria

In joining our analytical minds with our deep intuitive listening, we act as midwives in birthing a Design. This phase involves two key instruments, so to speak: *Design Alternatives* and *Design Criteria*. They help us to make concrete yet flexible Design recommendations. We create Alternatives before we settle on detailed Design recommendations. Alternatives are often schematic or sketchy, and they loosely imagine different possibilities of how to realize the project Purpose achieve project Goals. They are the fourth and final extension of the "What?", "So what?", and "Now what?" progression.

"WHAT?" ⟶	"SO WHAT?" ⟶	"NOW WHAT?" ⟶	"HOW??"
(Observations)	(Interpretations)	(Design Directions)	(Design Alternatives)

It can be extremely useful to create several Design Alternatives. There is power in not getting attached to one single idea. Coming up with Alternatives is beneficial by slowing down the process of solution emergence and making space to consider multiple angles. In doing so, emergent properties and new combinations that are greater than the sum of their parts can arise.

> ***Emergence is the way complex systems and patterns arise out of a multiplicity of relatively simple interactions.***
>
> – Nick Obolensky, *Complex Adaptive Leadership*

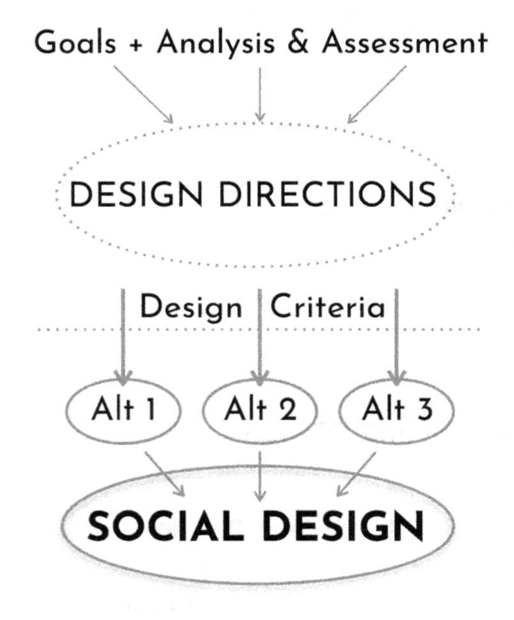

FLOW DIAGRAM FOR SOCIAL DESIGN

Design Criteria serve as a filter, shaping the specific forms that the Alternatives will take. Criteria, derived from project Goals, turn schematic ideas into feasible and detailed Designs. Rather than trying to design on a blank canvas, Criteria provide us with welcome boundaries for creating Alternatives.

Each criterion (a single criteria) should be specific and measurable. They can be either quantitative (in quantity/numbers) or qualitative (in quality, usually through general Observations or stories). In both cases, Criteria help designers set thresholds to determine if a specific Goal has been met.

As we design the project Evaluation, we can create ways to measure how successful we have been in meeting our Design Criteria. Are our Designs functioning as we had intended? Each time we make design decisions, we can pause for a short Evaluation, holding our decisions up to the Goals and Analysis and Assessment to see if they are responsive and relevant.

This part can be confusing, so let me give you an example of moving from a Design Direction to Criteria to creating Alternatives.

Example of Design Direction: Develop a clear pathway for farm and food systems job placement and entrepreneurship opportunities as part of people's reentry plans.

Example of Design Criteria: Create accessible reentry pathways available for men being released from all three units at the jail: Medium Security, Minimum Security, and Kimball Re-entry House.

Examples of Design Alternatives:

- Developing different approaches to educational programming for incarcerated participants; each Design Alternative could emphasize a different set of topics or content, pedagogical approaches, desired learning outcomes, and/or educational partners, etc.
- Creating a plan for reparations for those who have been wrongfully convicted; one Alternative could focus on economic reparation in the form of farm credit, another on land reparation, a third on investment strategies to support start-up businesses of those wrongfully convicted; a fourth Alternative could recommend a hybrid of these forms of reparations.

- Proposing policy recommendations that increase job placement and entrepreneurship opportunities; each Design Alternative could focus uniquely on the local, state, or federal level, or a customized combination of these for different Alternative Designs.

For each Alternative, the next step would be to create a list of respective *Benefits* and *Drawbacks* so that we can compare them against each other and ultimately decide on a final Design. How well does each function in terms of meeting the Goals and responding regeneratively to the Context? Are they equally viable? You may decide to take the "best of" each Alternative and create a composite Social Design. Or, you may choose one of the Alternatives for the stand-alone final Design if you deem it to be the most elegant solution after comparing its Benefits and Drawbacks to those of the other Alternatives.

EXERCISE 37: Creating Design Criteria

DESIGN LAB ➡ Return to your Holistic Goals (see page 140) for yourself, a group(s), and a larger social system(s). Then, create Design Criteria that are measurable, either qualitatively or quantitatively, for each of the three levels of Goals. Below are guiding questions to help you.

Journal: *Write down your responses to the following questions. When you've completed your responses, see if you can produce concise Criteria based on what you've written. The approaches for how you measure these things will be developed in chapter 13 on Evaluation. Here you are just identifying what you want to measure in order to know whether you've achieved specific thresholds articulated in your Goals. These outcomes can be measured through numbers, other indicators you can observe, or people's stories and narrative feedback.*

Yourself/Designer *– what measurable or observable indicator(s) can you identify to know if you:*

- *are feeling the way you want to feel through the realization of this project?*
- *are invoking the qualities you articulated in your Goals?*
- *have developed the new capacities you set your sights on?*

Organizations/Institutions/Communities *– what dimensions or outcomes will you want to measure in order to understand the:*

- *project's effect on and value for its Beneficiaries?*
- *impact of your project on the institution(s), organization(s) and/or community(ies) it is designed to influence?*
- *level of systems change your project has had within its group setting?*

Larger Social System *– clearly state what the following will look like:*

- *what shift will occur in a larger social system(s) as a result of your project?*
- *has this shift been transformational and regenerative?*

After you create the Design Criteria, use them as filters to develop and inform your Design Alternatives. Your recommendations in the final Social Design should reflect the Criteria you establish here.

Approaches to Developing Design Alternatives

Creating Design Alternatives is a great exercise in mental elasticity. Generating numerous solutions to one set of problems keeps our design thinking loose and open, and it forces us not to latch onto the first solution that arises in our minds or that others suggest to us. While it can be a laborious process to develop several Alternatives, it is well worth it! Setting a fixed amount of time to generate each Alternative keeps the ball rolling.

The Permaculture Designer's Manual, written by permaculture co-founder Bill Mollison, suggests a few different approaches to generating Design Alternatives.

Design by Random Assembly: Perhaps the most accessible, this approach expands our thinking and removes the boxes that commonly restrict our creative channels. First, we brainstorm all of the elements involved in meeting the Goals of our project. We write each of them on pieces of paper that we can move around in random configurations. Then, we watch for new connections and possibilities to pop out as the randomness reveals creative new ways of designing the relationships among the elements. Later in this chapter, Exercise 38: Three Designs in 30 Minutes leads you through this approach.

Design by Analysis Overlays: Constraints guide this approach to designing Alternatives. Through Analysis and Assessment, we come to understand the Opportunities and Constraints of the existing conditions of a project. When we look at the Constraints all together in a Summary of the Analysis, it's relatively easy to see the contours of what is possible. For instance, if a community's biggest Constraints are its lack of Financial and Material Wealth, then designing systems that draw upon its assets of Social and Cultural Wealth will be imperative. At the same time, we can create systems of exchange where existing assets can be transferred into Material and Financial Wealth when needed.

Design by a Master Pattern: This approach centers tried-and-true strategies for a specific end. Rather than innovating anew for each Social Design project, there may be a strategy we can adapt for our project, a form of social architecture so to speak, that usually works because of its universality. For an example at the level of the individual, one master pattern is understanding the existing conditions of zones and sectors of a person's life. At the collective level, organizations that build strategic movements often use social movement theory as a master pattern. Momentum, for example, is a training institute and movement incubator in Boston, MA, that builds on the foundation of resistance movements led by Gandhi and Dr. King, and exemplified by the "color revolutions" of Eastern Europe and the Arab Spring. Movement Generation is another excellent example in Oakland, CA. They developed a resilience-based organizing model that serves as a master pattern that can be adapted to the needs of different communities. Note how this approach to design is context-sensitive and differs from the use of best practices or predetermined formulaic solutions.

Design by a Pattern Language: We can choose the most appropriate pattern language that speaks to the issues we're designing for. This approach is a bit of a matching game. When we're reviving a city center through urban planning, for instance, we can consult the various pattern languages from vibrant cities that have evolved over centuries. Christopher Alexander's books are wonderful resources for projects related to the built environment. When we're thinking about social landscapes, there are excellent pattern languages outlined in numerous books such as *Change Here Now* by my Regenerate Change colleague, Adam Brock (see chapter 11 Further Reading for more resources on the topic). Becoming literate in pattern languages, either through our own observations and/or by studying ones others have identified, will allow you to become relatively efficient in this approach to designing Alternatives.

Design for the Weakest Link: This strategy of sending resources to the element that could hold back the success of a project comes from the Holistic Management movement. Managing the areas with the most limiting resources frees up more energy. Understanding where bottlenecks occur and how to alleviate them can make everything flow better. Some challenges that a team of mine uncovered in the GARDEN (Growing Agricultural Resilience and Developing Economic Networks) Project illustrates this approach. Knowing that economic dependence and food security were two of the primary reasons women stayed with abusive partners, we had created a successful proposal for the Women's Fund of Western Massachusetts, in which Greenfield Community College would forge partnerships with local social service agencies that served women in transition out of domestic violence. The college received a multiyear grant to offer courses to women in service of the project's Purpose. However, a lack of childcare limited the participation of the intended Beneficiaries. Once we identified this weak link and devised a plan for childcare during classes, we were able to fill all of the seats. The health of the system was restored.

Key Elements and Essential Functions

Designing by Random Assembly is often seizing the *lowest hanging fruit*, or the easiest approach to use, for getting traction with Design Alternatives. One useful way to work with this approach is to identify *Key Elements* and *Essential Functions*. Key Elements are the things/key players/the concrete nouns related to your project. Essential Functions are the processes/actions/outcomes that your project is designed to fulfill. You can pull these components out of your Goals Articulation. You can also brainstorm other components that are not in the Goals that would help the project achieve its Purpose. Continue to update your lists of Key Elements and Essential Functions as you move through each iteration of design. Then you can assemble them in different arrangements to create Alternatives that bring about more refinement.

Two permaculture design principles introduced before, functional interconnection and multiple functions, are highly relevant to this approach to Social Design. How can you arrange Key Elements to have functional interconnection with each other, increasing the Design's overall resilience? For each Element, how can you identify its multiple functions and design for the conditions it needs to express them?

To illustrate this approach, we'll use an example of an eco-social design project at Greenfield Community College. Shortly after I was hired to develop their Farm and Food Systems program, a group of inspired students in my Introduction to Food Systems class approached me. They wanted guidance on how to engage the community and design their own campus permaculture garden. Over the next four years, a coalition of students, staff, faculty, and community members established this multifaceted project.

The Goals were to increase access to healthy food, provide educational opportunities, and enhance the aesthetics of the campus. Here is a list of Key Elements (the important things or players) for the campus permaculture garden:

KEY ELEMENTS

- students
- faculty
- staff
- community members
- permaculture club
- campus food pantry
- dining commons
- related academic courses
- toolshed
- micro-orchard
- multi-layered forest garden
- annual vegetable beds
- greenhouse
- compost system

The Essential Functions (the processes/actions or outcomes) of the project included:

ESSENTIAL FUNCTIONS

- education
- nutrition
- leadership development
- food security
- water catchment
- soil regeneration
- pollination
- beautification
- demonstration
- vocational skills building
- confidence-building
- community-building
- research opportunities
- habitat creation

From these lists, we generated random assemblies that revealed new combinations of ways the components could fit together. Exercise 38 outlines just how to do this!

EXERCISE 38: Three Designs in 30 Minutes

This exercise moves us from *Conceptual Design* to *Schematic Design*. It comes from the Regenerative Design for Changemakers training at Omega Institute, where Keith Zaltzberg-Drezdahl and I developed this approach to help students move from analysis paralysis towards designing on paper.

Supplies needed: two stacks of Post-its in two colors, several large pieces of paper, markers, and a timer.

Begin by brainstorming a list of all the Key Elements (the things/key players/the concrete nouns) related to your project on a scrap piece of paper. You can pull these elements out of your Goals (try circling them in one color, ideally the same color as one of the Post-its you will use). You can also brainstorm other Elements not found in the Goals that would help the project achieve its Purpose. Then, write each Key Element on a Post-it of the same color (you'll use as many Post-its as you have Elements).

Next, brainstorm a list of all the Essential Functions (the processes/actions/outcomes) on a scrap piece of paper. Begin by circling these in your Goals in a second color. Again, you may want to add other Functions to the brainstorm list that are not in the Goals. Then, write each Essential Function on an individual Post-it of the other color (you'll use as many Post-its as you have Functions).

Set your timer for 10 minutes. Arrange your Post-its into different random assemblies on a large piece of paper. Move them around until you find a Conceptual Design that feels robust. Your assembly can be in the form of a mind map (see page 148), a flow diagram (see example on page 172), or any other visual layout that makes sense to you.

Use your markers to draw lines on the background piece of paper to connect the Post-its, i.e., the Elements and Functions, in various ways. You can draw lines between the Post-its to show relationships. You can draw arrows to show directionality, such as the flow of inputs and outputs. You can draw dotted lines to show potential or conditional relationships among Elements, Functions, or both. Severed sections in lines can show tension or conflict in relationships. You can draw circles around a cluster of components to show groupings, etc. You can also color-code your lines, if you like, to indicate different categories of relationships such as programmatic, economic, culturally connective.

Make sure to include a legend or key that communicates which color Post-it is a Key Element and which is an Essential Function, and what your different line types symbolize so that someone viewing your random assembly could understand it without your verbal explanation.

Once the timer goes off (or you have one Design Alternative that feels solid), stop working on this first round. You can take a photo of it for later quick reference, or as a record if you need to reuse the same background paper. Move onto a clean sheet of paper (if you have many sheets of paper to play with). Complete this process of setting the timer for three different rounds of 10 minutes each and create different Alternatives!

Continued on next page

EXERCISE 38: Cont.

DESIGN LAB ➡ Create a minimum of three Design Alternatives with this process. See how flexibly your mind can think about the project. Give yourself 10 minutes to generate one Alternative. Once the timer goes off, switch gears and see if you can generate a different Alternative for the next 10 minutes. See how many you can come up with. When you feel complete, after three (or seven or fifteen!), begin to evaluate their Benefits and Drawbacks relative to the others. On the margins of your paper where you have made each Design, list at least five Benefits and five Drawbacks for that Alternative. You can use your journal to do this if you only had one piece of large paper.

Journal: *What Alternative feels right in your body and why? Which aspects of different Alternatives might you want to combine into a final Social Design? Or is there one Design that is already perfect and can become the guiding schematic for the detailed Design to emerge?*

Frameworks for Developing a Detailed Design

Thinking about how to share your Design recommendations with others is equally as important as the details of your Design. If we cannot communicate our vision to diverse audiences and individuals, then we will not succeed in our change-making initiatives. Written, spoken, and visual means of communication let you share your project with all types of learners and in various settings.

Carefully decide on one or more frameworks to illustrate how your Design will function once it's been implemented. Remember, choose frameworks that best convey your recommendations of how the Goals marry the Analysis. When presenting your project, be explicit about how your Design solution meets the Goals and responds to existing conditions.

Here is a list of frameworks introduced in section I by which you can structure your Social Design recommendations and communicate them visually.

- Depict the sought-after conditions for the various **Sectors** of your project once the Design has been implemented, and your recommendations for how to arrive at this ideal scene. You can choose the Sectors that make sense for your project, e.g., community relations or environmental stewardship or financial resilience, and draw out a project sector diagram and shade in the level of health each sector will have as a result of your design. (see page 42)
- Develop a detailed plan for how you will identify and implement **Minimum Daily, Weekly, Monthly, and Yearly Requirements for Thriving**. These requirements can be for the wellness of your organization, institution, or community, and/or for yourself. Observe overlaps between your personal requirements and project requirements, and design for potential synergies. Make a diagram to showcase these requirements. (see page 43)
- Create a plan to manage, grow, and exchange your project's **Polyculture of Wealth** based on the Goals and Constraints. Make a diagram that shows what new Assets will come about as a result of the Design recommendations. Observe how regenerating the project's wealth relates to your own Polyculture of Wealth. (see page 161)

- Design the project toward increased resilience by designing strategic partnerships with one or more organizations. If you assess that your project is ready for it, can the Design recommendations include joining an existing coalition? Or, can it take a leadership role in creating a new coalition, if there is mutual need, with several other organizations? One approach is to develop recommendations for how you can transform existing relationships into **Regenerative Relationships**. Describe the impact this transformation will have on your project, and how it ties into the Goals and Analysis. A diagram and description of the project's ideal **Zones of Relationships** and the quality and purpose of those relationships can be useful here, too. Observe the Social and Cultural Forms of Wealth of the project and how that informs the ideal scene for its relationships. (see pages 85 and 84, respectively)
- Design complementary **leadership roles** within an organization, institution, community, or specific project based on patterns in nature by using the **Four Directions** model and map out the roles visually in the East, South, West, and North directions. (see page 56)
- Apply **Organizational Design** thinking, see the next topic below...

All Designs, regardless of their content or focus, can be worked out in *Design Phases* if need be. Oftentimes due to various factors such as funding, time constraints, capacity constraints, and unknown variables, it makes sense to create distinct phases for project Implementation. It's good to be thinking about this option in the Social Design portion of the process, and we will revisit the idea of phases in more detail in the next chapter on Implementation.

Introduction to Organizational Design

Taking some time to consider the broad structure of an organization you are starting or one that you are current a member of is well worth the investment. Oftentimes we don't question the guiding principles or organizational structures that we are working within. Making these things intentional, based on the Purpose of the organization, is a powerful way to harness design thinking in service of systemic change.

The Open/Closed/Hierarchical/Flat framework is illuminating. Two axes create quadrants into which organizations can be categorized (see diagram on the next page). Mapping an organization onto this framework helps illuminate its current structure and opens up the question if it's the best option for the organization's Purpose or could the structure benefit from a redesign?

The vertical axis represents a spectrum from Open to Closed Systems. *Open Systems* include organizations, movements, and facilities that anyone can join or access. In contrast, *Closed Systems* have some requirement for entry, making it more or less exclusive to join. On the horizontal axis, there's a spectrum of Hierarchical to Flat Systems. *Hierarchical Systems* use chains of command, sometimes transparent and sometimes opaque, that are often related to who has the power in decision-making processes. In contrast, *Flat Systems* have shared governance and decision-making models. Within these, there can be distinctive roles or differing pay grades, but each person has equal weight in decisions that affect them and the whole group.

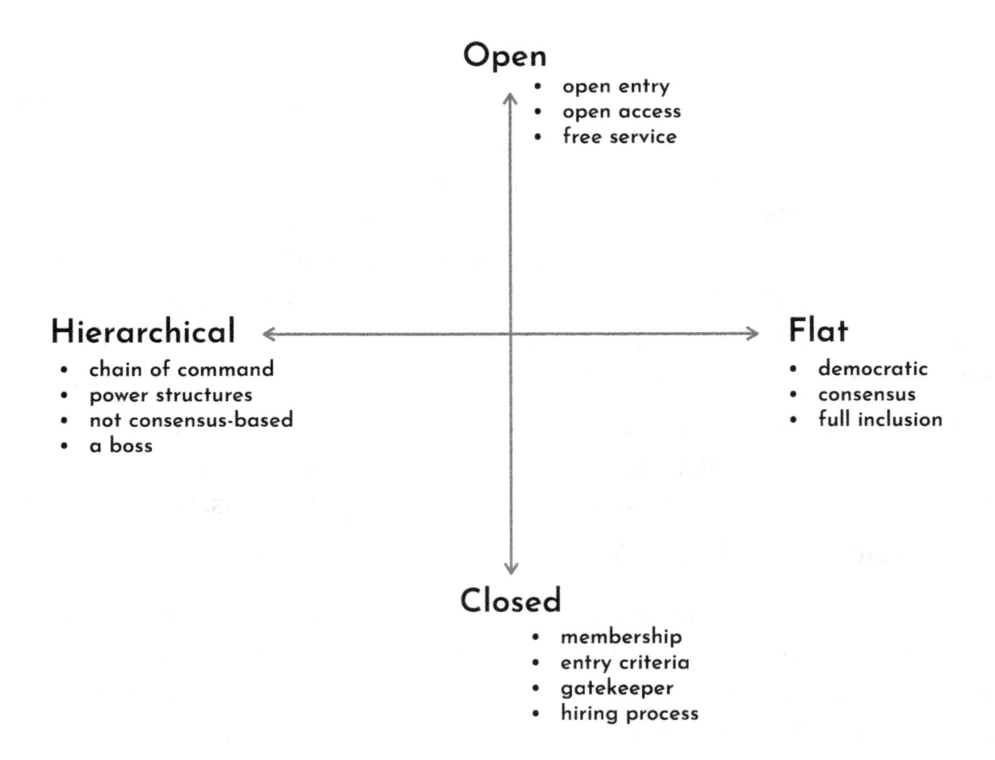

CHARACTERISTICS OF ORGANIZATIONAL DESIGN

Below are some examples of movements, clubs, and institutions mapped onto this framework. You can use this model to assess where your project and its related affiliations fall. This framework can also serve as a lens through which you can develop recommendations to change the organizational practices and structures of the entity(ies) your project is involved with so that they are designed to embody and best enact their Purpose(s).

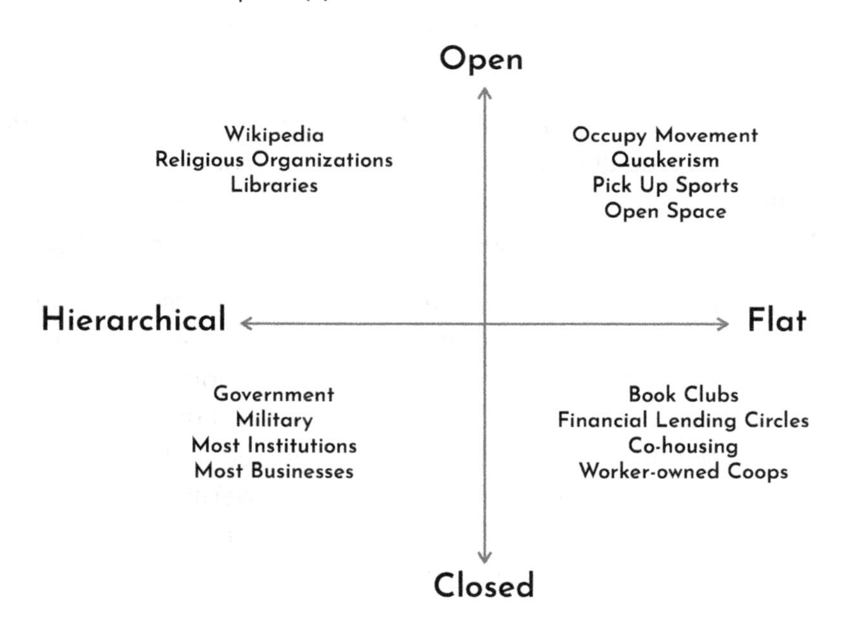

EXAMPLE ORGANIZATIONAL TYPES FOR EACH QUADRANT

As a reaction to closed/hierarchical systems, resistance movements like Occupy have swung to embracing open/flat systems. This combination is inclusive and often brings diverse representation to a project. One of its drawbacks, however, is lengthy group decision-making processes, which can slow down action. Groups that adopt open/flat systems also lack power structures. In individualistic societies, in particular, this circumstance often leads to the organization or movement becoming vulnerable to takeover or derailment. But design thinking can help us to refrain from viewing this conundrum in either/or terms. For example, designers can make modifications and achieve a middle ground with the Implementation of self-organizing systems (recall the introduction of this topic in the discussion of Paradigms under the 4 P's on page 120). Open Space is such a technology for organizing large groups. It provides non-hierarchical structure based on peer-leadership and facilitation. It works with individual consent versus group consensus and the principles of attraction/aversion and emergent properties.

Open Space Matrix at Northeast Prison Garden Educators' Retreat

Designs That Reinforce Solidarity Over Charity

Just like any technology, Social Design can be empowering or destabilizing to a community depending on the way it is used. If used as a tool by what Nigerian-American author Teju Cole refers to as the "White Savior Industrial Complex," it can inadvertently undermine the authority and community intelligence of people who have been the targets of *environmental racism* and colonization. *White saviorism*—a worldview so commonly held by and unquestioned in the Western world—often results in top-down approaches that do not recognize how they recapitulate colonial dynamics that originally brought about the environmental and social crises in the communities they are seeking to "save."

Alternately, a social designer can engage invisibilized communities in the design process through participatory stakeholder charettes (big community brainstorming sessions, see page 132) where their ideas are prioritized in the Design. Better yet, seasoned social designers can teach members of that community how to use the design process to regenerate their own land and culture, and do so under their own community's impetus. This is an instance of restorative justice, and especially so when a community targeted by oppression receives resources as reparations that they have explicitly asked for. In contrast, when handouts are given, especially when they do not respond to what the community expressly needs, then the white-savior charity Paradigm has crept in again.

Accept feedback and apply self-regulation is an important and often overlooked permaculture principle in designing the social dimensions of projects. A powerful practice for designers is to "step back," early and often, revisiting earlier phases to evaluate the morals of your Design:

- Does it reinforce conditions where gatekeepers (e.g., project directors, policy advocates, social workers), often without permission, speak on behalf of a community to funders or other outside institutions?
- Has "the problem" been determined by those who are outside of the community (such as charitable organizations, institutions, or even yourself) that the project is being designed for?
- Is anyone from the Beneficiary community included in the proposed Implementation of the Design?

Reflection and Integration: If your answer is yes to any of these questions ...Then go back and redesign your project so that its outcomes support liberation, solidarity, and community sovereignty. Without these outcomes, Designs can lead to an unintended abusive relationship, where gatekeepers can make demands on a community, but the community cannot make demands on the gatekeepers or related institutions. Our Designs will then reinforce historical and contemporary dynamics of power-over.

When we consciously move our work from a charity to a solidarity Paradigm, we need to work with gatekeepers to see themselves as equal human beings who hold shared interests. Most everyone wants safer neighborhoods and higher wages and less pollution. What is the issue you can see that will break down the rigid divisions between "self" and "other"? If we can shift gatekeepers from seeing themselves as having power-over and instead having power-with the project Beneficiaries, they will become your best project Accomplices.

If you are able to achieve this shift, then the next step is designing systems where gatekeepers agree to be accountable to the needs of the communities for which they are now an Accomplice. Gatekeepers can build authentic relationships with the communities they serve, and work in solidarity, by setting up mutual accountability structures, where the gatekeepers and the institutions involved receive and act on feedback and requests from Beneficiaries.

I hold a vision of healing and wholeness through the conscientious application of Regenerative Social Design. When we work together in multicultural coalitions to redesign the systems that created unequal distribution of power and resources, then we begin edging toward the horizon of systemic social regeneration.

Practices for Designing Democratic, Multicultural, Anti-Racist Organizations

Even though we may understand the importance of including many voices in leadership in our work, coming out of our silos and engaging in these efforts is more difficult than we realize. When designing your change-making project, here are some concrete practices that can help guide you in setting up organizations or other groups so that they are democratic, multicultural, and anti-racist.

Establish fully inclusive and participatory processes: *Multicultural democracy* is a process in which all parties, inclusive of socio-economic, cultural, and political diversity, participate in making the decisions that affect their lives. Are there ways to design your project so that Beneficiaries are democratically included in decision-making processes whose outcomes will affect them?

Increase multicultural competence: How well are the individuals who are part of your project's social ecosystem skilled in multicultural competence? Paul Kivel, author of *Uprooting Racism: How White People Can Work for Racial Justice*, offers resources for increasing multicultural competence in organizations. One concrete practice to incorporate into our Designs is to ensure that the makeup of an organization's members, staff, administrators, and directors mirrors the ethnic and racial identities, gender, economic status, and religion(s) of the larger community(ies) they serve.

The Climate Justice Movement is an example of a multicultural movement. They are vocal about structural equity issues, such as the whiteness of environmental organizations and the disproportionate lack of BIPOC representation in environmental leadership positions and in the implementation of solutions. In order for environmental organizations (which have far larger budgets than most organizations that address justice issues) to become multicultural, they must assess the makeup of their leadership teams and redefine their mission statements to include the messages of BIPOC frontline communities.

Challenge racism: Kivel advises that to become an anti-racist multicultural organization, the members, bylaws, and collective practices must actively and consistently challenge racism wherever it occurs. This steadfast commitment helps keep "multiculturalism" from being watered down. When designing social change projects to be anti-racist, it's imperative to watch out for patterns of tokenism. This insidious, too-common practice involves making small changes to pacify social tensions in lieu of undertaking fundamental transformation. For example, companies will hire a few BIPOC staff to give the appearance of racial equity without undertaking a sustained process to dismantle their own practices of white supremacy.

Be relational before transactional: *Urgency* is a common pattern of historically white organizations that are trying to diversify. Once they realize their reach has been exclusively for white people, and exclusively staffed by white people, organizations try to become multicultural overnight. Avoiding a longer process of building relationships with People of Color and BIPOC-lead organizations, white organizations often engage in transactional ways of relating as a means to hurry up and "fix" the problem of monocultural white representation. This behavior can look like marketing to and/or hiring BIPOC employees, which on the surface can seem like social progress, but without a longer process of building trust, accepting feedback when given, and uprooting institutional racism, quick-fix solutions sully good intentions. What remains are bad feelings and bad reputations.

Practice ongoing location of self-awareness: Part of the reason we begin the social designer's journey with location of self and Mapping Identities and Personal Histories (see page 12) is to increase our self-literacy. What are the belief systems, conditioning, and frames that we bring to any project? How will these worldviews harm others or unintentionally diminish the impact we hope our work will make? Samboja Lestari is an eco-social project that we have discussed as a case study in past iterations of the Regenerative Design for Changemakers training. This project takes a whole systems approach to solving orangutan abuse and poaching in Borneo, Indonesia. One of its biggest design interventions is the revival of the traditional sugar palm economy, which creates alternative livelihoods to poaching and to slash-and-burn charcoal production, which destroys orangutan habitat.

While Samboja Lestari is an incredible regenerative design project on many levels, it's also instructive for thinking critically about dynamics of power and privilege. Willie Smits, project founder and director, is a white, educated, English-speaking Dutchman. What of his values and assumptions did he bring to this project unconsciously? To what degree do project Beneficiaries have agency and power in decision-making processes?

It's well worth it to dedicate time and care to developing groups that truly value and uplift socio-economical, cultural, and politically diverse voices.

The Role of Case Studies

Some of the most convincing design proposals employ case studies. Case studies can be used to highlight success stories in other places with similar project conditions and can add legitimacy to an idea that seems far-fetched from the status quo. Seemingly unrelated but exciting case studies can be used to inspire hope and interest. In getting the attention of listeners, astute designer-storytellers can help make the connection between the case study and how it can be adapted to the conditions of a proposed project at hand, helping it gain validity.

Why reinvent the wheel? Case studies are also great for gleaning lessons learned. For instance, many people in the past have likely cared about an intersection of topics at the center of your personal Changemakers' Recipe. People I've worked with have designed and implemented projects at the intersection of children with disabilities and equestrian therapy or bicycle-powered composting and cooperative business owners. Likely all of these unique combinations have been experimented with. Do a little research and see what comes up, even if these ideas aren't regularly on the front page of the newspaper. Then, apply Analysis and Assessment thinking. Make some Observations and Interpretations about the Goals, processes, and outcomes of these projects. What pitfalls did they run into? Breakthroughs they had? What do they now know that they wish they'd known in the beginning? You can use design thinking to work out these factors ahead of time, on paper, saving your project money, time, and headache.

CASE STUDY on COALITION BUILDING ACROSS SECTORS:

INTERNATIONAL FOOD SOVEREIGNTY MOVEMENT

from *Harvesting Justice* by Beverly Bell and Tory Field

- The International Food Sovereignty Movement, also known as Via Campesina, is a coalition of 150 groups from 70 countries, representing around 200 million farmers from small and medium-sized farms, food producers, landless people, and Indigenous Peoples.
- The movement is rooted in the daily work of every small farmer, rancher, fisherperson, landless farm worker, and everyone else involved in local food production.
- The coalition includes groups as wide-ranging as the Indonesian Peasant Association, the Confederation of Farmers' Unions in Turkey, and the US National Family Farm Coalition.
- Together, Via Campesina achieved mandatory GMO labeling in 64 countries.
- Food sovereignty recognizes that transforming our food systems necessitates working in our communities, changing international policies, and everything in between.

Tamil Woman Processing Peanut Butter

This case study box highlights an example from the Food Sovereignty movement. I use this case study to inspire hopefulness about coalition-building across sectors with multicultural organizations. Although different in content, it relates to the work of my organization, Regenerate Change. Our Purpose is to connect and train changemakers, across sectors, in a common regenerative design framework, so they can intentionally co-design regenerative projects and leverage more influence collectively.

Which of the functions of case studies described above would be most helpful for you in presenting your Design recommendations to others? This question depends on who your audience is: Do you want engage strategic partners? Researchers? Funders, or others? Select the type of projects you want to highlight as case studies and for what reasons.

EXERCISE 39: Social Design and Presentation Board

After you have moved through all of the material presented in this chapter and completed the exercises, you have the ingredients needed for your recipe for social alchemy. It's time to assemble them all in a cohesive visual presentation to share with others!

DESIGN LAB ➡ Develop recommendations for your Social Design. Make a clear connection between what you are proposing and how it meets the project Goals. Be concise and specific in what you are proposing. And remember—this is a creative exercise, you are (likely) a new social designer, and you are not expected to be an expert at this process. Come from your passion and what you have learned from reading this book and beyond. Apply this new Experiential Wealth to creating the changes you wish to see. There are no wrong directions to take in this exercise.

The form of these recommendations might come from any of the suggested Frameworks for Developing a Detailed Design on page 178. And/or they might include other creative formats that communicate your Social Design, such as a series of images, a drawing with labels, a piece of writing, or a video to accompany your Presentation Board.

This is a good time to return to your project Purpose and Goals, and see if they feel fully reflective of where your project has evolved to at this point in the process. Or do you want to modify them?

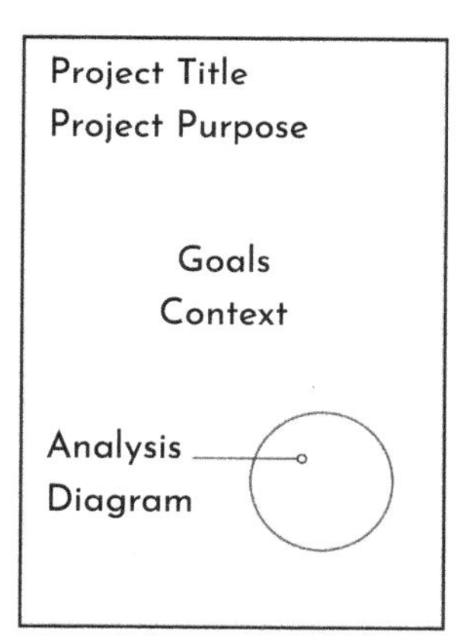

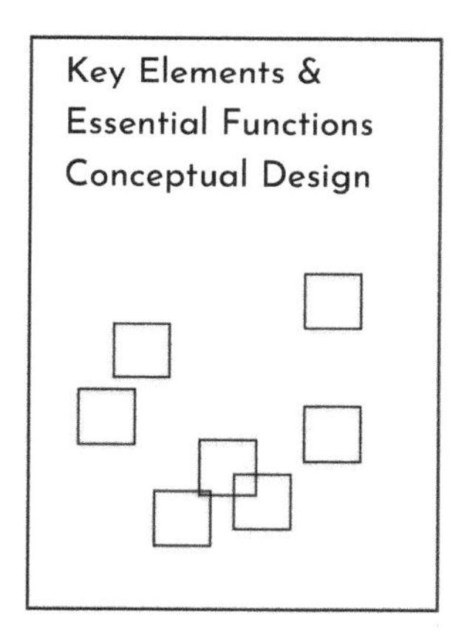

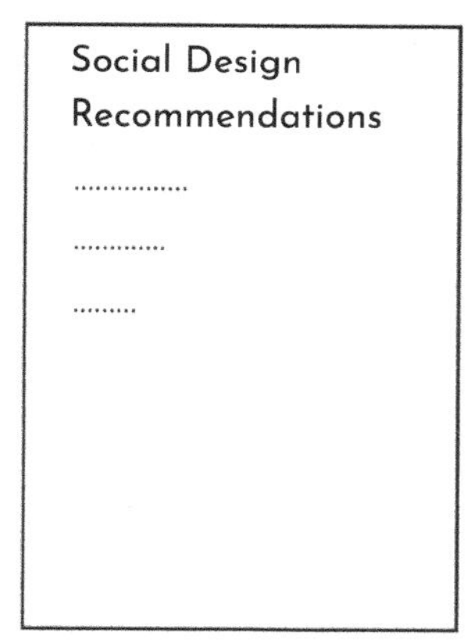

PRESENTATION BOARDS

DESIGN LAB ➡ Make a Presentation Board for your project. Three large sheets of flip chart or butcher paper (around 25" x 30") or large pieces of cardboard can serve as your background. On it, please include the following:

Project Title (catchy and short, no more than five words)

- Project Purpose, written out fully. The Title and Purpose typically go at the top of your Design Board, but you can be creative and place them anywhere that works well with your layout.

Continued on next page

EXERCISE 39: Cont.

- Reference to Goals: keywords from each of your project Goals. Refrain from writing whole sentences here. When you write a full proposal and/or make a formal project presentation, you should include your full Goals Articulation in present tense and active voice sentences.
- Reference to Context: keywords from your Holistic Context. You can use a Nested Wholes diagram, if you like, to show visually the three different sets of Goals on one side, and the keywords from your three Contexts on the other side.
- A minimum of one Analysis diagram. Refrain from writing Observations and Interpretations here. Again, if you're giving a presentation, you can read them or list them on a slide; if you're preparing a written proposal, you can write them out fully there. On the board, you can include brief Design Directions.
- Include on the second large piece of paper or cardboard your conceptual Social Design. This design could include Key Elements and Essential Functions or any other relevant and simplified pieces of your Design concept.
- Include your final concrete Social Design recommendations in one creative format or another with at least one visual diagram to communicate your ideas on the third piece of paper.

Reflection and Integration: After you create your Presentation Board, take a moment for Reflection and Integration. Choose three or more people with which you can share this stage of your creative process. Explain what you've developed for your project so far and use the Presentation Board as your map.

As you speak, make a mental note or jot down what you heard yourself say right afterwards. Do different angles of the project emerge? Based on who you're speaking with? Or the number of times you explain the project? Are there any new insights that arose in the sharing of your work?

After you record information that comes to you in this informal sharing process, take time for stillness before moving on to the next phase, Implementation. It may also be a good time to revisit not just your Purpose and Goals but also your Analysis and Assessment. This nonlinear process invites you to make tweaks or major reevaluations needed in the work you've generated so far. Looping back around is an important part of this creative and iterative process; embrace it and relinquish any feelings that may arise of "not making progress." Rest assured, the winding path holds more richness and integrity than the fastest straight line between two points. Brilliance is often messy in its process...

By the end of this chapter, I hope you are feeling how Regenerative Design unites the power of nature with human creativity to build life-affirming systems. With a positivist approach to social and ecological challenges, you can apply your whole systems thinking and the design tools you are learning to new projects able to transcend current limitations and create a world where all can thrive!

Please see Further Reading related to chapter 11 on page 248.

Social Design Lexicon for Chapter 11

Review the following key terms and write down what they mean to you. Then, reflect on how each of these concepts relates to your Social Design approach.

Solution Emergence vs. Mechanized Production:

Solutionary:

Platforms for Imagination:

Conceptual vs. Schematic vs. Detailed Design:

Late-Stage Capitalism:

Least Change, Greatest Effect:

50/50 Principle:

Social Alchemy:

Emergent Principles:

Adaptation:

Interdependence:

Decentralization:

Resilience:

Fractal Awareness:

Analysis Paralysis:

Form vs. Function:

Design Alternatives:

Design Criteria:

Benefits and Drawbacks:

Lowest Hanging Fruit:

Key Elements and Essential Functions:

Conceptual Design:

Schematic Design:

Ideal Scene:

Open vs. Closed Systems:

Hierarchical vs. Flat Systems:

Environmental Racism:

White Saviorism:

Accept Feedback and Apply Self-Regulation:

Multicultural Democracy:

Urgency:

CHAPTER 12: IMPLEMENTATION
RUBBER MEETS THE ROAD OF REALITY

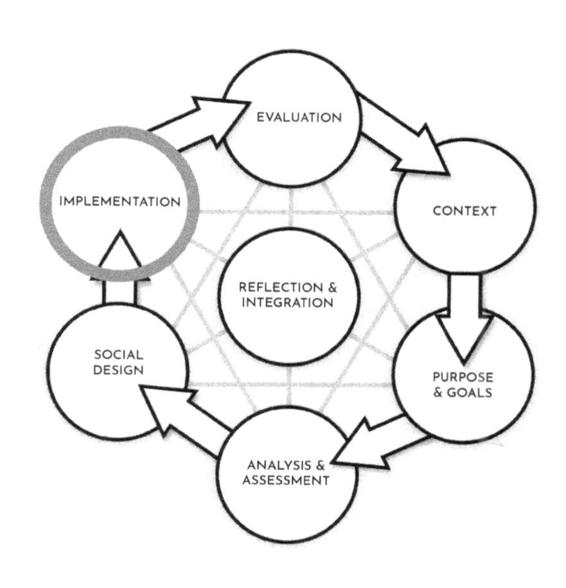

Take a deep breath and pause to recognize the incredible amount of Design work you have done thus far. Congratulations! You have come through the densest part of the journey, a portal of sorts, leading to a new creation. Here you've arrived at a clearing on the path. Behold the 360-degree view that surrounds you, and exhale...

Welcome to Implementation! This phase in the design process is where you get to take your ideas from paper and put them into action.

This chapter is designed to make sure you have the confidence, tools, and support necessary to succeed in Implementation. This is a multistage process, often with numerous subprojects and tasks in each stage. We'll be working with the permaculture principle from patterns to details. We start with broad brushstrokes, the *Stages of Implementation*. From there, we drill down a bit and explore strategies for project management. Lastly, we explore tools for prioritizing tasks in order to focus on what's most essential.

The Challenges of Implementation

Implementation has its own challenging Context that's important to name: resistance. Whether conscious or unconscious, resistance regularly arises when it comes time to actually implement our Designs. Permaculture certification courses often stop at the Design phase and do not engage with Implementation and Evaluation. Likewise, many planning projects, from regional planning to policy proposals, sadly sit on the shelves of planning departments and administrative offices, never to be implemented. It takes a different type of attention and level of dedication to implement a plan after all the hard work that's gone into creating a well-thought-out proposal.

This common phenomenon reflects a larger pattern in the dominant US culture, and in some Westernized parts of the world. If something is not a quick fix, the likelihood of it being adopted is slim. Agencies and state departments may be willing to invest in a planning processes to pacify constituents or advisory board members. But when it comes time to invest the resources to actually implement change, those plans get stalled or never happen. This can be a strategy to protect an entity's reputation by gaining credit for having a plan.

In other cases, there may be the willpower to implement changes, but bureaucratic dysfunction hinders progress. For instance, a changeover in a governmental or academic administration results in new decision makers in power. The new staff are now in the powerful role of gatekeepers, but if they inherited a plan and thus have little sense of ownership of it, they may not care enough to invest resources in seeing it through.

The Massachusetts Local Food Action Plan is a case in point. The state invested resources in a multiyear citizen-engaged planning process, comprising stakeholder charettes, surveys, interviews, and planning commissions working together to produce a comprehensive plan. A new entity, the Massachusetts Food Policy Council, was formed to execute the plan. However, with staff turnover in the governmental administration, the new commissioners and staff assigned to the council had little knowledge of the plan or a sense of obligation to it. The Policy Council meets, but it does not, as a united group, take action in advocating for policy change or enforcing the plan's Implementation. An ad hoc nonprofit, the Massachusetts Food Systems Collaborative, with far lesser resources, has had to step up to fill this void in the system.

You may be asking yourself, How do I, as an individual, go about implementing a social change project, one that can persist over time? This prospect can feel overwhelming. Luckily, we have tools to break down Implementation into several small and manageable stages. And we don't have to do it alone. Distributing the job of Implementation to several individuals and/or project partners takes the pressure off one heroic designer to implement a culture shift. Days of the lone wolf are no longer.

Setting up *mutual accountability structures* and designing clearly defined roles helps ensure we are not isolated in the process of Implementation. We can design the support we need to follow through on actions we commit to.

EXERCISE 40: Designing Your Role in Implementation

Designing your ideal role in the Implementation of a project is what regenerative business consultant Carol Sanford might refer to as a *developmental opportunity*. You can design the intensity and area of commitment for yourself as a "promise beyond ableness," a personal growth concept in her book, *The Regenerative Business*.

What areas of expertise would be just beyond the edge of your Conscious Competencies and Comfort Zone? Are you open to using the Implementation phase to expand your capacities for project management?

At the same time, it's important to strike a balance and refrain from stretching yourself too thin, taking into account the other things you are already committed to.

Reflection and Integration: Before diving into the nuts and bolts of Implementation, this is a good time for a cycle of Reflection and Integration questions. Take a moment to reflect on these questions below that I developed with my co-coach, Leora Fridman. This is where you can use your design skills to intentionally craft your level and area of involvement in project Implementation.

EXERCISE 40: Cont.

Journal: *Please write your responses to the following questions, and any other things you want to consider regarding the Implementation of your Social Design project.*

- ***Analyze:*** *Begin with Observation: list the current projects, jobs, and/or ongoing responsibilities you have committed to for the next six to 12 months.*
- ***Assess:*** *Then make Interpretations: what amount of time do you need every week for each of these responsibilities? (This includes time for preparation, execution, recuperation, and Reflection and Integration activities.) If your responsibilities are intermittent, then you can do this exercise on a monthly rather than weekly basis.*
- ***Assess:*** *Compare your calculations for time management with how you actually spend your time. Are you on target, or are you always trying to catch up? Are the sheer number of responsibilities you've agreed to possible or not? How well are your responsibilities spread out or paced so that you can have sufficient time to prepare, recuperate, etc.?*
- ***Design Directions:*** *Begin by taking a sober look at what activities you might need to let go of and/or turn down to establish a sustainable, if not regenerative, baseline for yourself. Which activities do not register in your body as a full Yes! when you bring them to mind? Be brave and honest with yourself here.*
- ***Design Directions:*** *Be realistic about what you can feasibly commit to taking on in the Implementation of your Social Design project. Is there a time in the seasonal cycle of the year when you have more capacity than at other times to commit to something new? Is there a project or job ending soon, after which you could allot more time to the project's Implementation?*
- ***Design:*** *What is the best fit in terms of a role for you, given your strengths, interests, and assessment of your availability? Where can you play with the idea of promise beyond ableness and explicitly craft your role as a personal growth opportunity? You may want to revisit your Social Niche Analysis* *(see page 17)* *and your list of skills generated from the Changemakers' Recipe* *(see page 101)* *when considering these questions.*
- ***Design:*** *Create an* Implementation Team. *Who in your network or in the project's ecosystem can you solicit to help with the Implementation? How often do you want to meet with your team as a whole? How frequently would you want to have* co-working dates*—for fostering connection and motivation for both parties, helping you both get things done?*

Based on the personal Constraints and Opportunities that you identified in this journal activity, and on the new capabilities you want to develop, consider what you can feasibly commit to. See if you can do so in a way that does not bring friction to your existing commitments or compromise your personal well-being. Then create a few different Alternative Designs for how you would ideally be involved in the Implementation of the project, the Benefits and Drawbacks each Alternative would have, and who would be on your team.

Take a moment to integrate this feedback you've given yourself before moving on.

■ <u>Social Designer Tip</u>: Ground-Truthing Before Implementing ■

In a moment, we will explore different ways to approach the designing of Implementation stages and selecting tools to turn large activities into small doable tasks. When beginning the process of making a clear Implementation plan, you have a ripe opportunity for *ground-truthing* your Design. The rubber meets the road, so to speak, at this intersection of potent ideas coming into material form. Ground-truthing, in a design process that's nonlinear, requires another visit to the Analysis and Assessment phase. Play somewhat of the devil's advocate here as you lay out your Stages of Implementation and related tasks. Be judicious in assessing what is plausible; remove or modify that which will create obstacles to successful Implementation. It could be that you're simply trying to do too much, and need to drop one thing or another. Alternately, there may be one or more aspects of the Design that will become a bottleneck and prevent other activities from progressing. Is there a little redesign that needs to happen for your Design to succeed once it's underway?

Other questions to consider at this stage include: Is the Design truly sensitive to the Context? Is it responsive to the needs of the people and beings it was originally intended to serve? What are all the ways the current Design could fail (see Pre-Mortem List on page 162)?

It is not necessary to answer all of these questions now. As you begin to map out the stages for Implementation, opportunities to ground-truth your plan will arise. Go back to your journal or Presentation Board when needed and find ways to tweak your project.

Big Patterns: Stages of Implementation

There are many tools for Implementation and project management from the fields of business development and non-profit management. I've found these two particularly useful in thinking about organizing a Social Design into clear Stages of Implementation:

Quarterly Timeline: One approach is to divide the year into quarters and create a timeline. What activities need to occur within the first three months to get the project up and running? If it's an existing project, what activities need to be added or amended to the current Implementation plan, if there is one? Within six months what needs to occur? What activities should happen at nine and 12 months? Some activities require more than three months to implement. They can be depicted as beginning at one of the quarters, and then continuing on into additional quarters. For example, it might be easy to develop a website within three months, but creating a professional promotional video showcasing your work for the website will likely take longer than a single quarter. You can indicate which quarter will mark the start of video making, and approximately how long you think it will take to be completed. (See the example timeline below.)

Once you've reached the 12-month mark, it's a good time for Reflection and Integration. The Year in Review Ritual exercise (see page 100) for the individual changemaker can be modified so that it is relevant to a project annual review. After taking stock, you can continue with quarterly planning for the second year. Alternately, you may decide to plan three years out, while remaining open to emergent processes and adjusting your Stages of Implementation as project conditions shift over time. No matter how you approach planning, taking the time at the end of each 12-month cycle to Reflect and Integrate, whether in an annual retreat or other form, is highly recommended.

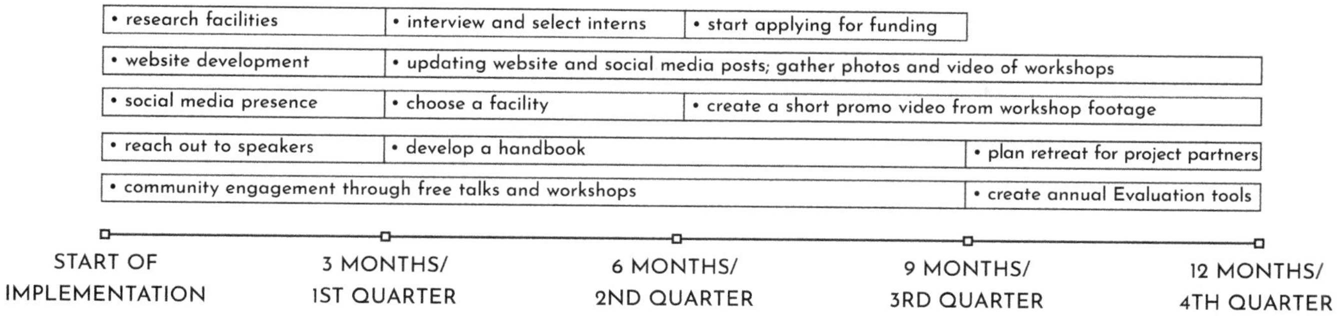

Start to 3 months	3 to 6 months	6 to 9 months	9 to 12 months
• research facilities	• interview and select interns	• start applying for funding	
• website development	• updating website and social media posts; gather photos and video of workshops		
• social media presence	• choose a facility	• create a short promo video from workshop footage	
• reach out to speakers	• develop a handbook		• plan retreat for project partners
• community engagement through free talks and workshops			• create annual Evaluation tools

START OF IMPLEMENTATION — 3 MONTHS/ 1ST QUARTER — 6 MONTHS/ 2ND QUARTER — 9 MONTHS/ 3RD QUARTER — 12 MONTHS/ 4TH QUARTER

EXAMPLE QUARTERLY IMPLEMENTATION TIMELINE

DESIGN LAB ➡ Develop a quarterly timeline for your project's Implementation for the next year.

Stages with the Four Directions: The Four Directions framework, which we used to discuss shared leadership roles in chapter 4, can be applied to planning stages of Implementation. This framework organizes rhythms in nature using the structure of the cardinal directions of East, South, West, and North. The chart, Four Directions and Project Stages, reviews what we've already covered. For Implementation, we will focus on the column that lays out the stages of a project.

This framework works well for either new Social Design projects or for reorganizing existing projects that you're amending with Regenerative Design. Recently, a group of young Jewish farm educators took a workshop with me on the Four Directions framework. They remarked that their organizations rarely made time for the North phase, Reflection and Integration, when their programs ended and before they started the next program (even though their practice was to take a weekly *Shabbat* for Reflection and Integration!). "Progress" and "product," values from the exploitation Paradigm, are so strong that even communities rooted in weekly sabbath practices forget to slow down and reflect in the professional sphere. By seeing the importance of the North phase—in natural cycles (think of the stillness of winter) and in their own *Shabbat* practice—they were able to bring this new awareness into their Conscious Competencies and organizational practices.

CARDINAL DIRECTION	TIME OF DAY	SEASON	STAGE OF LIFE	**STAGES OF A PROJECT**	SHARED LEADERSHIP ROLES
EAST	Sunrise	Spring	Birth	**Inspiration/ New Ideas**	Brings a welcoming presence; builds group connection/unity; focuses on inclusivity; provides inspiration
SOUTH	High Noon	Summer	Youth/ Adolescence	**Action/ Training**	Attends to details, e.g. in the role(s) of treasurer, notetaker, timekeeper, fundraiser, marketing, registration
WEST	Sunset	Autumn	Adulthood	**Service/ Creation/ Fruition**	Facilitates; convenes; acts as a spokesperson; serves as a master teacher; insures that celebrations of culminations occur
NORTH	Midnight	Winter	Elderhood	**Reflection/ Integration/ Senescence**	Knows the big picture; helps the group stay true to the Purpose; sees all the pieces; mentors/ advises; leads from behind

FOUR DIRECTIONS & PROJECT STAGES

EXERCISE 41: Syncing Implementation with Nature's Rhythms

Begin this exercise by listing all of the activities or sub-projects you'll want to accomplish in the Implementation of your project, in no particular order. This could include things like:

marketing ○ researching case studies ○ visiting other similar projects
creating a pilot ○ delivering project services ○ celebrating successes
gathering feedback ○ integrating Evaluation feedback ○ acquiring funding
building new relationships in the community ○ deepening relationships
mentoring others in this model ○ telling the story through social media

Here is how I would organize those tasks based on the Four Directions framework.

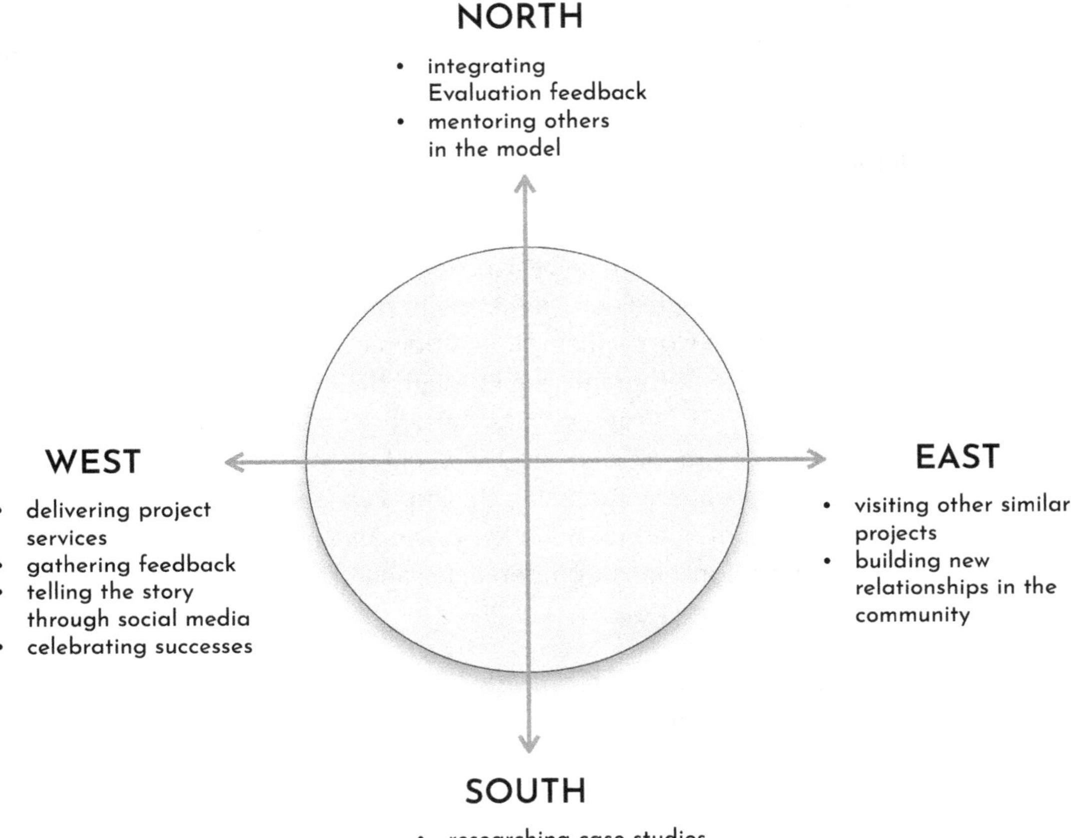

EXAMPLE STAGES OF IMPLEMENTATION

EXERCISE 41: Cont.

Now, it's your turn to brainstorm all of the big-picture stages and then organize them in the diagram below into four stages: East, South, West, and North. For instance, list tasks that build inspiration and set things in motion (as does the sunrise and spring's warmth) under East. List tasks that require focused work and logistical coordination (much like the midday workflow or agricultural production in the summer) under South, and so on. Then, start thinking of them as Stages of Implementation, with East being the first stage, South second stage, West third stage, and North fourth/final stage, before starting the cycle all over again. If your Social Design is for an established project, see if there any stages in its Implementation that have been missed or could be reorganized. Use the Four Directions chart to help guide your decisions for which stage to put subprojects in. Remember, one or more people on the Implementation Team can lead the management of each subproject.

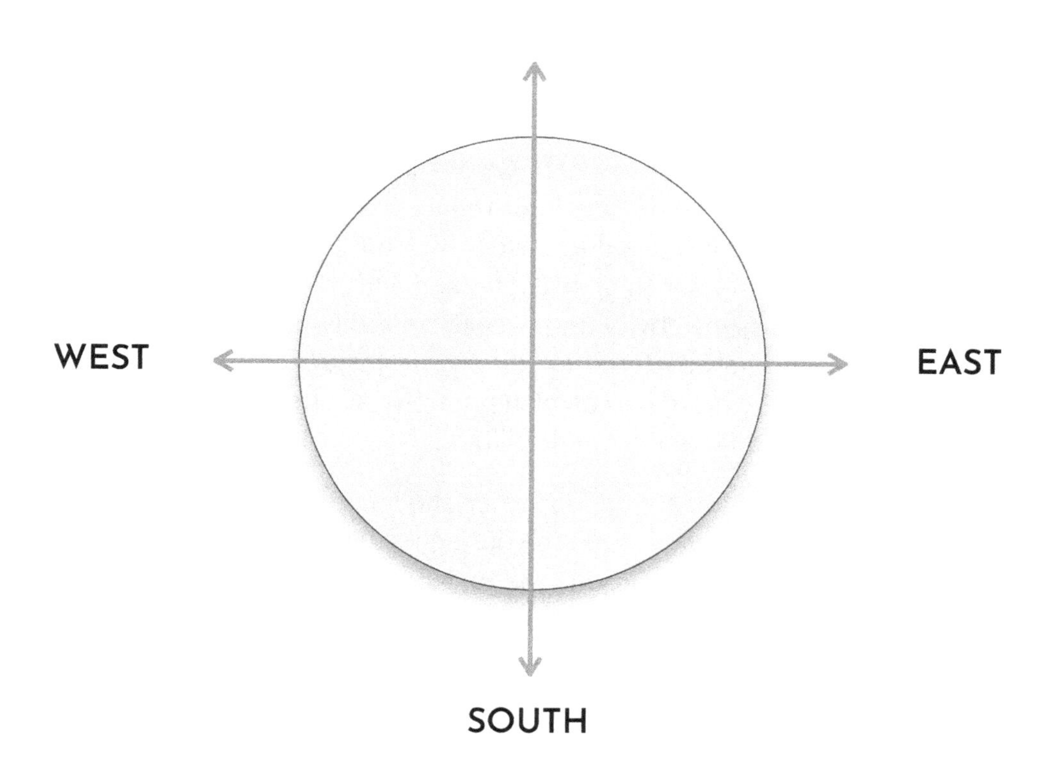

STAGES OF IMPLEMENTATION TEMPLATE

From Patterns to Smaller Details: Project Management

Implementation can have many moving parts. It's easy to become overwhelmed and lose confidence in our ability to manage all the variables and timelines. Numerous books, apps, and tools exist to help with this challenge. Here are a few that my colleagues and I have found useful for Social Design project management. Share these tools with partners on your Implementation Team, and see which ones you want to use in common.

Time-boxing: *Time-boxing* is a strategy for both project management and time management (yes, boxes can also be beneficial!). For those of us who tend to procrastinate or who seek perfectionism, this strategy is extremely useful for getting through several tasks in a defined period of time. Physical calendars with a big white space for each day can be a project manager's best Accomplice. Write out all the tasks that need to be completed each day of the upcoming week. Every morning of that week, take 20 minutes to set a defined amount of time (a time box) for each task. When you are ready to start working on the first task, set a timer for half the amount of time you've assigned for it. When the timer goes off, you will know that half of the time remains to complete the task and then reset the timer for the second half. Staying accountable to ourselves and the time boxes we've set is important for this strategy to work its magic. There may be moments when you decide to add extra minutes to the time box you set toward the end, and that is fine. However, you should keep moving forward to the next task, even if you did not finish the previous one. Eventually, your inner production system will calibrate to the amount of time you set for each item, while also adjusting timing when needed for the completion of each task.

Cycles of Requirements: Tracking the ebbs and flows of the requirements for project Implementation helps changemakers create a map of the process. Much like the swelling and receding of rivers during cycles of rainy and dry seasons, workflows follow similar patterns. We can use again that big physical desk calendar to draw circles and add colors or varying line thicknesses to map the busy times and the lulls in activity onto weekly, monthly, and yearly cycles. These visuals can depict past and present workflow patterns, improving our literacy of project needs. The more we can anticipate these cycles, the more we can plan proactive strategies to manage our precious energy in response to the ebb and flow of responsibilities.

Rotational Neglect: Sometimes there are periods when the rain of responsibilities seems relentless. You have a deadline to get your book to your editor plus you're getting readying to leave the country on a multiweek trip?! This is a good time to call on the strategy of *rotational neglect*. In the same way that rotationally grazing herd animals distributes resources to different plots of pasture, partitioned by time and movable fences, rotational neglect follows the same but inverted pattern. At moments, it may feel like there are too many mouths to feed and only one of you. Rather than getting overwhelmed and feeling paralyzed, you can set up a rotating schedule of purposeful neglect. How long is it feasible to neglect certain project responsibilities and relationships before they suffer? Start by identifying the thresholds of minimum contact needed to attend to each responsibility. Each one will be unique. Then, design a simple system where you attend only to the minimum requirements, so that you partition the resource of your time and attention strategically across each responsibility. Design your system in a way that doesn't neglect one or more relationship(s) or responsibility(ies) too long, resulting in negative consequences.

This counterintuitive strategy can be difficult to stomach for many changemakers whose baseline is hyper-responsibility, even if it means bottomless self-sacrifice in the name of the cause. However, rotational neglect is like a tonic, a strategy that respects and thinks about the well-being of each element of the ecosystem, especially the project manager! Maintaining sanity and stability with stacked deadlines and responsibilities all packed into the same month or week ensures that we can stay in the game and that things will get done. Designing a system of purposefully designed rotational neglect also sets up some assurance that balls won't get dropped in the midst of the chaos.

For me, the end of every semester is when I have the least energy after teaching and lovingly attending to students for months. It's also the time when I have to focus the most in order to give meaningful feedback on students' final projects and calculate course grades. At the same time, my other work-related projects need attending more than usual, with people sending their last emails before they go on winter or summer break. In this workflow swell when I have reduced energy, I aim for *good enough* rather than trying to maintain high standards of communication or perfectionism. I welcome time-boxing and rotational neglect at these two points in my year.

Levels of Activation: For each Stage of Implementation, you can zoom in and categorize each of the activities into their various *Levels of Activation*, much like the stages of building and tending a fire. As an entrepreneur, I have several streams of income as a strategy for financial resilience and to keep things interesting. When I take the time to assess the Level of Activation for each of my endeavors, I know what to prioritize and expect. This organizing tool, introduced to me by Keith Zaltzberg-Drezdahl, can help in categorizing and visually charting the changes in sub-projects of an Implementation plan:

- The *Ideation* level involves prospective endeavors with small flames that you can feed on occasion to keep them alive. You can choose if you want to invest in these ideas in hopes of turning them into fully ignited opportunities, based your Purpose.
- *On-boarding* projects, ones that are gaining momentum backed by your Implementation Team's decision to move forward, need kindling in the form of refined attention.
- Jobs and projects that are *Operational* require your daily or weekly fire-tending maintenance, which can be systematized to decrease the mental bandwidth they require.
- *Wrapping Up* is a senescence phase, when the fire that once fueled a project is now dying down. You can decide when it has met its benchmarks and lovingly transition it away from the forefront. Its ashes can go in the urn of Reflection and Integration.

EXERCISE 42: Charting Levels of Activation

You can chart the many subprojects nested within your Social Design with this tool, which is most useful once your Implementation activities are up and running.

Begin by brainstorming a list of subprojects that are part of your Implementation plan. For instance, if the project is about neighborhood food resilience, then these might be some of its subprojects: neighborhood work party, tool lending library, online meet-ups, neighborhood relationship building, neighborhood compost system, gardening workshops, tracking amount of food grown, and community greenhouse.

Put each subproject on a Post-it. Here you can choose to color-code the Post-its if you like, based on the content area of each subproject. For example, this project might include four categories: infrastructure, on pink Post-its; community engagement and outreach, on yellow Post-its; experiential learning, on turquoise Post-its; project Evaluation, on blue Post-its. See what makes sense as categories for your project and then assign them a color.

Remember to include a legend for the colors you choose! You can simplify and only use one color for all of your subprojects, too.

Then, make a chart like the one below on a large piece of paper or repurposed cardboard (ideally 25" x 30"). Categorize the level of activation for each subproject and then place the Post-its within the column that most corresponds to the level of each respective subproject's activation: Ideation, On-boarding, Operational, and Wrapping Up.

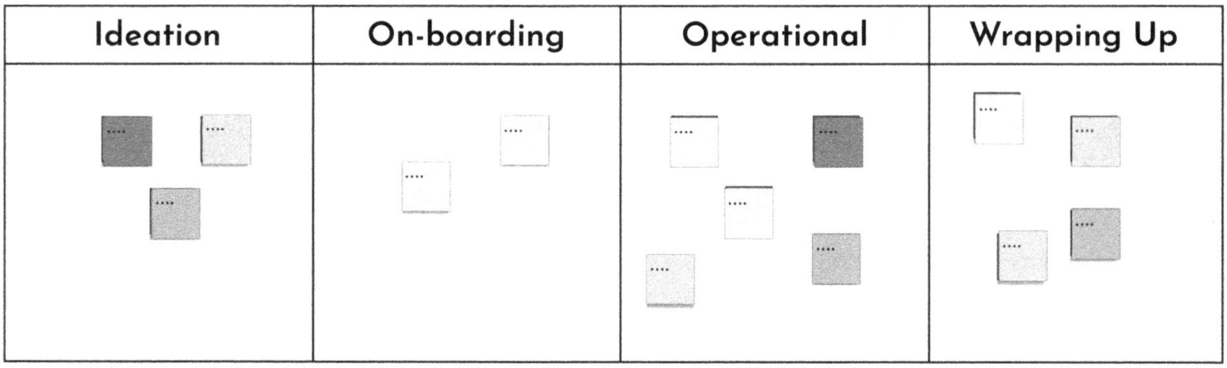

Ideation	On-boarding	Operational	Wrapping Up

EXAMPLE LEVELS OF ACTIVATION CHART

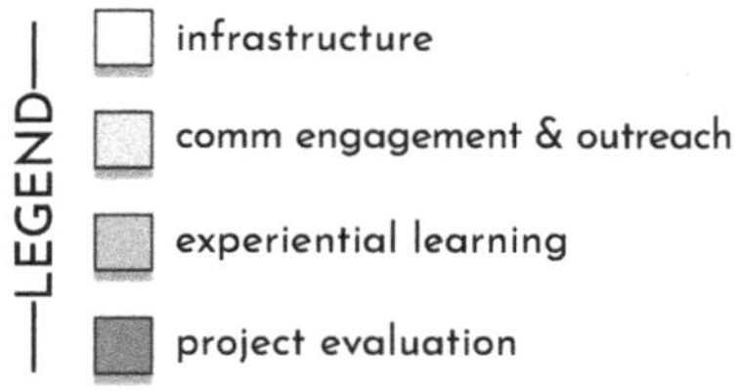

LEGEND
- infrastructure
- comm engagement & outreach
- experiential learning
- project evaluation

Nitty Gritty Details: Prioritizing Tasks

Once you have determined the Stages of Implementation and selected the best-suited tools for your style of project management, you can drill down to the micro level of task prioritization for each activity or subproject. Sifting out the nonessential from the essential can be difficult when you are in the moment, sitting in front of a computer screen for hours. Here are some tools for the micro level of project Implementation. There are also numerous books on these types of strategies, such as *Getting Things Done*, a work-life management system developed by Dave Allen.

After I introduce each of these tools for task prioritization below, Exercise 43: Mapping and Managing Tasks will ask you choose an activity or outcome in your Implementation plan and run through each of these tools.

Decision-Making Quadrants: There are numerous things that we'd like to do to make our projects fabulous. Our finite yet renewable resources of time and attention, however, mean that we need to decide which tasks are priorities. Each discrete activity in the various Stages of Implementation translate into several smaller tasks. The tool of Decision-Making Quadrants helps project managers identify those tasks and prioritize them in order to accomplish the outcomes desired. This tool originally comes from the Management Matrix in Stephen Covey's book *The 7 Habits of Highly Effective People*, another guide to increasing efficacy. I've adapted his language, and I use two spectra on axes rather than a matrix. I also incorporate the use of movable index cards to help lay out the priorities of tasks we need to get accomplished.

Looking through the lens of form versus function can help here. Evaluating the function of each element, rather than getting lured by its form, is important. Then you can decide if the function is essential to the outcome you're working toward. This utilitarian approach is great for moving forward on projects. For instance, if you were starting a permaculture landscape design business, you would brainstorm all of the Essential Functions that support its start-up stage. Then, you would decide which of the myriad forms would best support those functions, and hopefully other functions as well! Perhaps you want a bright, airy space in which to receive clients that would be comfortable and supplied with tea and snacks. This is one form of the function of being gracious. However, this welcoming space is not essential to the starting-up of the business. Instead, you decide to focus your energy on being gracious in your communications with clients on the phone and during site visits. These two forms—telephone communication and in-person communication—provide Essential Functions to the starting-up of the business, and have the potential to fulfill the function of graciousness at the same time. This is the multiple functions, also known as *stacking functions*, permaculture principle in action.

The Decision-Making Quadrants tool has four quadrants made with two axes. The vertical axis is a spectrum of importance: the top end represents highly important things, and the bottom end represents less important things. This axis helps us sort out the essential tasks from the things we might like to get to but that are not critical. The horizontal axis shows timeliness: the left end represents things that are not time-sensitive, and the right end represents things that are time-sensitive. This axis helps us organize the order of operations. Things that need immediate attention and that are essential go in the farthest upper-right-hand corner, such as calling back a prospective landscape design client who made an inquiry last week. There may be other tasks that you'd like to complete, such as adding new resource links on your website, but you've categorized this as being of mid-importance and not time-sensitive. You can return to these tasks when the more essential tasks are completed.

You may find that there are fewer tasks that fall in the important and time-sensitive quadrant over time. This is desirable, because the goal is to move as many of these into the important but not time-sensitive quadrant so that the bulk of your tasks are not emergencies that must be urgently addressed all the time. Anything you find in the time-sensitive but not important quadrant should be shed. These demand a lot of your attention, such as urgent emails about joining a particular campaign or a sale from a buyer you've purchased from before. Since you've determined that these activities are not important to you, they are degenerative to keep around in both your literal and mental inbox.

You can use painter's tape to create an X-axis and Y-axis on a table or a wall, or draw the lines on a very large pad of paper. Think about the tasks in your mental to-do list, and write each task on the front of an index card. Next, place the cards in order of importance and timeliness. For instance, you may have a task that is important to do eventually, but it may not be very time-sensitive, such as filing your receipts. That would go somewhere in the upper-left quadrant. Once you've placed all the index cards, take a picture of the arrangement and date it.

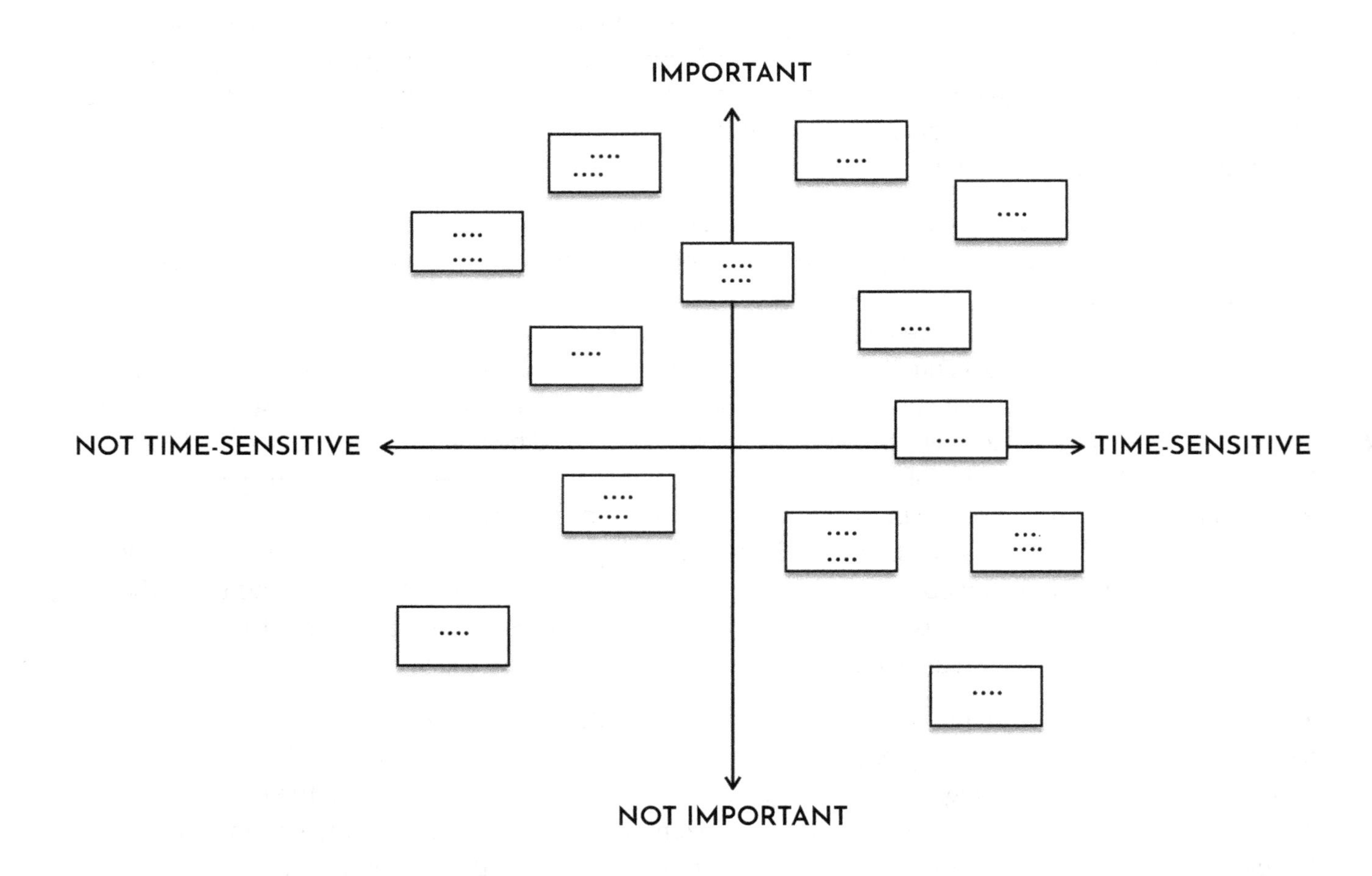

DECISION-MAKING QUADRANTS

Remember, this is a dynamic tool, where more essential items move toward the important and/or time-sensitive ends of the axes as days or weeks pass. Ones that you initially categorize as lower priority can become increasingly urgent when they are not attended to. Setting the date for regular check-in meetings with project volunteers and/or staff is an example of a task that becomes increasingly important as times goes by without meeting.

SMART Steps: Most tasks, although small themselves, may involve a few steps. James Stark, co-founder of the Ecology of Leadership program at Regenerative Design Institute in Bolinas, CA, uses the analogy of a *3-foot toss*. The game of horseshoes rewards the longest and most accurate throws. These tosses are hard to achieve. An alternate strategy for making strides is aiming for the short-distance throw, one that is close enough to hit accurately, again and again. With a series of 3-foot tosses, so to speak, we can actually achieve a great deal.

SMART Steps helps break down tasks and activities into short, discrete steps. SMART stands for:

Simple

Measurable

Attainable

Relevant

Timebound

You should be able to accomplish (and be able to tell when you've accomplished) a SMART Step within two weeks maximum. These short turnaround goals will activate the first stage of your Implementation plan, pushing against the inertia that can inhibit a Design's Implementation.

Using SMART Steps dovetails well with Decision-Making Quadrants. On the back of each index card, list the simple measurable steps needed to accomplish the task on the front. Next to each of the SMART Steps, add a deadline for accomplishing it. You can carry your index cards around with you to refer to often (a little "extra," I know). This process reduces the *mental load* we carry, as we try to remember everything that needs attending, and can help soothe anxiety associated with project management.

Critical Path: This prioritization tool helps project managers make swift decisions in the moment as things present themselves. The critical path organizes all of the important and time-sensitive tasks related to a single outcome from the Implementation plan. Usually, this outcome has a determined period of time by which it's ideally achieved. Continuing with the example of the landscape design business, say one of the desired outcomes for the first Stage of Implementation in the important and time-sensitive quadrant is to secure five new clients in the first three months. To engage with the Critical Path tool, you'll think of all the tasks that you need to accomplish this outcome. Write each one on its own Post-it.

Then, take out a new piece of unlined paper and draw a diagonal line from the bottom left corner up to the top right corner (see image below), with the desired outcome at the top right. This line represents the Critical Path. Place the Post-its next to the line, based on how critical each task is to accomplishing the outcome within the time period to achieve it. As other things arise, ones that would be nice to have happen but are not crucial, such as creating a business logo, can be added. These ancillary activities should be placed further away from the Critical Path line to show that they are less crucial to the successful delivery of the outcome.

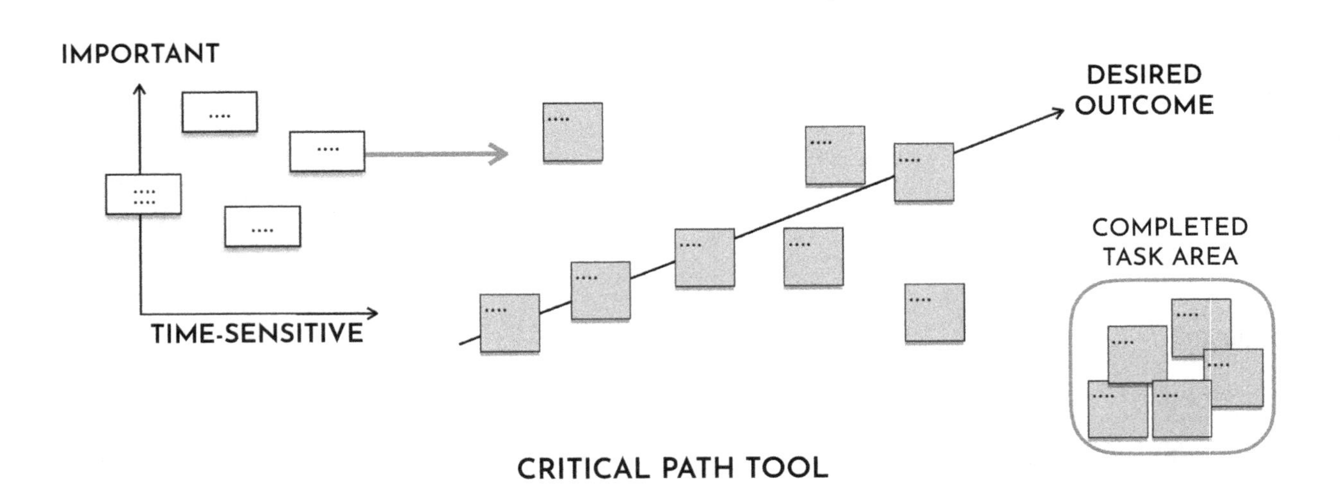

CRITICAL PATH TOOL

As you finish each task, and the SMART Steps embedded within it, you can remove related Post-its from the Critical Path and put them in a completed task area on the side. As new tasks get added to the important quadrants connected to the outcome you're planning for, you can create new Post-its for these tasks and add them to the Critical Path. When there's time and energy left before reaching the deadline, then you can decide if you want to work on the ancillary tasks adjacent to the Critical Path, but only after the most essential tasks are complete.

Backcasting: Building on the Critical Path tool, you can use the technique of Backcasting (imagine the opposite of forecasting) to see the sequence of steps needed to achieve the desired outcome. Working backwards, imagine the successful outcome first, then brainstorm all of the steps and inputs needed to achieve it. You can do two helpful things: order the steps (rearrange the Post-its on the Critical Path for appropriate sequencing) and quantify the time needed for each step (write the minutes or hours at the bottom of the Post-it). You'll also want to think about the inputs, such as landscaping tools, drafting equipment, or a pickup truck, that are needed to achieve the outcome. Write these on their related Post-its. Again, if you find yourself with surplus time or money in the budget, you can backcast from there and include some value-added padding, such as making business cards, hiring a website designer, and offering a free introduction to landscape design talk at the local nursery to increase your buzz.

EXERCISE 43: Mapping and Managing Tasks

1. Review what you have generated so far for **Stages of Implementation** and begin with the first stage.
2. Create an **Outline of Tasks** (with bullets, rather than sentences) for each activity within the first stage of Implementation.
3. Then, create a **Decision-Making Quadrants** diagram and write all of the tasks on index cards and plot them onto the four quadrants.
4. For all of the tasks that you decided are essential (the cards to the right of the vertical axis), write down **SMART Steps** on the back that will move you toward achieving the activity on the front. Again, these are simple, measurable, achievable, relevant, and timely steps you can take to accomplish the task.

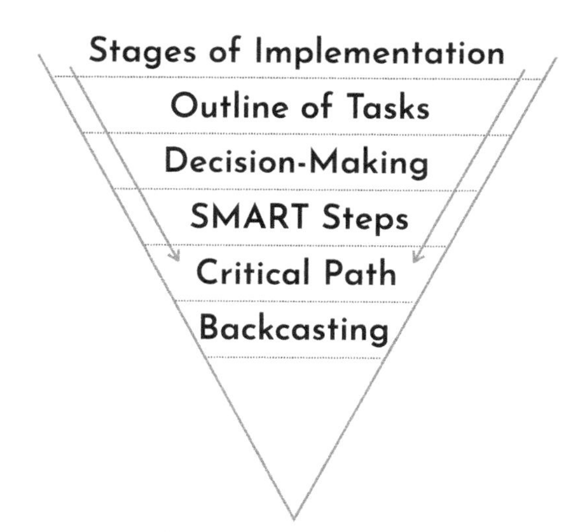

5. Then, take all of the index cards that you marked as important and time-sensitive related to one of the activities or outcomes (of your choice) and write them on Post-its. Plot them on, adjacent to, or further from the **Critical Path** line, based on how crucial they are for achieving the outcome. This action will help you sort out the essential from the nonessential tasks.
6. Employ the **Backcasting** technique to sequence the Post-its in the order tasks must occur. Then, determine the amount of time and inputs, if any, needed to complete each task and write these on the bottom of the Post-its. You'll see how long it will take to achieve this particular outcome.

Mutual Accountability Structures

Implementing change while staying connected to others helps motivate us and disrupts patterns of isolation that often keep us stuck in old ways. Regenerative Leadership Development, a topic we explored in chapter 4, also reminds us that when multiple people are responsible for a project, its success is fortified. Alone, we cannot solve the world's problems. The permaculture principles of redundancy and value diversity and the emergent strategy principle of decentralization remind us to distribute responsibility across our Implementation Team. With that distribution of responsibility also comes a collegial sense of co-ownership; project partners become vested in the project's development over the long haul. The adage "Many hands make light work" is also applicable here. Most importantly, when we create redundancy in the project's systems and diversify its champions, then we grow in resilience. If one person on the Implementation Team moves, quits, or burns out, for instance, then there are other strands of support in place. If instead we feel that we, as Designers, are solely responsible for the successful Implementation of our projects, then patterns of overextension, resentment, and burnout are inevitable, in only a matter of time.

Creating mutual accountability structures helps ensure the successful Implementation of the project. For those people and organizational partners on the Implementation Team, we can share the Social Niche Analysis tool to assess each individual's or project partner's potential role (see page 17). Understanding each player's strengths and interests more clearly lets us pair them with the Implementation activities with which they are most aligned. This pairing also means that people are more likely to be accountable to activities they feel connected to.

Once the team decides on clearly defined roles, much like a sports team, you can together articulate your terms and agreements for accountability. For instance, when do team members need to let others know that they will have to miss a meeting? What is the protocol when someone is unable to meet an agreed-upon deadline? Who do members call if they're feeling stuck and need some encouragement or resources?

Cardinal Direction	Shared Leadership Roles
EAST	Welcoming presence; builds group connection/unity; focuses on inclusivity; provides inspiration
SOUTH	Attends to details, e.g. treasurer, notetaker, timekeeper, fundraiser, marketing, registration
WEST	Facilitator; convener; spokesperson; master teacher; insures celebration of culminations occur
NORTH	Knows the big picture; helps the group stay true to the Purpose; sees all the pieces; mentors/advises; leads from behind

COMPLEMENTARY LEADERSHIP ROLES

To go one step further, you can creatively co-design an internal system of checks and balances in the leadership structure. One approach is to apply the Four Directions model. Each of the cardinal directions has an archetypal role associated with it based on nature's rhythms. Put together, the four roles balance and complement each other. In this arrangement, East, South, and West are ultimately accountable to the North person who holds the big picture and supports the three other roles in their specific functions. In addition, each direction works closely with and complements the opposite one on its axis.

Once you have some version of a web pattern established for your mutual accountability structure, you can focus on each individual's support system. Each person should identify at least one person in or outside of the Implementation Team who can be their Accountability Buddy. The Co-accountant Project is a peer support tool from StartingBloc that works in a similar fashion. Much like personal Wellness Buddies, Accountability Buddies provide mutual support and dissolve patterns of work isolation. The pair of buddies, on a mutually agreed-upon basis, shares with each other the tasks they need to accomplish and by when. Sharing these in the form of SMART Steps, in particular, has been most successful in my experience with this system. Buddies check in with each other, either by text, phone, email, Zoom, or other methods that each person requests. Some people may want a reminder message a few days before a deadline. Others may request a follow-up message on the deadline day to see if the task was accomplished. Ultimately, each person is in charge of how and when, and how often, they receive accountability support.

The key to making the Accountability Buddy relationship function well is being very specific. Each person should be clear about where their challenges lie and the exact type of support they need. Taking concrete steps such as setting co-work dates and reminders for ourselves and our buddies, putting those dates in our calendars, and committing to follow-up as requested is essential for success. As soon as one or both people forget to follow up with their buddy more than twice, the support structure begins to break down. This degradation may naturally happen over time. When it does, you can renew your agreements or decide that your time as buddies was fruitful and that it may be time to find new buddies. Having more than one Accountability Buddy can be helpful for different kinds of activities and for redundancy in case one or more of these relationships dissolves over time. Contemplate who can think well with you about the type of work you're doing, and then choose a buddy for that specific activity.

Reflection and Integration: At this point in the design process, we have a pretty good picture of what a project will require for its best shot at success. After mapping out the stages and steps of Implementation, we have 20/20 vision, able to see not just the broad contours but also the details of a project. There's a lot to digest! This is a good time for Reflection and Integration before Evaluation. Here are some questions to support this digestion. You can also choose to write freely about what's alive for you regarding your project at this stage in the journey.

Journal: *Does your Social Design project have any new needs or requirements that you uncovered through planning its Implementation? Are there Goals you want to modify? Is there new information to feed back into the Analyses and Assessments? How has your perception of your role as designer or project manager shifted after realizing that you can and should have an Implementation Team, mutual accountability structures, and buddies?*

Please see Further Reading related to chapter 12 on page 250.

Social Design Lexicon for Chapter 12

Review the following key terms and write down what they mean to you. Then, reflect on how these concepts relate to your approach to project Implementation.

Stages of Implementation:

Mutual Accountability Structures:

Developmental Opportunity:

Implementation Team:

Co-working Dates:

Ground-truthing:

Time-boxing:

Rotational Neglect:

Good Enough:

Level of Activation:

Ideation vs. On-boarding vs. Operational vs. Wrapping Up:

Stacking Functions:

3-foot Toss:

Mental Load:

CHAPTER 13: EVALUATION
MEASURING PROJECT IMPACT AND WHOLENESS

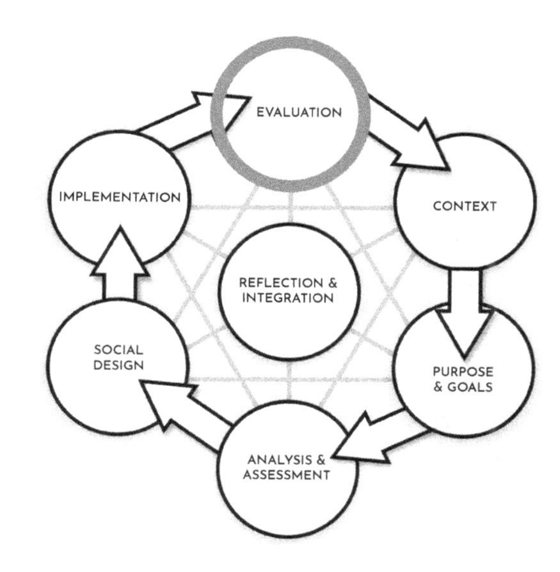

The Evaluation phase in the design process is a great synthesizer because it takes all the other phases into consideration. Evaluation tools provide information about how well the Design is functioning in its Context and the degree to which it's achieving its Goals. We can discern where a project's impacts can be leveraged for the greatest influence using the information that we gather through Evaluation processes. The motto of this phase is the permaculture principle accept feedback and apply self-regulation.

Even though Evaluation can and should occur throughout the design process, it is nestled between Implementation and Context in our conceptual diagram of the process for a few reasons. Its adjacency to the Implementation phase points to the role of Evaluation in measuring the success (or not) of Implementation. Likewise, Evaluation gives project managers feedback when they need to adjust the course of the Implementation plan.

Evaluation also ensures that the Context's 4 P's (People, Place, Power, and Paradigm, see page 120) will be remembered and incorporated into the measurement tools that gauge project outcomes. Evaluation tools can help reveal changing conditions within a project's Context. This valuable information lets designers know they need to revisit and redo related Observations and Interpretations of the project Analysis and Assessment.

Reflection and Integration, the central and recurring phase of the design process, also plays a role in Evaluation. In *Formative Evaluation*, designers evaluate as they go, pausing to observe outcomes at different *benchmarks* or intervals during a project's Implementation. Designers reflect on and integrate the data collected through Evaluations, and then use it to modify the Design as it unfolds. The feedback that an Evaluation provides about a Design—whether it occurs throughout Implementation or at an endpoint with a *Summative Evaluation*—helps designers and project managers guide project activities so that they stay in alignment with its Purpose.

Multiple Functions of Evaluation

Evaluation serves multiple functions in the living system of a Social Design. Unfortunately, this integral phase of the design process is sometimes left out in organizational cultures that are driven by urgency and that promote productivity over thoughtful pacing and whole systems thinking. In order to reap the many benefits of Evaluation, it's important to first understand its various functions and how to leverage them in order to achieve the most change. For instance, we can share the data that we gather as a way to initiate and incubate other projects with similar circumstances. This sharing supports the efficacy of new projects in other communities. This approach embodies the permaculture principle *catch and store energy,* whereby we can multiply the impact of an Evaluation to affect further concentric rings of change.

Please recall the Rings of Influence framework (see pages 80 and 115). In the diagram below, you can see how changemakers can apply this framework to leverage the impact of a well-designed project Evaluation.

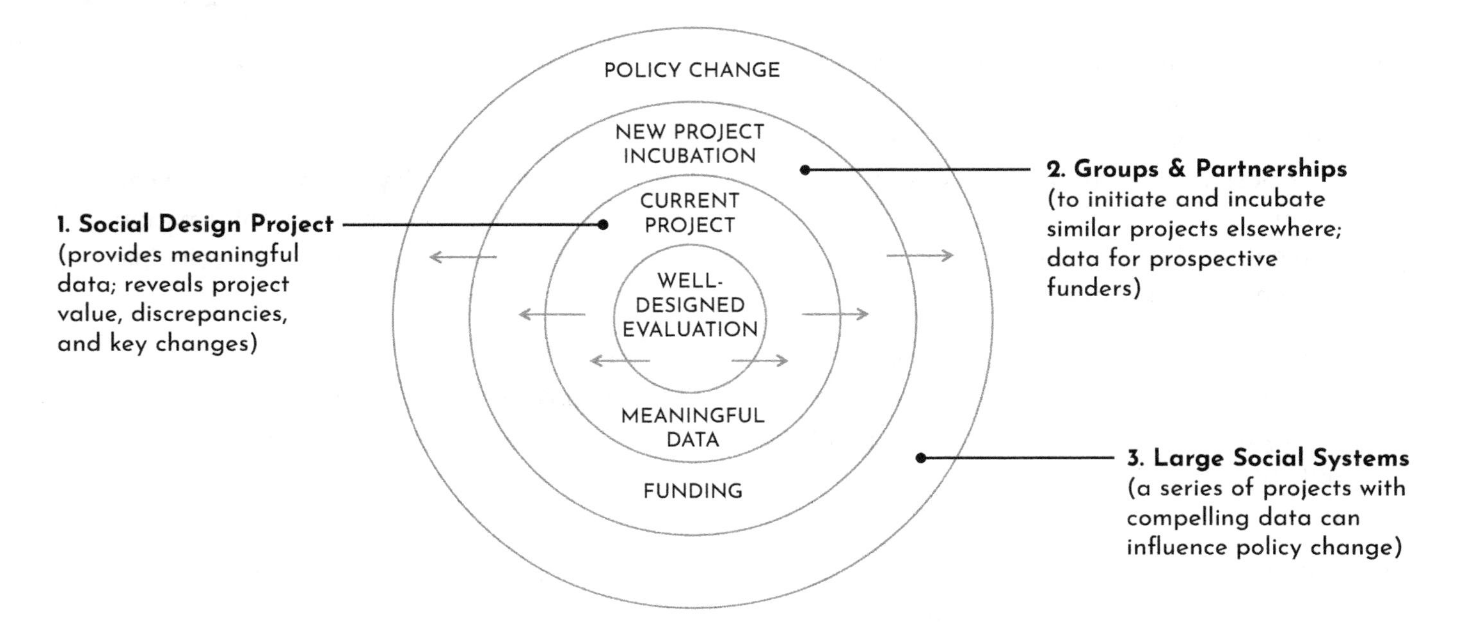

MULTIPLE FUNCTIONS AND INFLUENCE OF PROJECT EVALUATION

Function I—Finding Discrepancies: Evaluation helps project managers find discrepancies between a designer's stated intent and actual beneficial outcomes. This form of ground-truthing is valuable feedback. When an Evaluation reveals important discrepancies, designers can return to the project Purpose and Goals and rearticulate them more accurately.

I mentioned before that I co-developed a program proposal for the GARDEN Project for the Women's Fund of Western Massachusetts. The initial Purpose was to help remove two obstacles for women who wanted to leave abusive relationships: food insecurity and economic dependence. Four years later, at the conclusion of the project, I learned from the Evaluation consultant that the project had provided different Essential Functions than what our grant-writing team intended. The development of mutual aid networks among the participants, including community-building and trading and bartering food with each other, was most valuable to them. Their true needs were met through the activities of the project, regardless of what the Purpose Statement said in the grant proposal.

This Evaluation provided important feedback: The Purpose Statement and related Goals would require rewriting to better support these Essential Functions for future iterations of the project. As social designers, we will inevitably miss the mark sometimes, and that is encouraging because it means we are trying new things and looking for feedback on how to adjust our plans.

Function 2—Revealing Challenges: Evaluation also lets us zoom in on project details and locate unforeseen challenges. When feedback reveals new challenges, we can redesign one or more aspects of a project to respond to emergent conditions. The nonlinear and iterative structure of the design process creates moments that invite us to rework our design thinking.

We can also share information about unanticipated challenges with gatekeepers who have the ability to advocate for or make direct modifications to a project. Such modifications could include asking for resources, establishing clearer lines of communication among project partners, and/or adjusting project deliverables and expectations.

To continue with the GARDEN Project example, we saw challenges emerge in the third year. While the first two cohorts of participants had planted their gardens on private property belonging to partner agencies, the third cohort chose a city-owned park-let for their garden. Neither the city nor the neighbors were involved in the design or construction of the garden, which meant neither party had a sense of ownership or responsibility for it. The result was removal of plants and proliferation of litter, which left program participants feeling disrespected and discouraged.

These challenges—revealed through the Evaluation process—indicated that the project needed modifications in order to survive. The project manager deliberated over different plans to improve communication and social relations for this and future gardens on public property. They proposed that the foundation, one of the gatekeeper entities, fund a part-time position for a participant to serve as a project liaison with the city and neighbors. Feedback from Evaluations helps to locate these types of challenges and let us know where we need to make modifications so that the whole system can thrive.

Function 3—Showcasing Successes: Different Evaluation tools measure various dimensions of a project. When our projects are successful, we can choose data that best showcases a project's beneficial impacts. These, in turn, can influence broader social spheres beyond our initial project. For instance, changemaker colleagues in other organizations can use the Evaluation data from our projects in their applications for funding to help incubate similar projects in their organizations and bioregions.

We can also share data with policy advocates working to change institutional or governmental policies that affect larger social systems. Just Roots, the community farm in Greenfield, MA, researches the effects of fresh whole-food diets on public health in low-income communities. They use data from their Evaluation process to urge health insurance companies to change their policies and include coverage for local food shares as a form of preventative healthcare.

We can use *quantitative assessments* to generate concrete numbers, such as how many people in a community or institutional department were positively impacted by a program. Evaluators or other project spokespeople can use quantitative data, often presented as bar graphs or charts, when asking individual funders, foundations, or businesses for resources to continue or expand a project. Evaluation, when designed well, can showcase success and leverage a project's impact.

Function 4—Telling Key Stories: In contrast to quantitative tools, *qualitative assessments* produce measurements of outcomes in narrative form, such as stories, images, or quotes. This type of Evaluation is good for increasing people's empathy. A short film or interview can win project support at annual fundraisers, for example. Telling the story of the project is a powerful way to gain media attention. Images and quotes can be paired with quantitative data, too.

Media attention—whether from national news outlets, social media, or local radio stations—generates goodwill in a community, boosts the morale of project partners and Beneficiaries, and tells the story far and wide. For instance, the Jail-to-Farm-to-College and Employment Program received press in *American Jails Magazine*. Another reporter caught the story and published a piece in the national online publication *Ozy*, which led CNN to create a 10-minute film featuring the program. As a result of the media buzz, the project received an increased allocation of resources.

The more people who hear about your project, the more opportunities open up. Other places may be interested in piloting your project. Venues may invite you or another project spokesperson to give a presentation about it. Prospective project partners are more likely to contact you to collaborate. To use an ecological analogue: the more surface area a project has, the more opportunity there is for symbiosis with others. (With increased surface area also comes more opportunity for critique or attack. Being thoughtful about what messages and information we make public is of utmost importance.)

Even though it can be arduous and time-consuming to use Evaluations to prove that our project has value as a social enterprise, doing so is often regenerative; new opportunities arise to evolve the project Purpose and increase its influence.

Can you think of any additional beneficial functions of Evaluations?

■ Social Designer Tip: Flexibility and Evaluation ■

It's prudent to design an Evaluation lightly at the outset and in a way that's flexible. This approach is similar to the "50/50 principle": doing some planning while remaining open to change, knowing what we plan may not be applicable down the road. Likely you'll have new ideas and approaches to Social Design that emerge during the process; save yourself some time and make space for these emergent ideas by not over-designing the Evaluation early on.

The Building Blocks of Evaluation

Here are some building blocks with which to construct a well-designed Evaluation. Depending on what outcomes you want to measure, you can choose one or more of these approaches. The Objectives—which are concrete, measurable, and lead to specific ecological and social outcomes—that you articulated under each project Goal provide guidance on which outcomes are most important to measure. At this stage in the process, you may wish to return to your Objectives, and possibly update some of them based on the type of impact you wish to assess.

There are frequent bumps with Evaluation in grant writing and delivery. Often, we don't allot enough time to choose the best Evaluation tools, implement them, and analyze the data we collect. The people who write grants or proposals are not (usually) going to be project Beneficiaries. As such,

Goals and Objectives can be laden with assumptions and may not be relevant to the people that the project is trying to serve. When this happens, there's a gap between what project Beneficiaries receive and what they actually need. To make matters worse, evaluators then have the challenge of trying to assess irrelevant Objectives, and may miss the more potent aspects of a project's true impact. Instead of institutional gatekeepers solely determining how "social good" projects are evaluated, ongoing input from Beneficiaries about Goals, Objectives, and Evaluation procedures can avoid these issues.

Here in the Social Design Lab, you can play with the various approaches to Evaluation in your project and/or across different projects and see what types of results emerge. Remember, don't be afraid to experiment and learn as you go! These Evaluation methods are not mutually exclusive, but can be used in various combinations:

Evaluation Criteria: You may be wondering, How will I determine success? To some degree, this depends on what *thresholds of change* you are seeking. Developing *Evaluation Criteria* is a good way to determine if your project has made the magnitude of change you wanted it to, returning to your big-picture Purpose. Oftentimes Design Criteria (see page 171) relate to Evaluation Criteria. Get specific about which numbers or qualities must be reached in order to achieve your Goals. An example Design Criterion could be: Each year 12 women will have successfully completed all four college courses in the GARDEN Project (quantitative). Another Criterion could be: Each participant has articulated a positive impact (on their self-esteem, confidence, self-sufficiency, etc.) from learning food preservation skills (qualitative).

Quantitative Assessment: Measuring concrete variables in numerical data comes about through quantitative assessment. Within the world of funding and annual reporting, there is often an emphasis on quantitative or numerical data over qualitative forms of data. Designing an Evaluation well means choosing the best tools based on the Goals and Objectives. Please keep in mind that quantitative assessments are powerful, but they can be limited; they tend to measure only one or two dimensions of a project, such as the amount of vegetables grown or the number of children who consumed them. Without information about what these outcomes meant to the individuals or communities involved, impact reports can be dry.

Qualitative Assessment: This form of assessment values narratives, personal experiences, and feelings. It is most useful for telling a story, capturing nuance, and expressing how a project is relevant to audiences far and wide. While numerical data can be impressive, what stands out more often in people's minds are images and words.

The data collected through qualitative assessments can be coded and translated into quantitative measurements when needed. A survey with a place for open-ended questions, for example, can be coded; an evaluator will look for themes within the written data, e.g., how often something is said, patterns in stories, which can then be expressed in numerical form. Filtering for biases here is critical, however.

Formative Evaluation: This type of Evaluation occurs at different times throughout the period of Implementation, rather than all at once at the conclusion of a project. You can design this form of assessment to happen at regular intervals, at randomly dispersed times, and/or when sub-projects are completed. Formative Evaluation can include planning regular check-ins with project partners as you go. If it's an educational project, you can schedule classroom observations to see how students interact with their peers, the content, their mentors, etc. Or, you can use it as a *reflective practice* after a class or an event, and share what the Objectives were and capture what actually happened. This information will help you to plan the next class or event. One thing to note about Formative Evaluation, in particular, is that ultimate project outcomes are harder to track and assess because conditions can change quickly midway through a project. Surveys, data tracking sheets, and *rubrics* are tools that lend themselves to Formative Evaluation. Rubrics are grids that help evaluators code qualitative data with a numerical ranking of questions or categories, which turns qualitative data into quantitative data.

Formative Evaluation also lines up nicely with quarterly Implementation plans (see page 192). If you created a quarterly plan, please review the activities and phases that you projected. What effects, outcomes, or successes do you want to measure at the completion of three, six, nine, and twelve months? Using a reflective practice, you can ask yourself, Is it still important that I achieve what I thought I would at each of these benchmarks? Do other project activities depend on one or more outcomes to happen first? Or was the timing I assigned to some activities arbitrary, and thus can be adjusted to make way for priorities?

A word of advice from Ang Roell, a food justice colleague at University of Massachusetts-Amherst and Franklin County Jail and a professional evaluator: Taking a Formative approach to Evaluation requires discipline to stay on top of it. Roell remarks, "Formative Evaluation is very valuable. It's also important to acknowledge there are limitations because so much else going on with a project. It's a great tool if built into [a regular] practice."

Summative Evaluation: This type of Evaluation comes at the conclusion of a project or subproject. It looks at the big picture and assesses the overall impacts of project activities. Without Summative Evaluation, it's difficult to measure concrete change. Understanding when and what changes occur between the beginning and the end of a project, and in the period afterward, is crucial for measuring cultural shifts and whether they sustain over time.

Summative and Formative Evaluations complement each other nicely and can be used together on the same project. For instance, a survey or test at the end of a project that measures the degree of change, such as a new skill learned or a decrease in microaggressions, helps build more accuracy if our Formative Evaluations were somewhat subjective. Formative Evaluations provide opportunities to make adjustments along the way, yielding greater value and impact. Using both, we can see if the project is veering off course midstream *and* know what it accomplished at the end.

The information to gather in Summative Evaluations is most ripe just as a project is ending, when participants are still engaged and the changes they experienced are still fresh in their minds. Don't wait to gather data once the project has been over for some time. Participants may not be available any longer or forget the details of their experience.

Again, remember to be adaptable in your Summative Evaluation design, especially if you plan it early on in a project. And, be clear about *how* you will measure the smaller Objectives and the broad-brush changes that occurred as result of your project.

EXERCISE 44: Designing Your Evaluation

DESIGN LAB ➡ Please think about the type of impact that you want to measure for your project. This is a good time to revisit your Holistic Goals and related Objectives.

Journal: *Please record your responses to the following questions.*

Evaluation Criteria:

- *If you developed Design Criteria (see page 171) earlier in the Goals phase of the design process, determine if these are the same set of Criteria you want to use to measure project impact.*
- *Or, do you want to use different or additional Criteria?*
- *Then, develop Criteria for each of the three Nested Wholes that you articulated in your Holistic Goals: yourself/the Designer, the Group Context, and the Systems Context (see page 118). Use the criteria you've developed to inform your answers to the questions below.*

Quantitative Assessment:

- *What numerical data related to your project's impact do you want to measure, if any?*
- *What tools will you use to gather this data, e.g., observation with rubrics, surveys, a logbook, measurements of weight or social media followers or number of participants?*

Qualitative Assessment:

- *What outcomes or effects do you want to measure in narrative form, if any?*
- *What tools will you use to gather this data, e.g., questionnaires, note-taking, audio or film interviews, photographs?*

Formative Evaluation:

- *Does it make sense to evaluate project conditions as you go? If yes, when in your Implementation Plan and for what purpose(s) would you use Formative Evaluation? Mark when these assessments will occur on your plan and/or in your calendar.*
- *Would you use quantitative or qualitative assessment, or both, for the Formative Evaluations? Which tools will you use? Record these on your Implementation Plan as well.*
- *What might be the Benefits and Drawbacks of using or omitting Formative Evaluation?*

Summative Evaluation:

- *Do you want to assess the effects and outcomes of your project at the end rather than periodically? Or do you want to use both Formative and Summative Evaluation approaches?*
- *For your Summative Evaluation, would you conduct quantitative or qualitative assessments, or both? Which Evaluation tools would you use?*
- *What would be the Benefits and Drawbacks of using or omitting Summative Evaluation?*

Formative Evaluations for Entrepreneurs' Financial Wellness

If you plan to become or are already an entrepreneur, a professional designer of change, or at least want your independent change-making projects to produce income, then please respond to the following Formative Evaluation questions for entrepreneurs. If that is not your goal, then you can skip this topic.

You may want to consider the following questions:

How frequently do you want to review your bookkeeping? Every 30 days, 90 days, once a year? How will you determine if an arm of your business is not doing well?

- How often do you want to evaluate where you are, in terms of the number of projects you have or the income you've generated, in relation to your annual projections? This can help you figure out if you need to seek more work or pause in taking any new work.
- How will you measure which contracts are secured, which contracts closed, how they went, interactions with clients or funders, etc.? One idea is to make a rubric, which can include questions that you rank 1 to 5, such as: How well did the client communicate? Were you paid on time? How many times did you send an invoice? Would you work with this client again?
- How will you determine which of your business Goals and Objectives you achieved each quarter or year? How will you make space to observe places where you did things differently than you thought you would?

You can ask an Accountability Buddy to help you stay on track by checking in with you quarterly, or on whatever basis you choose to undertake a business Formative Evaluation. Consider scheduling regular co-working dates during these times so that you're not sitting at a computer all alone, entering data in spreadsheets into the wee hours of the night. Make it fun! Put on some music and take breaks to chat with your buddy. This type of co-working date helps ensure that you are taking care of the business upkeep you need to, which in turn ensures your change-making work is viable over the long run.

Designing Regenerative and Ethical Evaluations That Measure Wholeness

This book has guided you toward deliberately designing your change-making projects to express the permaculture ethics of Earth Care, People Care, and Resource Share. Even, and especially, in Evaluation we want the processes and tools we use to reflect our ethics. This worthy aim requires a commitment to intentional Evaluation design, rather than cutting corners and using industry standards. When we design an Evaluation protocol that is customized to measure wholeness—the nuances of the People, Place, Power, and Paradigms of a project—we can incorporate insightful information that we gather back into the Social Design, thus fortifying it. Evaluators use this *feedback loop* of data to evolve the project's Purpose and expand its potential for broad-scale change-making. This is one way that Evaluation can play a role in regenerating the vitality and efficacy of a project's impact.

In contrast to context-sensitive tools, standardized tools reflect the assembly-line mentality, which values efficiency over quality. Standardized tools clump unique People and Places into a homogenized "Context." This approach is fraught with Unconscious Assumptions, the effects of which can be degenerative and undercut a project's integrity. For instance, it might lead to reporting on percentages with a small sample size or using forms to collect demographic information that misses fine distinctions.

Facilitator Evaluation is one important tool for attending to the ethics of the Evaluation process. Just as anthropologists reflect on themselves as researchers and their impact on the social situations they study, evaluators can and should do the same. Here are a few questions that are important to incorporate in the design of ethical Evaluations:

- Who is administering the Evaluation process, and how are their identities, roles, and power positions likely to affect the information they choose to gather?
- How might Evaluation results be different when an assessment tool is administered to participants by someone in a power-over position rather than a peer?
- What happens when only one person is an evaluator versus numerous people?
- How might results change if project participants or other Beneficiaries give input on the Evaluation design and then administer it to each other? This approach is called *Participant-Centered Evaluation.*

There is an art to designing Evaluations that measure wholeness rather than pieces. In systems thinking, we know there will always be emergent properties and sometimes chaos that we didn't foresee. Permaculture principles *use protracted and thoughtful observation* and accept feedback and apply self-regulation remind us that in order to make changes that endure and evolve over time, it takes perseverance and openness to system feedback. A counterintuitive but complementary idea from the innovation world is "make mistakes faster." Through rapid trial and error, we can determine the best routes to success, and sooner!

Center for Whole Communities has developed Whole Measures, an assessment tool that considers the ecological, economic, and social dimensions of a project. They use a research method that is cyclical, participatory, qualitative, reflective, and responsive to the emerging needs of a situation. This method is unique in that it involves Participant-Centered Evaluation; participants select which outcomes are the most relevant to assess. Participants then use rubrics that they modify to reflect and measure the "fields and practices" that they actually experienced, such as strong communities, healthy people, and justice and fairness.

Under the guidance of Center for Whole Communities, Ang Roell is piloting the use of their Whole Measures for Community Food Systems tool within the Franklin County Jail in Greenfield, MA. Exemplifying a multicultural approach to project leadership, Jeanette Abi-Nader and the Community Food Security Coalition Center worked with Center for Whole Communities to assemble a fantastic team to create this food systems-specific assessment tool, including Adrian Ayson, Keecha Harris, Hank Herrera, Darcel Eddins, Deb Habib, Jim Hanna, Chris Paterson, Karl Sutton, and Lydia Villanueva.

The Participant-Centered Evaluation process that Roell uses is context-sensitive, engaging participants who are trauma survivors and disempowered in their current circumstances in ways that are ethical and *trauma-informed*. Roell works with the men in the Jail-to-Farm-to-College and Employment Program to: 1) form Evaluation teams, 2) understand and modify the rubrics, 3) define intended outcomes, 4) rate program components, 5) participate in reflective group dialogue, and 6) apply the results. We hope that this pilot assessment will help provide meaningful whole systems results so that other jails and prisons will elect to design similar programs and work toward culture shifts that will improve food justice in the correctional system.

Please return to your Evaluation design and see what modifications you would like to include, such as ways that it can be more ethical and better measure wholeness. Information about how to access the Whole Measures tool is in the Further Reading section, as are other resources related to chapter 13, on page 250.

Social Design Lexicon for Chapter 13

Review the following key terms and write down what they mean to you. Then, reflect on how these concepts relate to your approach to project Evaluation.

Formative Evaluation:

Benchmarks:

Summative Evaluation:

Catch and Store Energy:

Quantitative Assessment:

Qualitative Assessment:

Thresholds of Change:

Evaluation Criteria:

Reflective Practice:

Rubrics:

Feedback Loop:

Facilitator Evaluation:

Participant-Centered Evaluation:

Use Protracted and Thoughtful Observation:

Trauma-informed:

CHAPTER 14: REFLECTION AND INTEGRATION
TAKING STOCK BEFORE STARTING ANEW

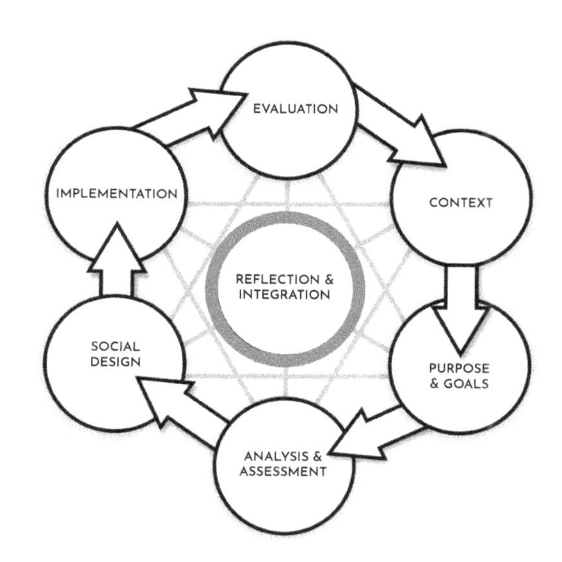

When we slow down to practice *Reflection and Integration*, we stay attuned with the rhythms of nature. *Senescence* is a beautiful form of letting go, nature's way of exhaling. We, too, can slow down and release, turn inward to reflect on all of the creating we've done, and integrate lessons from our recent experiences. In this way, we grow in wisdom. And so too, each phase of the design process benefits from and becomes fortified by reflecting on what we've learned and incorporating that information into our design thinking.

Thoughtful Reflection and Integration practices are antidotes—sometimes even political acts of resistance—to the progress, profit, and product-centered values of the exploitation Paradigm. When we default to these dominant practices that privilege urgency over contemplation, we miss the opportunity to cultivate new insights that are available to us at every bend in the road. The insights we glean are like deposits in our bank of Experiential Wealth that we can draw from to guide us in future scenarios. When don't reflect on lessons learned, we end up in the same situations over and over again.

In permaculture we call many of the herbaceous plants with large taproots, such as burdock, comfrey, and dandelion, *dynamic accumulators*. These plant allies penetrate the dense, dark subsoil with their long roots and bring trace minerals from the depths up to the surface. They pump these minerals through their vascular systems and store them in their leaves. When the autumn comes and the leaves senesce and fall to the Earth's surface as mulch, the deep mineral resources that these plants have accumulated are made available to other plants whose roots only grow in top layers of the soil.

This metaphor from nature reminds us humans of our opportunity to harvest the richness that is underground, so to speak. When we pause for Reflection and Integration, we too are digging deeper than what's available on surface, in search of rare gems. We can then integrate these gems into our conscious awareness, from our icebergs floating below the surface. This practice, in turn, increases our range of awareness and our competencies to take on more complex projects. We are better prepared for the next cycle of creation that follows this period of rest. When we commit to regular practices such as taking full weekends off, going on annual retreats, or taking sabbaticals, these restful periods of Reflection and Integration regenerate us and revivify our change-making work. And, much like the plant communities that abide with the dynamic accumulators, our social ecosystems benefit too when we return from the depths recharged, wealthy with new resources to share with our friends.

EXERCISE 45: Social Design Lab Reflection and Integration

If you have engaged in the short cycles of Reflection and Integration suggested throughout the Social Design Lab, then you will be already feeling the benefits of that work in your project and in your bones. Here, we have one last exercise that will encourage you to reflect on and integrate the broad patterns that have emerged in your project journey with the design process.

Journal: *Ideally, you can discuss these questions with a Learning Buddy or classmate. The listener takes notes in your journal while the speaker shares their responses, and vice versa. If you don't have another person with you, please write your responses to these questions in your journal.*

- *What did you learn about yourself, personally, during the course of the Social Design Lab?*
- *What new capabilities did you develop as a social designer? As a changemaker?*
- *What did you learn about relationships and power in your project?*
- *What did you learn about Regenerative Social Design, as a whole?*
- *What did you learn about yourself in regard to working alone? And in regard to working with buddies and mutually supportive teams?*
- *What practices will you begin or continue with in order to integrate your responses to these questions? Meditation, journaling, regularly visiting a spot in nature, recording nighttime dreams, tending a fire, sitting by a river, and talking with a good friend are all practices that I have found useful for letting the body and mind do its natural work of Integration.*
- *What inspirations or stirrings are arising in you regarding next steps? What beginnings of yet another creation cycle can you see just past this moment of twilight, where this book and your first full iteration of the Regenerative Social Design Process have reached their completion? Is there a small ritual you want to create to mark the ending of one cycle and the dawning of the next?*

Conclusion / Transition / Blessing

May your change-making work spread like prolific fruit, gifted to the beautiful and hardened places that surround you. May you be blessed with the ability to take root in both soft, fertile soil and rough, impervious concrete.

We all are the ones we've been waiting for, so why hesitate to step boldly into our brilliance? We have the great privilege and responsibility of being alive right now in the intergenerational web of humanity, linking the past with the future through the actions we make in each and every moment. We have the power to generate rippling rings of change through the small and big dreams we speak aloud to the world. The more we can imagine and design a new world into reality with each other, the more justice and liberation that world will bestow on its beings.

You have a powerful tool in your hand; never forget to use what you've learned about design for healing and renewal. As changemakers with a common prayer on our lips and wildly different Purposes in our hearts, we scatter and take root, working at our respective nodes toward coordinated Paradigm shifts. The butterflies that feed from our nectar will whisper our recipes for social alchemy to each other, as they migrate back and forth, pollinating our fruits, our gifts, our creations yet to come.

Please see Further Reading related to chapter 14 on page 251.

> *Never doubt that a small group of thoughtful, committed citizens can change the world; indeed, it's the only thing that ever has.*
>
> – Margaret Mead, cultural anthropologist

> *And the day came when the risk to remain tight in a bud was more painful than the risk it took to blossom.*
>
> – Anaïs Nin, culture-shifting novelist

Social Design Lexicon for Chapter 14

Review the following key terms and write down what they mean to you. Then, reflect on how these concepts resonate at this stage.

Reflection and Integration:

Senescence:

Dynamic Accumulators:

CLIENT INTERVIEW QUESTIONS

APPENDIX

Context

When did your organization, business, or project begin? Who started it?

Where is it located? Are there multiple locations?

Do you generate products? Services? Both?

Who do you serve? What is the Purpose/what are the issues you are trying to address?

What is the scope of the geographic or demographic area you serve? (e.g., neighborhood-scale, city-scale, regional-scale, national-scale)

What are your funding streams?

Organizational / Business / Cultural Practices

What is the management structure like? Who makes decisions? Who has power?

What is the work culture like of your project? (Does it operate in the Comfort Zone, minimally taking risks? Or is there always a crisis in the Panic Zone and people spending their time putting out fires? Or is there thoughtful observation then action taken?)

What is the personal well-being like for those involved? Is the baseline overworking? Are there cultural connection experiences? High turnover? High employee satisfaction?

Are you in collaboration with other organizations, institutions, or businesses? How?

What would you say is the level of awareness and training within the organization/business/project about racism and white supremacy? Classism? Other forms of oppression? What might be Unconscious Assumptions?

How multiracial is your management? Staff? Board of directors, if applicable?

Please define your current approach: Single-issue? Charity? Solidarity? Systems change?

Is the current business/project model sustainable? Financially sustainable? Reliable and well-trained staff? What have been your financial challenges and successes?

What kind of marketing do you do? Who/what is the public face of your organization/business/project?

CLIENT INTERVIEW QUESTIONS Con't.

Labor

How many entry-level employees? Management positions? Cooperative/democratic decision-making structure? Pay range? Or is work all done through volunteer efforts?

For each level of position, how diverse are people's ages? Races? Genders? Class? Education level?

Are there job benefits? Insurance? Non-financial forms of compensation?

What are your biggest challenges with labor or staffing?

Ecological Practices (if applicable)

How do you manage the land you reside on?

What are your energy practices? Efforts for energy efficiency?

What do you do with waste? E.g., compost, repurpose, upcycle, dump?

How, if at all, do you acknowledge and/or make reparations to the original stewards' land you operate on (if your people were not the original stewards)?

Big Picture

What are your Goals for the organization, business, or project in three to five years?

What would you say is the weakest link for the project? For instance, if one issue could move forward then the whole system would be improved?

What larger social systems does you aim to change? E.g., transportation system, education system, etc.

What is your vision for that change? Who else in the project shares that vision?

ENDNOTES

Chapter 2

1. Anthony Giancatarino and Simran Noor, *Building the Case for Racial Equity in the Food System*, New York: Center for Social Inclusion, 2014.

Chapter 5

1. Frank Biermann, Philipp Pattberg, and Fariborz Zelli, eds., *Global Climate Governance Beyond 2012: Architecture, Agency and Adaptation*, Cambridge: Cambridge University Press, 2010.

2. Natasha Gilbert, "One-Third of Our Greenhouse Gas Emissions Come from Agriculture," Nature News, nature.com, October 31, 2012.

3. Paul Hawken, *Drawdown: The Most Comprehensive Plan Ever Proposed to Reverse Global Warming*, Penguin Books, 2017.

4. Mark Leon Goldberg, "Pakistan Floods Facts and Figures," UN Dispatch. undispatch.com, August 16, 2010.

5. Mark Leon Goldberg, "Typhoon Haiyan in the Philippines Facts and Figures," UN Dispatch, undispatch.com, November 11, 2013.

Chapter 10

1. Jasmine Bell, "5 Things to Know About Communities of Color and Environmental Justice," Center for American Progress, americanprogress.org, April 25, 2016.

2. DeNeen L. Brown, "The High Cost of Poverty: Why the Poor Pay More," Washington Post, washingtonpost.com, May 18, 2009.

3. Tory Field and Beverly Bell, *Harvesting Justice: Transforming Food, Land, and Agricultural Systems in the Americas*, New Orleans, LA: Other Worlds, 2013, 74.

4. "Fighting Racism from the USDA: Black Farmers Gain Power Through Co-Ops," Food Sov Price, foodsovereigntyprize.org, accessed December 9, 2019.

5. Kilolo Kijakazi, Karen E. Smith, and Charmaine Runes, *African American Economic Security and the Role of Social Security*, Washington, DC: Urban Institute, July 23, 2019.

6. Andrianna Natsoulas and Beverly Bell, "Challenging Racism in the Food System: The Federation of Southern Cooperatives Fights for Black Lands, Agriculture, and Equal Justice," World Pulse, worldpulse.com, October 14, 2015.

7. "Statistics About Diabetes | ADA," American Diabetes Association, diabetes.org, March 22, 2018.

8. Marc Seitles, "The Perpetuation of Residential Racial Segregation in America: Historical Discrimination, Modern Forms of Exclusion, and Inclusionary Remedies," *Journal of Land Use and Environmental Law,* Vol. 14, no. 1, 1998: 89–124.

9. U.S. Government Accountability Office, *Workplace Safety and Health: Additional Data Needed to Address Continued Hazards in the Meat and Poultry Industry*, www.gao.gov/products/GAO-16-337, May 25, 2016.

10. Mengyao Zhang and Debarchana Ghosh, "Spatial Supermarket Redlining and Neighborhood Vulnerability: A Case Study of Hartford, Connecticut," *Transactions in GIS*, Vol. 20, no. 1, February 2016: 79–100.

FURTHER READING BY CHAPTER

Introduction

Decolonizing Permaculture

"Decolonizing Permaculture," Jesse Watson, www.resilience.org,

"Decolonizing Permaculture," Permaculture Activist magazine, #98, Winter 2015

"How to Decolonize the Permaculture Movement," Tobias Roberts, huffpost.com

Earth-Based Judaism

"Adamah: The Jewish Farming Fellowship," https://hazon.org/adamah/

Envisioning Sabbatical Culture: A Shmita Manifesto, Yigal Deutscher, Hazon

The Hebrew Priestess: Ancient and New Visions of Jewish Women's Spiritual Leadership, Jill Hammer and Taya Shere, Ben Yehuda Press, 2015

The Jewish Book of Days: A Companion for All Seasons, Jill Hammer, Jewish Publication Society, 2006

Jewish Farm School, www.jewishfarmschool.org

JOFEE (Jewish Outdoor, Food, Farming, and Environmental Education), https://hazon.org/jofee/overview/

Magic of the Ordinary: Recovering the Shamanic in Judaism, Gershon Winkler, North Atlantic Books, 2003

Seasons of Our Joy: A Handbook of Jewish Festivals, Arthur Waskow, Simon & Schuster, 1986

A Time for Every Purpose Under Heaven: The Jewish Life-spiral as a Spiritual Path, Arthur Waskow and Phyllis Ocean Berman, Farrar Straus & Giroux, 2002

Urban Adamah, https://urbanadamah.org

Wilderness Torah: Center for Earth Based Judaism, https://wildernesstorah.org/

Human Development and Nature

Nature and the Human Soul: A Road Map to Discovering our Place in the World, Bill Plotkin

Soulcraft: Crossing into the Mysteries of Nature and Psyche, Bill Plotkin

Omega Institute's Center for Sustainable Living

Omega Center for Sustainable Living, www.eomega.org/omega-center-for-sustainable-living

Permaculture

Edible Forest Gardens: Ecological Design and Practice for Temperate-climate Permaculture, Dave Jacke and Eric Toensmeier, Chelsea Green, 2005

"Permaculture," researchgate.net, Kevin Morel, François Léger and Rafter Sass Ferguson

Permaculture: A Designers' Manual, Bill Mollison, Tagari, 2nd ed., 1997

"Permaculture for Agroecology: Design, Movement, Practice, and Worldview. A Review," in Rafter Sass Ferguson and Sarah Taylor Lovell, Agronomy for Sustainable Development, 34, 2014, pp. 251–274

Permaculture: Principles and Pathways Beyond Sustainability, David Holmgren, Holmgren Design Services, 2002

Permaculture One: A Perennial Agricultural System for Human Settlements, Bill Mollison and David Holmgren, Tagari, 5th ed., 1990

Perma/Culture: Imagining Alternatives in an Age of Crisis, Molly Wallace and David Carruthers, Eds., Routledge, 2018

Regenerative Design

Regenerative Development and Design: A Framework for Evolving Sustainability, Pamela Mang and Ben Haggard (Regenesis Group), Wiley, 2016

"Regenerative Design Institute: Cultivating Skills and Deepening Awareness of Our Place on Earth," www.regenerativedesign.org/

Regenerative Design Group, www.regenerativedesigngroup.com/

Regeneration International, https://regenerationinternational.org/

Regenerative Thinking for Social Change, http://interactioninstitute.org/regenerative-thinking-for-social-change/

Systems Thinking

Thinking in Systems: A Primer, Donella Meadows, Chelsea Green, 2008

Systems Archetypes I: Diagnosing Systemic Issues and Designing High-Level Interventions, Daniel H. Kim, Systems Thinker

Systems Thinking for Social Change: A Practical Guide to Solving Complex Problems, Avoiding Unintended Consequences, and Achieving Lasting Results, David Peter Stroh, Chelsea Green, 2015

The Work That Reconnects

Joanna Macy, www.joannamacy.net/main

The Work That Reconnects Network, https://workthatreconnects.org/

Overview of Section I

Emergent Strategy and Nested Wholes

Emergent Nested Systems: A Theory of Understanding and Influencing Complex Systems as Well as Case Studies in Urban Systems, Christian Walloth, Springer, 2018

Emergent Strategy: Shaping Change, Changing Worlds, adrienne maree brown, AK Press, 2017

"Nested Social Change," Curtis Ogden, www.interactioninstitute.org

"The Regenerative Practitioner: Nested Systems of Place," Regenesis Group, www.regenesisgroup.com

Fractals

"Design for Living: The Hidden Nature of Fractals," Kim Tingley, www.livescience.com

"Emergence: The Remarkable Simplicity of Complexity," Andy Martin and Kristian Helmerson, www.theconversation.com

Chapter 1

Ancestral/Intergenerational Healing

Ancestral Medicine, https://ancestralmedicine.org

"Family Constellations," www.goodtherapy.org/learn-about-therapy/types/family-constellations

"What Are Systemic Constellations," www.nasconstellations.org/

Wounds into Wisdom: Healing Intergenerational Jewish Trauma, Tirzah Firestone

Center for Whole Communities

Center for Whole Communities, http://wholecommunities.org/

Class Oppression

The Activist Class Culture Kit, www.activistclasscultures.org/#about-marquee

"Class Action: Building Bridges Across the Class Divide," https://classism.org/

"Classism," class definitions, https://nccj.org/classism-0, Maurianne Adams, Lee Anne Bell, and Pat Griffin, Eds.

Created Equal: A Curriculum for High Schoolers and Middle Schoolers on Class and Classism, Class Action, https://classism.org/

Greenwashing

"How Can Consumers Find Out If a Corporation Is 'Greenwashing' Environmentally Unsavory Practices?" Roddy Scheer and Doug Moss, www.scientificamerican.com, June 29, 2013

"The Troubling Evolution of Corporate Greenwashing," Bruce Watson, www.theguardian.com, August 20, 2016

Gender Oppression and Undoing the Gender Binary

"Gender Logic and (Un)doing Gender at Work," Elisabeth K. Kelan, *Gender, Work and Organization*, February 12, 2010

MERGE for Equality, https://www.mergeforequality.org/

"The Struggles of Rejecting the Gender Binary," Daniel Bergner, *New York Times Magazine*, June 4, 2019

Undoing Gender, Judith Butler, Routledge, 2004

Mindfulness in Education

"The Five Literacies of Mindful Learning," Daniel Rechtschaffen and Taylor Rechtschaffen, *Educational Leadership*, Vol. 73, No. 2, October 2015

Mindful Life Project, www.mindfullifeproject.org

The Way of Mindful Education: Cultivating Well-Being in Teachers and Students, Daniel Rechtschaffen, WW Norton, 2014

Social Location/Location of Self

"Intersectionality, Social Locations of Privilege and Conceptions of Women's Oppression," Lee MacLean, www.cpsa-acsp.ca/papers-2009/MacLean.pdf

"The MSW@USC Diversity Toolkit: A Guide to Discussing Identity, Power and Privilege," Jeremy Goldbach, https://msw.usc.edu/

Tokenism

"8 Ways People of Color Are Tokenized in Nonprofits," Helen Kim Ho, www.medium.com

"There Is a Fine Line Between Tokenism and Diversity," Ella Wilks-Harper, www.gal-dem.com

"Tokenism: The Result of Diversity Without Inclusion," Tonie Snell, www.medium.com

Undoing Racism and Caucus Work

"Being Black in the Age of Wokeness," teaser article on nytimes.com for *Still Processing* podcast, with Wesley Morris and Jenna Wortham

"Caucus and Affinity Groups," *Racial Equity Tools*, www.racialequitytools.org/act/strategies/caucus-affinity-groups

"Going to the Root: How White Caucuses Contribute to Racial Justice," Alex Vlasic, *The Arrow*, arrow-journal.org, July 3, 2019

"Race Caucusing in an Organizational Context: A POC's Experience," Kad Smith, www.compasspoint.org

"Understanding and Dismantling Racism: A Booklist for White Readers," Charis Books and More, www.charisbooksandmore.com

Undoing Racism: The People's Institute for Survival and Beyond, www.pisab.org

"United to End Racis," www.rc.org/publication/uer/contents

"Why People of Color Need Spaces Without White People," Kelsey Blackwell, *The Arrow*, www.arrow-journal.org, August 9, 2018

Whiteness

"The Social Construction of Whiteness: Racism by Intent, Racism by Consequence," Teresa J. Guess, *Journal of Critical Sociology*, July 1, 2006

"Whiteness and White Privilege," Racial Equity Tools, www.racialequitytools.org/fundamentals/core-concepts/whiteness-and-white-privilege

Chapter 2

Abolition and Reparations

"Abolition and Reparations: Histories of Resistance, Transformative Justice, and Accountability," Patrisse Cullors, *Harvard Law Review*, April 10, 2019

Abolition Democracy: Beyond Empire, Prisons, and Torture, Angela Y. Davis, Seven Stories Press, 2005

The Abolitionist, www.abolitionistpaper.wordpress.com

Reparations Map for Black-Indigenous Farmers, Soul Fire Farm, www.soulfirefarm.org

Reparations: The Movement for Black Lives, www.policy.m4bl.org/reparations/

Competence Cycles

"Four Stages of Competence," www.wikipedia.org

The Fallacy of "Scientific Racism"

"Born That Way? 'Scientific' Racism Is Creeping Back into Our Thinking: Here's What to Watch Out For," W. Carson Byrd and Matthew W. Hughey, *Washington Post*, September 28, 2015

"A Brief History of the Enduring Phony Science That Perpetuates White Supremacy," Michael E. Ruane, *Washington Post*, April 30, 2019

"How Can We Curb the Spread of Scientific Racism?" John Horgan, www.blogs.scientificamerican.com, October 17, 2019

Intergenerational Trauma

"Can We Really Inherit Trauma?" Benedict Carey, *The New York Times*, December 10, 2018

"The Legacy of Trauma," Tori DeAngelis, American Psychological Association online journal

Intergenerational Trauma: The Transgenerational Impact of PTSD on the (Military) Family, Kimberly Copeland, www.deploymentpsych.org, July 7, 2018

Post Traumatic Slave Syndrome: America's Legacy of Enduring Injury and Healing, Joy DeGruy, Uptone Press, 2005

Wounds Into Wisdom: Healing Intergenerational Jewish Trauma, Tirzah Firestone, Monkfish Book Publishing, 2019

Power, Privilege, and Identity

James and Grace Lee Boggs School, www.boggsschool.org/

"Liberation Theory: A Working Framework," Ricky Sherover-Marcuse, *Films for Action*, June 16, 2017

Master's Program in Leadership for Sustainability at UVM, www.uvm.edu/rsenr/leadership-sustainability

"The Perpetuation of Residential Racial Segregation in America: Historical Discrimination, Modern Forms of Exclusion, and Inclusionary Remedies," Marc Seitles, *Journal of Land Use and Environmental Law*, Vol. 14, No. 1, Fall 1998

"Privilege as Practice: A Framework for Engaging with Sustainability, Diversity, Privilege, and Power, in the Journal of Sustainability Education," Matthew Kolan and Kalynn Sullivan TwoTrees, *Journal of Sustainability Education*, December 27, 2014

Racism and the Food System

African American Economic Security and the Role of Social Security, Kilolo Kijakazi, Karen E. Smith, and Charmaine Runes, Urban Institute, www.urban.org, July 2019

Building a Case for Creating Racial Equity in the Food System, Anthony Giancatarino and Simran Noor, Center for Social Inclusion, July 17, 2014

"A Critical Mass for Real Food," Anim Steel, www.yesmagazine.org, August 8, 2012

*Farming While Black: Soul Fire Farm's Practical Guide to Liberation on the Lan*d, Leah Penniman, Chelsea Green, 2018

Food Justice Now! Deepening the Roots of Social Struggle, Joshua Sbicca

Karen Washington: It's Not a Food Desert, It's Food Apartheid, Anna Brones, www.guernica.com, May 7, 2018

Resources for Racial Equity and Healing

Continuum on Becoming an Anti-Racist, Multi-Culturalist Institution, aesa.us, Crossroads Ministry (Adapted from original concept by Baily Jackson and Rita Hardiman, and further developed by Andrea Avazian and Ronice Branding), n.d.

Dismantling Racism Works Web Workbook, www.dismantlingracism.org

Interaction Institute for Social Change, https://interactioninstitute.org/

"Towards a Perspective on Eliminating Racism: 12 Working Assumptions," Ricky Sherover-Marcuse, Films for Action, May 16, 2017

Restorative and Transformative Justice

Centre for Justice and Reconciliation, http://restorativejustice.org/#sthash.OhSEv3rr.dpbs

Justice Compromised: The Legacy of Rwanda's Community-Based Gacaca Courts, Human Rights Watch, May 31, 2011

"Restorative Justice and Transformative Justice: Definitions and Debates," Candace Smith, *Sociology Lens*, March 5, 2013, blog post on www.restorativejustice.org

"Restorative or Transformative Justice?" Howard Zehr, blog post on www.emu.edu, March 10, 2011

"Rwanda's Community Courts: A Unique Experiment in Justice," Homa Khaleeli, *The Guardian*, January 11, 2010

Social Construction of Race

"A History: The Construction of Race and Racism," Western States Center, Dismantling Racism Project, www.racialequitytools.org, n.d.

Race: The Power of an Illusion, PBS film series, Larry Adelman, Executive Producer, and the California Newsreel, 2003

"Race: The Power of an Illusion, Background Readings, The Historical Origins and Development of Racism," George Fredrickson, www.pbs.org, 2003

"Race and Racial Identity Are Social Constructs," Angela Onwuachi-Willig, *New York Times*, September 6, 2016

Seeing White: Scene on Radio, podcast, www.sceneonradio.org/seeing-white, n.d.

"The Social Construction of Race: Some Observations on Illusion, Fabrication, and Choice," Ian F. Haney Lopez, *Harvard Civil Rights-Civil Liberties Law Review*, Vol. 1, 1994

Understanding White Supremacy

"Dismantle White Supremacy," Unitarian Universalist Association, www.uua.org/justice/dismantle-white-supremacy

"Hate Beyond Borders: The Internationalization of White Supremacy," Anti-Defamation League, www.adl.org, n.d.

Me and White Supremacy Workbook, Layla F. Saad, 2018

"White Supremacy Culture," Showing Up for Racial Justice, www.surjpoliticaledsite.weebly.com, n.d.

"White Supremacy's Insidious Presence in Our Elections," Amira Elghawaby, *Commentary*, www.globalnews.ca, October 4, 2019

White Fragility

"The Sugarcoated Language of White Fragility," Anna Kegler, huffpost.com, July 22, 2016; updated December 6, 2017

White Fragility: Why It's So Hard for White People to Talk About Racism, Robin DiAngelo, Beacon Press, 2018

"Why White People Freak Out When They're Called Out About Race," Sam Adler-Bell, AlterNet, March 10, 2015

White Privilege

White Awareness: Handbook for Anti-racism Training, 2nd ed., Judith Katz, University of Oklahoma Press, 2003

"White Culture," Judith Katz, www.pps.net, n.d.

"White Privilege: Unpack the Invisible Knapsack," Peggy McIntosh, *Peace and Freedom*, July/August, 1989

Chapter 3

Crowd-Funding Platforms

Kiva Zip, www.kiva.org/

GoFundMe, www.gofundme.com/

Patreon, www.patreon.com/

YouCaring, www.youcaring.com/

Gratitude Studies

"Giving Thanks Can Make You Happier," *Healthbeat*, Harvard Health Publishing, www.health.harvard.edu, n.d.

The Science of Happiness Podcast Episode 7: How Gratitude Benefits Your Brain, UC Berkeley, www.greatergood.berkeley.edu/, March 12, 2018

"7 Scientifically Proven Benefits of Gratitude That Will Motivate You to Give Thanks Year-Round," Amy Morin, *Forbes*, November 23, 2014

Internal Family Systems

"Internal Family Systems Model," www.wikipedia.org

"Internal Family Systems (IFS)," www.selfleadership.org/

"Internal Family Systems (IFS)," *Good Therapy*, updated February 12, 2018

Jewish Cycles of Seven

"Cycles of Seven," *Ohr Chadash*, www.thetrugmans.com, 2020

Envisioning Sabbatical Culture: A Shmita Manifesto, Yigal Deutscher

Rav Kook's Introduction to Shabbat Ha'aretz, Rabbi Abraham Isaac Kook, Rabbi Julian Sinclair, trans., Hazon, 2014

Shmita Sourcebook, Yigal Deutscher, Anna Hanau, and Nigel Savage, www.hazon.org

Personal Wellness and Self-Care

"Caring for Ourselves as Political Warfare," adrienne maree brown, adriennemareebrown.net, December 10, 2014

Pleasure Activism: The Politics of Feeling Good, adrienne maree brown, AK Press, 2019

"Radical Self Care: 6 Ways Activism Is Good for You," Victoria Albina and Julie Netherland, huffpost.com, October 6, 2017

The Radically Selfish Podcast, Michelle Keinan

Regenerative Business

Financial Permaculture Institute, www.financialpermaculture.com/about

nRhythm: Regenerative Organizational Design, https://nrhythm.co/

"Episode 1236: Financial Permaculture with Eric Toensmeier," *Permaculture Podcast*, Scott Mann, www.thepermaculturepodcast.com, December 27, 2012

The Regenerative Business: Redesign Work, Cultivate Human Potential, Achieve Extraordinary Outcomes, Carol Sanford, Nicholas Brealey, 2017

The Regenerative Business Summit, https://theregenerativebusinesssummit.com/

Regenerative Enterprise: Optimizing for Multi-capital Abundance, Ethan Roland and Gregory Landua, Lulu.com, 2015

Reinventing Organizations: An Illustrated Invitation to Join the Conversation on Next-Stage Organizations, Frederic Laloux, Nelson Parker, 2016

The Responsible Entrepreneur: Four Game-Changing Archetypes for Founders, Leaders, and Impact Investors, Carol Sanford, Jossey-Bass, 2014

Solidarity Economics

Blue Heart, https://www.blueheartaction.org/divestment

Compost Co-op, www.thecompostcooperative.com/

Evergreen Cooperatives, www.evgoh.com/about-us/

Fossil Free Movement, https://gofossilfree.org/

"How I Can Offer Reparations in Direct Proportion to My White Privilege: What It Looks Like to Pay for the Unearned Advantages My Whiteness Has Afforded Me," Chris Moore Backman, www.yesmagazine.org, October 25, 2017

J. K. Gibson-Graham's work. Retrieved from https://en.wikipedia.org/wiki/J. K. Gibson-Graham

"Local Currencies Program," Schumacher Center for a New Economics, n.d.

"Michael Eric Dyson Believes in Individual Reparations," interview by Ana Marie Cox, *New York Times Magazine*, January 4, 2017

New Economy Movement, retrieved from https://en.wikipedia.org/

Regenerative Enterprise Institute, www.regenterprise.com/regenerative-enterprise/

Sacred Economics: Money, Gift, and Society in the Age of Transition, Charles Eisenstein, North Atlantic Books, 2011

Schumacher Center for a New Economics, https://centerforneweconomics.org/

Toolbox for Education and Social Action (TESA) Collective, www.tesacollective.com/

U.S. Solidarity Economy Network, https://ussen.org/

"What Reparations Might Look Like: How Could Reparations Manifest at an Individual and Collective Level, and What Might This Say About Unrelenting Systemic Racial Inequality?" Jennifer Epperson, *The Outline*, September 17, 2019

What Is Divestment? YouTube video, www.350.org, January 7, 2016

Worker-owned Cooperatives, www.usworker.coop/what-is-a-worker-cooperative/

See also Chapter 10 Further Reading on "Valuing Non-Financial Forms of Wealth"

Zones of Use

"Permaculture and Social Zoning," Pedro Valdjui, *Terra Alta* blog, January 15, 2019

"Zones and Sectors: Efficient Energy Planning," *Deep Green Permaculture*, n.d.

Chapter 4

Ancestral Futures

Active Hope: How to Face the Mess We're in Without Going Crazy, Joanna Macy and Chris Johnstone, New World Library, 2012

Hebraic Futurism nascent movement, catalyzed by Regenerate Change.

"How to Be Better Ancestors," Winona LaDuke, *Center for Humans and Nature*, February 27, 2017

Queer Ancestors Project, www.queerancestorsproject.org

Queer Ancestral Futures Zine, booklet by Queer Eco Project

Biomimicry

Biomimicry Institute, https://biomimicry.org

"How the Wonder of Nature Can Inspire Social Justice Activism," adrienne maree brown www.yesmagazine.org, February 1, 2018

Cultural Mentoring

"Art of Mentoring," *Wilderness Awareness School*, www.wildernessawareness.org/adult-programs/art-mentoring, n.d.

Coyote's Guide to Connecting to Nature, Jon Young, Ellen Haas, and Evan McGown, Owlink Media, 2nd ed., 2010

8 Shields, http://8shields.org/

"Kamana Independent Study," *Wilderness Awareness School*, https://wildernessawareness.org/adult-programs/kamana

Vermont Wilderness School, https://vermontwildernessschool.org/

Cultural Orphans

"Bolad's Kitchen," www.floweringmountain.com/boladskitchen

"The 'Sin' of Cultural Appropriation from Within an Orphan Culture," Aimee K. Shaw, www.medium.com

Group Dynamics and Social Justice

"Calling-in Versus Calling-out: 'Throwing Out My Activist Armchair,'" Jennifer Mahan, *If/When/How*, June 6, 2017

Emergent Strategy: Shaping Change, Changing Worlds, adrienne maree brown, AK Press, 2017

Guide to Working in Diverse Groups, Spirit in Action

"In Good Faith: Intent & Impact in Social Justice," Han Koehle, www.medium.com, May 2, 2017

"Intent vs. Impact: Why Your Intentions Don't Really Matter," Jamie Utt, www.everydayfeminism.com, July 30, 2013

Leading Diverse Communities: A How-To Guide for Moving from Healing to Action, Cherie Brown and George J. Mazza

"A Practical Guide to Calling In," Mel Mariposa, www.theconsentcrew.org, May 29, 2016

Safe Spaces, Brave Spaces: Diversity and Free Expression in Education, John Palfrey, MIT Press, 2017

Peacemaking and Communication Skills

Center for Non-violent Communication, www.cnvc.org

Haudenosaunee Guide for Educators, guide on www.americanindian.si.edu, National Museum of the American Indian Education Office

"Intro to Listening," *White Ally Toolkit*, www.whiteallytoolkit.com

"Tree of Peace Society," revolvy.com, content from www.wikipedia.com

What Is Active Listening? United States Institute of Peace, n.d.

White Roots of Peace: Iroquois Book of Life, Paul A. W. Wallace, Clear Light Publishing, 1990

Rites of Passage

Animus Valley Institute, https://animas.org/

Living on Land (LOL) program at Wildseed Farm and Healing Village, www.wildseedcommunity.org/

Nature and the Human Soul: Cultivating Wholeness and Community in a Fragmented World, Bill Plotkin, New World Library, 2008

Oaks Counsel Day Quests, https://oakscounsel.com/dayquests

"Rites of Passage," *Ojai Foundation*, https://ojaifoundation.org/project/rites-of-passage

The Roaring of the Sacred River: The Wilderness Quest for Vision and Self-healing, Steven Foster and Meredith Little, Prentice Hall Press, 1989

School of Lost Borders, http://schooloflostborders.org

Tree of Life: A Woman's Initiation Journey, www.treeoflifeinitiation.org

Wild Mind: A Field Guide to the Human Psyche, Bill Plotkin, New World Library, 2013

Social Justice Focused Design Courses

"Zone In: Social Permaculture for Regenerative Change," *Denver Permaculture Guild*

"Ecological Literacy Immersion Program," *Omega Center for Sustainable Living*

"Permaculture FEAST: For Ecological and Social Transformation, (Oct – Dec 2014, Holyoke, MA, USA)," Jonathan Bates, *Permaculture News*, June 23, 2014

"Regenerative Design for Changemakers Training," *Regenerate Change*, n.d.

Sociocracy

Sociocracy and Permaculture: Designing the Future, Erin Young and John Schinnerer, YouTube webinar, June 9, 2017

Sociocracy: Solutions That Guarantee a Deeper Democracy, www.sociocracy.info

Whole Systems Social Change Approaches

Center for Whole Communities, http://wholecommunities.org

Spirit in Action's Guide to Working in Diverse Groups, spiritinaction.net

Chapter 5

Climate Change and Climate Justice

The Carbon Farming Solution: A Global Toolkit of Perennial Crops and Regenerative Agriculture Practices for Climate Change Mitigation and Food Security, Eric Toensmeier, Chelsea Green, 2016

Drawdown: The Most Comprehensive Plan Ever Proposed to Reverse Global Warming, Paul Hawken, ed., Penguin Books, 2017

Hurricane Season Curriculum, Climbing PoeTree

Proceedings of the National Academy of Sciences, www.pnas.org

"Sustaining All Life," www.rc.org/publication/environment/sustainingalllife

See also Chapters 8 and 11 Further Reading

Food System Transformation

Farming While Black: Soul Fire Farm's Practical Guide to Liberation on the Land, Leah Penniman, Chelsea Green, 2018

Harvesting Justice: Transforming Food, Land, and Agriculture Systems, Tory Field and Beverly Bell, Other Worlds, 2013

Rebuilding the Foodshed: How to Create Local, Sustainable, and Secure Food Systems, Phillip Ackerman-Leist, Chelsea Green, 2013

Grief Work

Coming Back to Life: The Updated Guide to the Work That Reconnects, Joanna Macy and Molly Brown, New Society, rev. ed., 2014

"Grief Ritual with Sobonfu Somé," School of Integrated Living (SOIL)

Joanna Macy, www.joannamacy.net/main

Malidoma.com, http://malidoma.com/main

My Grandmother's Hands: Racialized Trauma and the Pathway to Mending Our Hearts and Bodies, Resmaa Menakem, Central Recovery Press, 2017

North American Systemic Constellations, www.nasconstellations.org/what-are-systemic-constellations.html

The Smell of Rain on Dust: Grief and Praise, Martin Prechtel, North Atlantic Books, 2015

Sobonfu Somé, www.sobonfu.com/about-sobonfu/

What Is Spiritual Bypassing? Diana Raab, www.psychologytoday.com, January 23, 2019

Wounds into Wisdom: Jewish Intergenerational Healing, Tirzah Firestone, Adam Kadmon Books, 2019

Jewish Practices for Personal Growth

At the Well, www.atthewellproject.com

Miriam's Well, poem by Barbara Holender, ritualwell.org

"Netivot: Paths of the Priestess," Kohenet Hebrew Priestess Institute, kohenet.com

"Tzav," *Rabbi Shefa Gold*, www.rabbishefagold.com, 2006

Personal Transformation and Leadership

BOLD (Black Organizing for Leadership and Dignity), www.boldblackorganizing.org

"The Ecology of Leadership: A Transformational Pathway to Thrive and Serve in a Changing World," *Regenerative Design Institute*, https://regenerativedesign.org/programs/ecology-leadership#.XdstcjJKigQ

On the Fringes of Place: A Blog About Identity and Indigeneity, http://onthefringesofplace.com/

Re-evaluation Counseling, www.rc.org

Wounded Healer Archetype

The Wounded Healer: A Jungian Perspective, Kathryn C. Larisey, Jung Society of Atlanta, 2012

"The Wounded Healer as Cultural Archetype," Galia Benziman, Ruth Kannai, and Ayesha Ahmad, *Comparative Literature and Culture*, Vol. 14, No. 1, 2012

Chapter 6

Accomplices & Solidarity

Accomplices Not Allies: Abolishing the Ally Industrial Complex, Indigenous Action, www.indigenousaction.org/accomplices-not-allies-abolishing-the-ally-industrial-complex/

Allyship (& Accomplice): The What, Why, and How, Michelle Kim, www.Medium.com

Learn & Unlearn: Anti-racism Resource Guide Lesson 1: Actor, Ally, Accomplice, John M. Flaxman Library, https://libraryguides.saic.edu/learn_unlearn/foundations1

Opportunities for White People in the Fight for Racial Justice, www.whiteaccomplices.org/

Solidarity Vigil: 3 Ways to Stand with the Sikh Community Now, www.solidarityvigil.com

Building Alliances

Alliances for Change: Organizing for the 21st Century, Building Movement Project, www.racialequitytools.org, n.d.

Anti-oppression Resource and Training Alliance (AORTA), http://aorta.coop

Chris Crass, www.chriscrass.org/essays--resources.html

Resilience Alliance, http://resiliencealliance.com

"Women in Leadership: Finding and Leveraging Allies and Mentors," Zoe Mackey, Berrett-Koehler Publishers, www.ideas.bkconnection.com, August 22, 2018

Grief Work

See Resources in Chapter 5 Further Reading

Indigenous Worldviews vs. Western Scientific Worldviews

Braiding Sweetgrass: Indigenous Wisdom, Scientific Knowledge, and the Teachings of Plants, Robin Wall Kimmerer, Milkweed Editions, 2015

Dancing with the Cannibal Giant: New Stories for the Great Transition, documentary narrated by Sherri Mitchell, BALE — Building a Local Economy, 2019

Gathering Moss: A Natural and Cultural History of Mosses, Robin Wall Kimmerer, Oregon State University Press, 2003

Neurodecolonization and Indigenous Mindfulness, Michael Yellow Bird, www.indigenousmindfulness.com

Sacred Instructions: Indigenous Wisdom for Living Spirit-Based Change, Sherri Mitchell, North Atlantic Books, 2018

Tending the Wild: Native American Knowledge and the Management of California's Natural Resources, M. Kat Andersen, University of California Press, 2013

White Earth Land Recovery Project, http://welrp.org/

Keystone Species in General, and Humans as Necessary Keystone Species

"Aboriginal Land Management and Care," J. Korff, creativespirits.info, updated December 2, 2019

The Benefits Associated with Caring for Country: Literature Review, Dr. Jessica K Weir, Ms. Claire Stacey and Dr. Kara Youngetob, www.aiatsis.gov.au, 2011

Farming with the Wild: Enhancing Biodiversity on Farms and Ranches, Daniel Imhoff, Sierra Club Books, 2003

How Reintroducing Wolves Helped Save a Famous Park, BBC film

Indigenous Land Management in Australia, by Rosemary Hill, Petina L Pert, Jocelyn Davies, Catherine J Robinson, Fiona Walsh and Fay Falco-Mammone, www.agriculture.gov.au, May 2013

Inhabit: A Permaculture Perspective, film, www.inhabitfilm.com, Costa Boutsikaris and Emmett Brennan, 2015

Nested Wholes and Interconnection

Carol Sanford, https://carolsanford.com

Leadership and the New Science: Discovering Order in a Chaotic World, 3rd ed., Margaret Wheatley, Berrett-Koehler Publishers, 2006

The Hidden Life of Trees: What They Feel, How They Communicate, Discoveries from a Secret World, Peter Wohlleben, Greystone Books, 2016

"The Integral Theory of Ken Wilber," Julian Scott, New Acropolis, www.library.acropolis.org, August 22, 2019

The More Beautiful World Our Hearts Know Is Possible, Charles Eisenstein, North Atlantic Books, 2013

A Pattern Language: Towns, Buildings, Construction, Christopher Alexander, Murray Silverstein, and Sara Ishikawa, Oxford University Press, 1977

Relational Reality, Charlene Spretnak, Green Horizon Books, 2011

A Theory of Everything: An Integral Vision for Business, Politics, Science and Spirituality, Ken Wilbur, Shambhala, 2001

Thinking in Systems: A Primer, Donella Meadows, Chelsea Green, 2008

Undoing Racism

Black Lives Matter, https://blacklivesmatter.com

"Counting the Omer for Black Lives," *Jews for Racial and Economic Justice*, www.jfrej.org, March 30, 2018

Dimensions Educational Consulting, www.dimensionsedc.com/

In Search of Our Mothers' Gardens, Alice Walker, Mariner Books, 2004

Raising White Kids: Bringing Up Children in a Racially Unjust America, Jennifer Harvey, Abingdon Books, 2018

Showing Up for Racial Justice, www.showingupforracialjustice.org

Uprooting Racism: How White People Can Work for Racial Justice, 3rd ed., Paul Kivel, New Society Publishers, 2011

We Rising Up (featuring Carolyn Malachi), YouTube music video, Climbing PoeTree

See also Resources for Chapter 1 Further Reading

Chapter 7

Backcasting Tool

"Backcasting in Design," Aga Szóstek, www.uxdesign.cc

Backcasting Timeline, https://openchangeideas.files.wordpress.com/2015/06/backcasting-a0.pdf

Changemakers' Recipe

"Ikagai," wikipedia.org

"Ikigai: The Japanese Secret to a Long and Happy Life Might Just Help You Live a More Fulfilling Life," Thomas Oppong, www.medium.com

Climbing PoeTree

Climbing PoeTree, www.climbingpoetree.com

Climbing PoeTree, Alixa Garcia and Naima Penniman, book of poems

Collective Care

"From Self Care to Collective Caring," Leah Harris, www.madinamerica.com

Harriet's Apothecary, www.harrietsapothecary.com

More Than Self-Care: A Workbook for Holistic Liberation, Serena Yeager, 2020

Ways of Wielding the Force: 13 Exercises in Collective Care and Effectiveness, Zainab Amadahy, CreateSpace Independent Publishing Platform, 2013

Facing Death

"Death and Dying," Pam Geyer, www.rc.org, reprinted from the RC e-mail discussion list for leaders of elders

"Death and Dying, Life and Living," www.rc.org, excerpts of talks by Joan Karp

"Death Meditation: Meet Your Death Before You Die Actually," www.spirare.name

"Doula Givers: Certified End of Life Doula Training," www.doulagivers.com/positive-passings/death-doula

Jewish Practices of Reflection and Integration

"5 Offerings for a Deep and Powerful Yom Kippur," Rabbi Arthur Waskow, www.theshalomcenter.org

"Renewing Ourselves and Our Visions in the Month of Elul," Tamara Cohen, www.ritualwell.org

"Rosh Hashanah: Missing Words from a Hidden God," Rabbi Jill Hammer, sermon on www.rabijillhammer.com

"Yom Kippur Katan," Rabbi Shefa Gold, www.rabbishefagold.com

Internal Family Systems (IFS)

See Resources in Chapter 3 Further Reading

Modern Health Crises

"Depression as a Disease of Modernity: Explanations for Increasing Prevalence," Brandon H. Hidaka, *Journal of Affective Disorders*, 140(3), 2012

National Academy of Sciences Engineering and Medicine: Committee on Population Division of Behavioral and Social Sciences and Education, https://sites.nationalacademies.org/DBASSE/CPOP/index.htm

Sabbatical Consciousness: Modern Adaptive Practices of Cyclical Periods of Rest and Renewal

"Envisioning Sabbatical Culture," Yigal Duetscher, blog post on www.schusterman.org

"5 Major World Religions: How Do They Worship?", *Deseret News*, www.deseret.com

Rav Kook's Introduction to Shabbat Ha'aretz, Rabbi Abraham Isaac Kook; Rabbi Julian Sinclair (trans.)

"The Sabbath: An Ancient Holiday in the Modern World," Richard Stockton, www.allthatsinteresting.com

The Sabbath: Its Meaning for Modern Man, Abraham Joshua Heschel

Shmita Sourcebook, Yigal Deutscher, Anna Hanau and Nigel Savage, www.hazon.org

Story of the Day and Other Core Routines

See "Cultural Mentoring" in Chapter 4 Further Reading

Overview of Section II

Beginner's Mind

"Approaching Life with Beginner's Mind" Leo Babauta, www.zenhabits.net

"The Beauty of Beginners Mind," Jack Kornfield, www.jackkornfield.com

Insight Timer App, https://insighttimer.com/meditation-app

Emergent Strategy

"Emergent Strategy Ideation Institute," www.alliedmedia.org/esii

Emergent Strategy: Shaping Change, Changing Worlds, adrienne maree brown, AK Press, 2017

How to Survive the End of the World, Autumn Brown and adrienne maree brown, podcast, www.stitcher.com/podcast/brown-sisters/how-to-survive-the-end-of-the-world

Regenerative Design Process

Conway School of Landscape Design, https://csld.edu/

Edible Forest Gardens: Ecological Design and Practice for Temperate-Climate Permaculture, Dave Jacke and Eric Toensmeier, Chelsea Green, 2005

Permaculture One: A Perennial Agricultural System for Human Settlements, Bill Mollison and David Holmgren, Tagari, 5th ed., 1990

Regenerative Development and Design: A Framework for Evolving Sustainability, Pamela Mang and Ben Haggard, Wiley, 2016

"Stockbridge School UMass: Intro to Permaculture Course," https://onlinesustfoodfarm.com/permaculture/

Resilience Theory in Planning and Design

"From Fail-Safe to Safe-to-Fail: Sustainability and Resilience in the New Urban World," Jack Ahern, *Landscape and Urban Planning*, Vol. 100, No. 4, April 30, 2011

Resilience Thinking in Urban Planning, Ayda Eraydin and Tuna Taşan-Kok, Springer, 2012

Social Permaculture Design

"Building a Toolbox for Social Permaculture," Abrah Dresdale and Connor Stedman, *Permaculture Activist Practicing Democracy*, Issue 89

Change Here Now: Permaculture Solutions for Personal and Community Transformation, Adam Brock, North Atlantic Books, 2017

Lisa Marie DePiano, http://lisamariedepiano.com

People and Permaculture: Caring and Designing for Ourselves, Each Other and the Planet, Looby McNamara, Permanent Publications, 2012

"Starhawk: Regenerative Culture, Earth-based Spirituality, and Permaculture," https://starhawk.org/

"Stockbridge School UMass: Social Permaculture for Food Justice Course," https://onlinesustfoodfarm.com/social-permaculture

See also Chapter 10 Further Reading on "Social Design Trainings with Critical Analysis"

Chapter 8

Climate Change and Farmer Suicides in India

"Crop-damaging Temperatures Increase Suicide Rates in India," Tamma Carleton, *PNAS*, 114(33), August 15, 2017

Failure to Yield: Evaluating the Performance of Genetically Engineered Crops, Doug Gurian-Sherman, *Union of Concerned Scientists*, www.ucsusa.org, 2009

"Farmer-suicide in India: Debating the Role of Biotechnology," Gigesh Thomas and Johan De Tavernier, *Journal of Life Sciences, Society and Policy*, Vol. 13, May 2017

Climate Debt and Climate Justice Resources/Reparations

This Changes Everything: Capitalism vs. The Climate, Naomi Klein, Knopf Canada, 2014

Climate: A New Story, Charles Eisenstein, North Atlantic Books, 2018

"The Cruel Irony of Climate Debt," Francesco Bassetti, www.climateforesight.eu, 2019

"It's Time to Pay Our Climate Debt to Countries Like Mozambique," Ben Ehrenreich, www.thenation.com, April 22, 2019

On Fire: The Burning Case for a Green New Deal, Naomi Klein, Knopf Canada, 2019

"Reparations Map for Black-Indigenous Farmers," www.soulfirefarm.org

The Shock Doctrine: The Rise of Disaster Capitalism, Naomi Klein, Vintage Canada, 2008

See also Chapter 5 and 11 Further Reading sections

Myth of Meritocracy

"Five Myths About Meritocracy: No, Rich Families at Elite Schools Aren't Really Paying Their Own Way," Daniel Markovits, *Washington Post*, September 13, 2019

"The Myth of Meritocracy: Assuming That Meritocracy Is Real and Justifiable Is Just Another Racial and Sexual Micro-aggression," Jackie Labonite, www.theodysseyonline.com, July 4, 2016

"Why the Myth of Meritocracy Hurts Kids of Color: A New Study Finds That Believing Society Is Fair Can Lead Disadvantaged Adolescents to Act Out and Engage in Risky Behavior," Melinda Anderson, *The Atlantic*, July 27, 2017

Paradigm Shifting

Climate: A New Story, Charles Eisenstein, North Atlantic Books, 2018

"Bronte Velez On the Pleasurable Surrender of White Supremacy, Pt. 1," *For the Wild*, podcast episode 139, October 2, 2019, https://forthewild.world/listen/bronte-velez-on-pleasurable-surrender-of-white-supremacy-1-139

"Imbalanced Spheres of Activism and 'The Great Turning' that Needs to Get Turning," Troy Wiley, www.medium.com, April 24, 2018

Music, Spirit and Protest: An Interview with Climbing PoeTree on the Laura Flanders Show, YouTube

Thinking in Systems: A Primer, Donella Meadows, Chelsea Green, 2008

Pattern Language

Change Here Now: Permaculture Solutions for Personal and Community Transformation, Adam Brock, North Atlantic Books, 2017

The Nature of Order: An Essay on the Art of Building and the Nature of the Universe, Christopher Alexander, Center for Environmental Structure, 2002

A Pattern Language: Towns, Buildings, Construction, Christopher Alexander, Murray Silverstein, and Sara Ishikawa, Oxford University Press, 1977

Regenerative Thinking and Carol Sanford's Work

No More Feedback: Cultivate Consciousness at Work, Carol Sanford, Interoctave, 2019

The Regenerative Business: Redesign Work, Cultivate Human Potential, Achieve Extraordinary Outcomes, Carol Sanford, Nicholas Brealey, 2017

The Responsible Entrepreneur: Four Game-Changing Archetypes for Founders, Leaders, and Impact Investors, Carol Sanford, Jossey-Bass, 2014

The Seed Communities, https://seed-communities.com/changeagentmenu/

Understanding White Supremacy

See Further Reading section for Chapter 2

Chapter 9

Afrofuturism

Afrofuturism Reading List and Resources: Starting Place, Maurice Broaddus, mauricebroaddus.com

Black Panther, 2018 film, Ryan Coogler, Dir.

Earthseed: The Complete Series, Octavia Butler, Open Road Media Sci-Fi & Fantasy, 2017

It's Not Just Black Panther: Afrofuturism Is Having a Moment, Alex Fitzpatrick, April 20, 2018

Kindred, Octavia Butler, Beacon Press, 2003

Lilith's Brood, Octavia Butler, Grand Central Publishing, 2000

Octavia's Brood: Science Fiction Stories from Social Justice Movements, Walidah Imarisha and adrienne maree brown, Eds., AK Press, 2015

Walidah Imarisha, www.walidah.com/home-1

Charettes

The Neighborhood Charrette Handbook, James A. Segedy and Bradley E. Johnson, www.michigantownships.org

Planning and Conducting Integrated Design (ID) Charrettes, Joel Ann Todd, www.wbdg.com, updated November 19, 2016

Holistic Management

Holistic Management International, https://holisticmanagement.org

Paicines Ranch, https://paicinesranch.com/index.php

Savory Institute, www.savory.global

Integral Theory

"The Integral Theory of Ken Wilber," Julian Scott, library.acropolis.org, August 22, 2019

"Integral Theory Primer: A Reader's Guide to Ken Wilber," Ali Akalin, www.shambhala.com

Reinventing Organizations: An Illustrated Invitation to Join the Conversation on Next-Stage Organizations, Frederic Laloux, Nelson Parker, 2016

Present Tense Active Voice for Goals Articulation

Edible Forest Gardens: Ecological Design and Practice for Temperate-climate Permaculture, Dave Jacke and Eric Toensmeier, Chelsea Green, 2005, p. 148

Prison Food Justice Network and Programs

Conference on Social and Ecological: Infrastructure for Recidivism Reduction at Yale University, retrieved from www.prisongardenjustice.org

Jail-to-Farm-to-College and Employment Program, Abrah Dresdale, issuu.com

"The New Garden Society: Transforming Landscapes, Transforming Lives," www.thenewgardensociety.org/welcome

Strategic Planning: Gatekeepers and Project Champions

"Making Change Sustainable with Champions," Ivan Colic, www.wndyr.com, October 31, 2019

"The Politics of Innovation: Why Innovations Need a Godfather," D. J. Smith, *Journal of Technovation*, Vol. 27, Issue 3, March 2007: 95-104

"Strategic and Planning Issues of Knowledge Management: Key Players," Sirje Virkus, www.tlu.ee

Visionary Social Design and Art-making

Ashara Ekundayo Gallery, www.asharaekundayogallery.com

Center for Artistic Activism, https://c4aa.org

Center for Story Based Strategy, www.storybasedstrategy.org

Claudia Rankine, http://claudiarankine.com

"Gloria E. Anzaldúa," www.wikipedia.org

Intelligent Mischief, www.intelligentmischief.com

The Million Person Project, www.millionpersonproject.org/about

Oakland Art Murmur, https://oaklandartmurmur.org

Chapter 10

Decolonizing via the Nervous System

Dr. Michael Yellow Bird, https://www.indigenousmindfulness.com/

My Grandmother's Hands: Racialized Trauma and the Pathway to Mending Our Hearts and Bodies, Resmaa Manakem, Central Recover Press, 2017

Just Transition

Climate Justice Alliance, https://climatejusticealliance.org

"From Banks and Tanks to Cooperation and Caring: A Strategic Framework for a Just Transition," booklet, Movement Generation Justice and Ecology Project, www.movementgeneration.org

Mindmapping Tools

Coggle, https://coggle.it

Imindq, www.imindq.com

MindMaple, www.mindmaple.com

Sketchboard, https://sketchboard.io

Racism and the Food System

See Further Reading section for Chapter 2

Social Design Trainings with Critical Analysis

"Zone In: Social Permaculture for Regenerative Change," Denver Permaculture Guild, 2020

"Planting the Seeds of Change," Earth Activist Training

"Regenerative Design for Changemakers," www.regeneratechange.com

Social Permaculture for Food Justice Course, Stockbridge School UMass, https://onlinesustfoodfarm.com/social-permaculture/

Valuing Non-Financial Forms of Wealth

8 Forms of Capital, Ethan Roland and Gregory Landua, appleseedpermaculture.com, 2011

Gift Economy, retrieved from www.en.wikipedia.org

"Guide to the Barter Economy and the Barter System History," Kelly Anderson, mint.com

"Mutual Aid Societies," https://wiki.p2pfoundation.net/Mutual_Aid_Societies

"Regenerative Enterprise: 4 Years Later," Ethan Roland Soloviev, medium.com, March 14, 2017

U.S. Solidarity Economy Network, https://ussen.org/

Also see Chapter 3 Further Reading on "Solidarity Economics"

Chapter 11

Climate Justice Movement

Climate Futures: Reimagining Global Climate Justice, Kum-Kum Bhavnani, John Foran, Priya A. Kurian, and Debashish Munshi, Eds., Zed Books, 2019

Climate Justice Alliance, https://climatejusticealliance.org

Climate Justice: Hope, Resilience, and the Fight for a Sustainable Future, Mary Robinson, Bloomsbury, 2019

Drawdown: The Most Comprehensive Plan Ever Proposed to Reverse Global Warming, Paul Hawken, Penguin Books, 2017

"Hurricane Season Curriculum," www.climbingpoetree.com

No One Is Too Small to Make a Difference, Greta Thunberg, Penguin Books, 2019

On Fire: The Burning Case for a Green New Deal, Naomi Klein, Knopf Canada, 2019

Storms of My Grandchildren: The Truth About the Climate Catastrophe and Our Last Chance to Save Humanity, James Hanson, Bloomsbury, 2010

"Sustaining All Life," www.rc.org/publication/environment/sustainingalllife

Toward Climate Justice: Perspectives on the Climate Crisis and Social Change, Brian Tokar, New Compass Press, 2014

See also Chapter 5 and 8 Further Reading sections

Context-Sensitive Design

See "Regenerative Design Process" in Overview of Section II Further Reading

Democratic Multicultural Organizations and Movements

Anti-oppression Resource and Training Alliance (AORTA), http://aorta.coop

JIMENA: Preserve and Protect the Heritage of Sephardic and Mizrahi Jews, www.jimena.org

Movement Generation Justice and Ecology Project, https://movementgeneration.org

"Multicultural Competence," Paul Kivel, www.paulkivel.com

Regenerate Change, www.regeneratechange.com

SoulFire Farm, www.soulfirefarm.org

Training for Change, www.trainingforchange.org

US Food Sovereignty Movement, http://usfoodsovereigntyalliance.org

Via Campesina, www.viacampesina.org

Design by Pattern Languages and Master Patterns

Change Here Now: Permaculture Solutions for Personal and Community Transformation, Adam Brock, North Atlantic Books, 2017

Liberating Voices: A Pattern Language for Communication Revolution, Douglas Schuler, MIT Press, 2008

Momentum: Training Institute and Movement Incubator, www.momentumcommunity.org

Movement Generation Justice and Ecology Project, https://movementgeneration.org/

The Nature of Order: An Essay on the Art of Building and the Nature of the Universe, Book 3: A Vision of a Living World, Christopher Alexander, Center for Environmental Structure, 2005

Pattern Language, wikipedia.org

A Pattern Language: Towns, Buildings, Construction, Christopher Alexander, Murray Silverstein, and Sara Ishikawa, Oxford University Press, 1977

Regenerative Development and Design: A Framework for Evolving Sustainability, Pamela Mang and Ben Haggard, Wiley, 2016

Emergence and Adaptation

Complex Adaptive Leadership: Embracing Paradox and Uncertainty, 2nd ed., Nick Obolensky, Routledge, 2014

Emergent Strategy: Shaping Change, Changing Worlds, adrienne maree brown, AK Press, 2017

Emergent Strategy Ideation Institute, www.alliedmedia.org/esii

How the Wonder of Nature Can Inspire Social Justice Activism, adrienne maree brown, www.yesmagazine.org, February 1, 2018

Open Space Technology

Open Space Technology Introduction, YouTube, www.batfishcreations.com

Open Space Technology: A User's Guide, 3rd ed., Harrison Owen, Berrett-Koehler, 2008

Open Space Technology, Harrison Owen, liberatingstructures.com. Short form developed to fit in Liberating Structures milieu by Henri Lipmanowicz and Keith McCandless.

Systemic Constellations

"About Systemic Constellation Work (SCW)," Diana Claire Douglas, knowingfielddesigns.com

All My Relations Constellations, https://allmyrelationsconstellations.com

I Carry Your Heart in My Heart: Family Constellations in Prison, Dan Booth Cohen, Carl Auer International (1831), 2009

Love's Hidden Symmetry: What Makes Love Work in Relationships, Bert Hellinger, Zeig Tucker & Theisen, 1998

North American Systemic Constellations, www.nasconstellations.org/what-are-systemic-constellations.html

White Saviorism

"The White-Savior Industrial Complex," Teju Cole, *The Atlantic*, March 21, 2012

"Unpacking White Saviorism: How White and Western Society's Desire to Help Can Do More Harm Than Good," Annie Windholz, www.medium.com, June 26, 2017

Chapter 12

Backcasting Tool

See "Backcasting Tool" in Chapter 7 Further Reading section

Critical Path

"20 Free Critical Path Templates (MS Word, Excel and PDF)," www.templatelab.com

"How to Use the Critical Path Method for Complete Beginners," Esther Cohen, www.workamajig.com, April 18, 2018

Project Management and Implementation Strategies

"30+ Project Plan Templates and Examples to Visualize Your Strategy," Sara McGuire www.venngage.com, January 21, 2020

Getting Things Done: The Art of Stress-Free Productivity, Dave Allen, Penguin Books, rev. ed., 2015

The 7 Habits of Highly Effective People, Stephen Covey, Simon & Schuster, 2013

Three Popular Ways to Prioritize a Hectic Schedule, itadmin, www.examinedexistence.com

Promise Beyond Ableness

"The Regenerative Organization, Part IV," Carol Sanford, November 9, 2015, www.carolsanfordinstitute.com

SMART Steps/Goals

"SMART Goals: How to Make Your Goals Achievable," www.mindtools.com

"Write Achievable Goals with the SMART Goals Framework," Kat Boogaard, *Productivity*, www.atlassian.com, January 25, 2019

Timeboxing

Timeboxing, www.clockify.me

"Timeboxing: Maximizing Your Productivity," www.mindtools.com

Chapter 13

Action Research Method

"A Beginner's Guide to Action Research," Bob Dick, www.aral.com

"Guiding School Improvement with Action Research," Richard Sagor, Association for Supervision & Curriculum Development, 2000

Context-Sensitive Evaluations

Ang Roell: Organizational Change-Making Consultant, https://angelaroell.com/services/project-design-evaluation

"Context in Evaluation," Beth Snow, www.drbethsnow.com, February 17, 2016

"Context Is Critical," Brad Rose, www.bradroseconsulting.com, December 17, 2012

"Context-sensitive Evaluation: Determining the Context Surrounding the Implementation of a Government Policy," Lyn Alderman, *Evaluation Journal of Australasia*, Vol. 15, No. 4, December 1, 2015

Media about Franklin County Jail Farm/Food Program

"Can This Small Town Lead America in Fighting the Opioid Crisis?" Mattea Kramer, www.ozy.com, April 18, 2018

"Garden of Possibility," Richie Davis, *Greenfield Recorder*, July 10, 2014

"GCC Food and Farming Courses Open Doors for Jail Inmates," Richie Davis, *Greenfield Recorder*, December 26, 2017

"Inmates to Learn Organic Gardening," Richie Davis, *Greenfield Recorder*, November 28, 2013

"Jail Sees Food and Farming as Track for Learning, Jobs, Nutrition — and Change," Richie Davis, Greenfield Recorder, June 17, 2016

Rehab Jail for Heroin Addicts, CNN video by BEME, April 12, 2018, www.cnn.com/videos/us/2018/12/04/rehab-jail-for-heroin-addicts-beme.beme

Whole Measures Evaluation Framework

"Whole Measures," Center for Whole Communities, www.wholecommunities.org/whole_measures

Whole Measures for Community Food Systems: Stories From the Field, Obiora Embry, Deborah Fryman, Deb Habib, and Jeanette Abi-Nader, 2019, http://wholecommunities.org/wp-content/uploads/2015/12/WholeMeasuresStories-copy-2.pdf

Chapter 14

Reflection and Integration Resources

"8 Critical Learning Reflections That Promote Deeper Thinking," Lee Watanabe-Crockett, www.wabisabilearning.com

Alliance of Artists Communities, www.artistcommunities.org/arts-ecology-residency-programs

Barre Center for Buddhist Studies: Meditation and Retreat Center, www.buddhistinquiry.org

"The Best Meditation Retreats in the U.S.," Lori Brookhart-Schervish, outsideonline.com, June 22, 2014

Better Farm, www.betterfarm.org

Coming Home to Yourself: 10-Day Distance Course, Sarah Blondin. https://insighttimer.com/sarahblondin

"How a Daily Self-Reflection Practice Improves Leadership Performance," Naz Beheshti, *Forbes*, September 28, 2018

"Insight Timer App: #1 App for Meditation and Sleep," www.insighttimer.com

"Nature, Eco and Wilderness Retreats," www.retreatsonline.com

"Reflective Practice," www.learningforsustainability.net

Spirit Rock: An Insight Meditation Center, www.spiritrock.org

Abrah Dresdale, MA, (she/her)—often called a *force of nature*—is a social designer, consultant, and educator. Named a New England Fixer by Grist Magazine, she is Co-founding Director of Regenerate Change and serves as Social Permaculture Faculty at the University of Massachusetts and Omega Institute. Abrah lives on a multi-family farm on occupied Mohawk and Lenape land in the Mahicantuck / Hudson River Valley, NY.

Visit her website at AbrahDresdale.com

CPSIA information can be obtained
at www.ICGtesting.com
Printed in the USA
LVHW021159080822
725381LV00006B/316

9 780578 857459